medieval russia's epics, chronicles, and tales

St. George in the garb of a medieval Russian knight.
A sixteenth-century icon.

medieval russia's epics, chronicles, and tales

EDITED, TRANSLATED, AND WITH
AN INTRODUCTION BY

Serge A. Zenkovsky

Professor and Director of Russian Studies,
Stetson University

A Dutton **dep** *Paperback*

NEW YORK
E. P. DUTTON & CO., INC.

Acknowledgments

Grateful acknowledgment is made to the following for
permission to quote from copyright material:

Selections from *The Russian Primary Chronicle* as
translated by Samuel H. Cross in *Harvard Studies and
Notes in Philology and Literature,* Volume XII, 1930,
reprinted by permission of the Harvard University Press.
Copyright, 1930, 1958, by The President and Fellows of
Harvard College.

Selection from *The Correspondence between Prince
A. M. Kurbsky and Tsar Ivan IV of Russia* translated by
J. L. I. Fennell, 1955, reprinted by permission of the
Cambridge University Press, London and New York.

LIBRARY OF CONGRESS CATALOG CARD NUMBER: 63-8606

SBN 0-525-47117-0

PREFACE

PREPARING this volume for publication, I felt that at the
[pre]sent level of American and British scholarship in the field of
[Ru]ssian studies the time has come to offer readers and students
[a] comprehensive anthology of Russia's medieval literature in
[tra]nslation. The works of modern Russian writers of the nine-
[tee]nth century, especially those of the age of the great Russian
[no]vel as represented by Dostoevsky and Tolstoy, have long since
[be]come an inalienable part of American and British curricula of
[lite]rary studies and of collections in public and school libraries.
[Als]o rather well known are the contemporary writings of Rus-
[sia]'s Soviet period. Very different is the situation regarding the
[lite]rature of previous centuries, especially that of the Russian
[Mi]ddle Ages, which lasted until the beginning of the eighteenth
[cen]tury. Indeed, there are available in English translation such
[ma]sterpieces of medieval Russian letters as the *Primary Chroni-
[cle]*, the *Lay of Igor's Campaign*, some adaptations and transla-
[tio]ns of the *Life*, or autobiography, of Avvakum, and of some
[oth]er works written from the eleventh through the seventeenth
[cen]turies. Most of these translations, however, are either out of
[pri]nt or not readily available, having appeared in rare or ex-
[pen]sive editions. Moreover, the tremendous remaining part of
[Ru]ssian medieval writings has never been translated either into
[En]glish or into any other Western language.

[T]he present anthology is therefore a pioneering effort to pre-
[sen]t to Western readers the finest works, a few in excerpt, of
[Ru]ssian literature from its very beginning, in the early eleventh
[cen]tury, through the seventeenth century, when Peter the Great
[for]ced Russia to rejoin the European family of nations and dis-
[car]d its medieval culture.

[R]ussian medieval literature is very extensive. According to
[inc]omplete statistics, for example, there are over seven thou-
[san]d versions of lives of saints written during Russia's Middle
[Ag]es, and many thousands of chronicles and tales. Therefore,
[the] task of selecting for translation the most outstanding of these
[i]s not easy. I attempted to solve this problem by offering here
[as] many recognized masterpieces of that period as possible, to-
[get]her with some lesser known works that also contribute to an
[und]erstanding of the mentality, culture, and literary manners
[of] Old Russia. My guiding principle was to offer entire works
[wh]enever possible, or at least complete narrative passages from

v

such longer writings as the chronicles, in order to give reader an opportunity to grasp the style and spirit of the R sians of that age. In a few cases—as, for instance, the long torical and polemical writings of the sixteenth and early sev teenth centuries—I decided, owing to the limitations of volume, to include the most characteristic and interesting p sages, in order to convey a more complete picture of the evc tion of Russian letters.

When possible, already existing translations have been us but the major part of the works published in this book app for the first time in English. The translation of medieval Russ letters presents a number of technical difficulties. Their synt structure, and style are very different from the methods devices of contemporary writers. Therefore, the translation many passages required some adaptation to the mode of expr sion of modern English for them to be comprehensible readers. For the sake of those who are not well acquainted w Russian medieval history, geography, and terminology, the wo "prince," "city," or "river" have been added to avoid possi confusion. Since the Russian medieval calendar was 5,508 ye behind the Western one, the corresponding Western dates h been supplied where necessary.

A customarily difficult problem is that of the transliteration Russian names. For the titles of original Russian sources system of the Library of Congress has been used, except for diacritical signs. In the transliteration of Russian names terminology, the Library of Congress system underwent so minor modification: for instance, the initial Russian soft vow rendered by *ia* or *iu* have been changed to the more reada *ya* or *yu* (that is, "Yaroslav," not "Iaroslav"); the final *ii* and have been replaced by *y* (that is, "Kurbsky" instead of "Ku skii"); and the final *iia* has been rendered by *ia* ("Dobrynia' place of "Dobryniia"). Most of the proper names are given their Russian form. Those of the clergy, such as "Theodosius' "Sergius," are usually given in their original Greek or L version, and those of foreign rulers and writers in their orig form, while common Christian names, such as "Alexand "Nicholas," "Andrew," or "Helen," are given in the usual Eng manner.

Of the works previously translated into English and incor rated in the present collection, many have been revised aga the original Russian texts and their transliteration of Russ names altered for the sake of consistency. It is my pleasant d to acknowledge my gratitude to the following publishing hou persons, and institutions for their permission to reproduce here the material listed:

1. to Harvard University Press, Cambridge, Massachusetts, for permission to reprint passages from *The Russian Primary Chronicle*, translated by Samuel H. Cross;

2. to G. P. Putnam's Sons, New York, and London, for permission to use portions of Leo Wiener's *Anthology of Russian Literature*;

3. to the Editorial Board of the *Slavonic and East European Review*, London, for permission to reprint *Adam's Address to Lazarus in Hell*, translated anonymously and published in Volume X (1932), pp. 145–152;

4. to Mr. Nicholas Zernov and The Society for the Promotion of Christian Knowledge, London, for permission to reprint *The Acts and Miracles of Our Dear and Holy Father, Sergius*, by Epiphanius the Wise, from *St. Sergius, Builder of Russia*, translated by Nicholas Zernov;

5. to Cambridge University Press, London and New York, for permission to reprint J. L. I. Fennell's translation of Prince Andrew Kurbsky's "First Epistle to Ivan IV," from *The Correspondence between Prince A. Kurbsky and Tzar Ivan IV of Russia*;

6. to Miss U. M. Lane and The Hogarth Press, Ltd., London, for permission to use *The Life of Archpriest Avvakum by Himself*, translated by Jane Harrison and Hope Mirrless.

In the preparation of this volume I was assisted by students in my graduate seminar on ancient Russian literature at the University of Colorado. The Reverend George Benigsen helped in translating *The Life of Yuliania Lazarevskyaya*, while Mr. Dan B. Chopyk translated Bishop Serapion's *Sermon on Merciless Heathens*. The remaining translations were made by myself in cooperation with my graduate student and assistant, Mr. Richard White. It is evident, however, that I am the only person responsible for all possible errors or shortcomings in selecting, translating, and commenting on the works in this book.

I am grateful to the Graduate School of the University of Colorado for financial help toward the completion of this volume when I was Professor of Slavic Languages and Literatures at that University.

Only I can fully appreciate the contribution made by my wife and colleague, Betty Jean, whose interest and editorial skill were so helpful in the planning and completion of *Medieval Russia's Epics, Chronicles, and Tales*.

SERGE A. ZENKOVSKY

CONTENTS

ILLUSTRATIONS

MAPS

СЛЫШАТИ ДАСЛЫ
ШИТЬ ⁘

ЦА МАРТА · СТРА
ТЫХЪ МК̅ · И
Г   В
ЕВА · ОТЪ МАТ · ГЛА · С̅ ⁘

РЕЧЕ Г̅Ь ПРИТЪ
Ч УЖСНИЖ ПОДО
БЬНО ЕСТЬ ЦР̅Ь
СТВИИ НБ̅СЬНОЮ
ЧЛКОУ ДОМОВИ
ТОУ ИЖЕ ИZИДЕ
КОУПЬНО Zа ОУТРА

A page from the Gospel of Ostromir written in 1056.
It is the oldest Russian book in existence.

INTRODUCTION

The Literature of Medieval Russia

THE term "Middle Ages" has a somewhat different connotation and time span for Russia than for Western Europe. In the West the Middle Ages began in the fifth century, when the Western Roman Empire fell under the blows of Germanic barbarians. They ended at the close of the fifteenth century or the beginning of the sixteenth, when Columbus discovered the New World, Luther broke the spiritual unity of the West, and secularized thought put an end to the "Age of Faith." The Russian Middle Ages began much later, only in the ninth century, and her Age of Faith came to an end in the early eighteenth century, when Russia adopted the secularized culture of Western Europe.

During the years that witnessed the fall of Rome, the Slavic tribes inhabiting the territory of present Russia were still in the age of prehistory. Only scattered data about the apparently Slavic "Antes" point to the inception of a loosely organized statehood in that area. Four additional centuries were needed for the appearance of a more solid national structure among the Eastern Slavs and for their emergence on the stage of history. The first indications of a firmly founded government among the Eastern Slavs, in the cities of Novgorod and Kiev, can be observed only in the ninth century when, in 862, according to legend, a certain Rurik became the prince of Novgorod. Since that time the word "Rus," or Russians, rapidly won a place in the pages of historical annals. In the tenth century the Kievan prince and conqueror Sviatoslav built a vast empire spreading from the Volga to the Dnieper and Danube rivers, and from Kiev to Novgorod. Despite these military and political successes, however, the culture of this early Russian state remained at a modest level. Only after the Christianization of Russia in 988 or 989 by Sviatoslav's son, Vladimir, did literacy and literature appear among these Slavs, and only from that time can historians observe the first blossoming of early Russian culture.

I. THE KIEVAN PERIOD (1030–1240)

1. CHURCH SLAVONIC

CHRISTIANITY came to Russia from Byzantium, or, as it was often called, the Eastern Roman Empire, at that time a powerful and highly developed nation culturally. Its flourishing capital, Constantinople, was still the most important political and cultural center of Europe and commanded a vast empire comprising the Balkan Peninsula, the Aegean Archipelago, all of Asia Minor, and parts of Italy. Its literary and state language was Greek; and Byzantium, as the preserver of both Christian thought and Greco-Roman arts and letters, was the main luminary of knowledge for still "dark" Western Europe. Despite Russia's conversion to Byzantine Christianity, however, Greek never won a position in Russia similar to that of Latin in the West, where for centuries Latin remained the exclusive liturgic and educational medium for medieval Catholic Europe. Indeed, from the very beginning of evangelization in Russia, the mass was read in Russian churches in Slavic, not in Greek. This does not mean that the Byzantine Greeks were not nationalists. To be sure, they always placed their language, the tongue of Homer, Plato, and the Gospel, above all others. Still, the wealth of the native cultures of non-Greek provinces of Byzantium compelled them at an early stage to permit the churches of the Middle East to use languages other than Greek. Later, when in 863 the Moravian prince Rostislav asked Constantinople to send missionaries for the Christianization of his realm—which occupied the present territories of Slovakia and Hungary—the Byzantine Church did not hesitate to permit the use of the Slavic tongue in the new churches.

The tasks of creating an alphabet for the Slavs and forming out of the primitive Slavic vernacular a suitable language for the mass and Gospel was entrusted to two brothers, Cyril and Methodius, Greek monks from the city of Saloniki. Linguists of genius, Cyril and Methodius created a Slavic alphabet (commonly called "Cyrillic") on the basis of the Greek one. They translated the ecclesiastic literature into one of the dialects of the Slavs of Macedonia, using Byzantine Greek stylistics and syntax. This new, somewhat artificial literary language—now called "Church Slavonic"—was perfectly Slavic in its vocabulary and grammar but rather Byzantine in its stylistic aspect.

Transplanted to Russia as a liturgic and literary language, Church Slavonic, which was very close to Old Russian, proceeded to absorb specific features of this Eastern Slavic language. Thus there developed a very interesting Russian literary language composed of Church Slavonic, with its original South Slavic linguistic features, interspersed with purely Russian characteristics. Surviving some periods of Russification, this adopted language remained the official literary language of Russia until the end of the seventeenth century, and the literary monuments written in it often have an elevated, solemn, even esoteric, coloration. As there were in medieval Russia no definite standards for the literary language, an erudite or sophisticated writer or cleric would couch his literary prose exclusively in Church Slavonic—which strongly reflected the refined and adorned stylistics of Byzantine letters—while in the same given period private correspondence, state documents, and even some simpler literary works were written in an almost pure and stylistically more naïve Old Russian vernacular. The possibilities for interweaving these two very close yet contrasting linguistic strata were innumerable and, since strict linguistic rules for the written language were established only in the eighteenth century, many Old Russian texts have a particular charm owing to a mingling of the vernacular with Church Slavonic. Unfortunately, this aspect of Old Russian literary monuments can not be reproduced at all in translation.

2. THE ADVANTAGES AND LIMITATIONS OF CHURCH SLAVONIC

The entire subsequent development of medieval Russian culture and literature was thus determined by the introduction and example of the Byzantine literary legacy in Church Slavonic translations. Initially, such adoption of a new culture in a linguistically comprehensible version offered a very considerable advantage for the Russians, who, contrary to the experience of the Catholic Germans or Poles, had not to learn a difficult foreign language, that is, Latin or Greek, in order to absorb the new religion and civilization. Byzantium's ecclesiastic and some of its secular literature, with all its stylistic patterns and genre models, became readily available to the Eastern Slavs in translation, and Russian letters were given a rapid start. Their beginning appears even spectacular when compared with the literary destinies of the Western Slavs—the Czechs and the Poles—who, having been Christianized by Rome, were obliged to adopt Latin in their mass and in their writing. Poland's first literary work in its native language did not appear until some three hundred years after its conversion to Christianity, and even five hundred years after evangelization the Poles continued to write in Latin more often than in Polish. A very similar delayed development can be observed among the Czechs. The first original Russian writings, however—some sermons by the Novgorodian and Kievan preachers, Bishop Luka Zhidiata and Metropolitan Hilarion—appeared as early as forty or fifty years after Russia's conversion. The *Primary Chronicle*, a significant work of literary, historical, and ideological interest came into being just a little over a century after the appearance in Kiev of Christian priests and Church Slavonic manuscripts, while the *Lay of Igor's Campaign,* Russia's greatest monument in the heroic epic tradition, had already been written within two centuries after her Christianization.

The spread of Byzantine culture to Russia in its Church Slavonic versions, however, also had negative aspects. Because Russian priests officiated in Church Slavonic, they were not obliged to study Greek, and the knowledge of this language and of antique, classical, culture for centuries remained extremely limited in Russia. While Western Europe did not forget Virgil and classical Latin even during the darkest years of its cultural dormance—the fifth to eighth centuries—during the Russian Middle Ages knowledge of the Greek language and acquaintance with Byzantine literature in the original was restricted to but a few representatives of the upper cultural strata. Numerous translations from Greek into Church Slavonic were made in Russia but most of these were of theological or historical works. Neither the wealth of pre-Christian Greek literature nor the entirety of Byzantine secular writings became known to medieval Russians. The Russian clergy was apparently afraid to translate and propagate the works of pagan writers, while the Greeks themselves were not especially interested in spreading education and their cultural heritage among the Slavs. It can be surmised that Byzantium was content to keep Russia as a cultural colony not expected to attain the level of civilization of its cultural "mother country." In any case, the Greeks sent to Russia neither teachers for the purpose of forming a sophisticated cultural elite nor the works of ancient Greece. Moreover, they preferred to appoint Greeks to the head of the Russian Church than to prepare Russians for such positions, and did very little to raise the intellectual standard of the native Russian clergy. Thus, the humanistic, scientific, and philosophic traditions of Byzantium put down no substantial roots in Russia, and Byzantium's influence remained limited primarily to the religious, political, and artistic spheres, while the bulk of classical Greek, as well as Latin, thought and letters remained almost unknown to Russians until the late seventeenth century.

3. Kievan Russia

As has been pointed out, the cultural history of Russia begins largely with its Christianization at the end of the tenth century. While an early Russian state had existed at least since the mid-ninth century, and some scattered information concerning the national-state organization of the Russian, or Eastern, Slavs can be traced from the seventh century after Christ, or even the fifth (the state of the Antes), disappointingly little is known about the life of the pagan Russians and their culture. Judging from the quick flowering of their letters, art, and architecture after Christianization in 988–989, it can be presumed that the earliest contacts of the Eastern Slavs with Greece, Byzantium, the Caucasus, and peoples of the Eurasian steppes led to the formation in Eastern Europe of a very definite cultural type even before Christianity and letters came there. The trade routes from Scandinavia to Byzantium, from Central Asia and the Far East to Western Europe, passed through the territory of this early Russian state and certainly contributed to its cultural growth. The city of Kiev was at the crossroads of these two important trade routes, and its rise as the capital of a Russian state was largely due to the prosperity brought it by merchants who traveled to or through the city. After the Russians' conversion to Christianity at the instance of the Kievan Prince Vladimir (ruled 978–1015), Byzantine culture in its Slavicized forms won the dominant position among the Russians for the next seven centuries, and the years from A.D. 1000 to 1700 can be called the medieval or "Byzantinized" period of Russia.

Kiev itself became one of the wealthiest and most animated cities of medieval Europe, richer and more brilliant than Paris or London of the time. It was adorned with innumerable churches, and by the time of the reign of Vladimir's son, Yaroslav (ruled in Kiev 1019–1054) there were already numerous schools, hospitals, and libraries. In the eleventh and twelfth centuries Russia was an integral part of Europe, and Kievan princes maintained close dynastic ties with the ruling houses of Western countries. Their children married the sovereigns or princesses of England, Germany, France, Sweden, Hungary, and Byzantium. A daughter of Prince Yaroslav, Anna, married King Phillip of France and was the only literate member of the French royal family, for whom she signed state documents herself. Prince Vladimir Monomakh (who ruled in Kiev from 1112 to 1125), the grandson of Yaroslav, married Princess Gita, daughter of the last Anglo-Saxon king, Harold, whose family had been obliged to abandon England after the Norman Conquest and to live as emigrés in Kiev, where there were many foreigners. Western chronicles often mention the wealth and beauty of this early Russian capital. The German chronicler, Tittmar of Magdeburg, remarks that, during a fire, over four hundred churches burned in Kiev. The city's main cathedral, St. Sophia (Holy Wisdom), was lavishly decorated with delicate frescoes and mosaics. Its marble pillars were brought from the Crimea, and even now, despite centuries of mutilation and restoration, the cathedral's proportions and dimensions produce a strong impression.

The Kievan era, however, was short-lived: from the late tenth century to the early thirteenth. Yaroslav's children and grandchildren sundered the unity of Kievan Russia by indulging in fratricidal feuds and Vladimir Monomakh was the last Kievan sovereign recognized as leader by all the Russian princes. After his death the Kievan state disintegrated into a number of large and small principalities that competed and fought with one another. In the face of increasingly frequent raids into the South Russian territories by Turkic nomads—Pechenegs and, later, Kumans (Polovetsians)—the Slavic population began to migrate from the southern area of Kiev to the forests in the north, or westward to the plains of Galicia and the Carpathian Piedmont. The prosperous merchant city of Novgorod in the northwest, Galich—the capital of Galicia—in the extreme southwest, and the cities of Suzdal and Vladimir—precursors of Moscow—in the northeast outgrew Kiev in prominence. With the conquest of the Holy Land and Constantinople by the Crusaders, new trade routes opened up from West to East and Kiev's importance as a trading center rapidly diminished. The Mongol (Tatar) invasion that took place in 1237–1240 under the leadership of the heirs of Genghis Khan dealt the final blow to the dying Kievan state. Kiev itself was sacked and burned, not to recover for centuries; most other Russian cities were also devastated, and some two-thirds of the Russian population perished. Thus weakened, most of western and southern Russia then fell to the Lithuanians and Poles, while the rest of Russia remained a vassal state of the Mongol (Tatar) Empire for the following two centuries.

4. The Byzantine Literary Heritage of Kievan Russia

When Russia was Christianized by Prince Vladimir, some Christian literature and several secular Byzantine works had already been translated from the Greek into Church Slavonic by Cyril and Methodius or by Bulgarians, who formed a powerful Slavic state in the Balkans in the ninth and tenth centuries. Bulgaria's proximity to Byzantium stimulated the knowledge of Greek among the Bulgarians and an active translation of Greek works into Church Slavonic, as well as the transmission of Byzantine literary patterns from the Greeks to the Slavs. These outh Slavic translations from Greek became the first writings vailable to the Russians. Later, a considerable number of Byantine writings were translated in Russia itself. Among the ormer, of capital importance were, of course, the Gospel and arts of the Old Testament, particularly the Psalms, which in hurch Slavonic were readily understandable to all Russians ho attended the Church service. Many of the liturgic texts ad been composed by Byzantine theologians who were at the ame time talented religious poets, such as St. John Damascene. heir aesthetic perfection, so clearly reflected in the ornate eauty of the Russian Church service itself, greatly influenced ie subsequent spiritual and artistic development of the Russian eople, while the stylistic and compositional influence of patristic ritings on all genres of ancient Russian literature remained ery great.

Among the translated literature, of prime importance also ere writings of the early Christian Fathers and the "lives," or *itae* (*zhitie*), of early Christian and Byzantine saints. Of the ormer, the most popular in Russia were the writings of St. John hrysostom, which were continually translated and recopied iroughout the whole seven centuries of the Russian Middle ges. The spirit of this great Antiochian preacher of Christian ocial teachings influenced Russian religiosity almost as much as ie Gospel itself; in any case, much more than the Old Testaient—which, with the exception of the Psalms, was not often ead by Russians. A collection of St. John Chrysostom's serions, *Marguerite* (*The Pearl*), was printed in the 1630's long efore the publication of the first full text of the Bible.

Saints' lives, often enhanced by fictional elements, were comiled in special collections in which the *vitae* were arranged in ie order of the calendar; they remained for centuries the most difying reading for Russians. Even as late as the nineteenth entury, Greek, Syrian, Egyptian, and Russian *vitae* found an :ho in the works of Tolstoy, Dostoevsky, Leskov, Turgenev, nd other Russian authors, while for early Russian writers, espe- ially the compilers of the *vitae* of native Russian saints, trans- .ted Byzantine hagiography constituted the main source for :ylistic and spiritual inspiration.

Of similar attraction for the Russian reader were the Apocry- ia—writings on subjects of the Old and New Testaments not :cognized by the Church as authentic or canonic, translated om Greek into Church Slavonic either in Bulgaria or in Russia. mong them the apocrypha on King Solomon—whose wisdom

eclipsed for Russian minds that of Aristotle and Plate—as well
the apocryphal tale *Descent of the Virgin Into Hell*, particular
absorbed the Russian reader. The latter was apparently co:
siderably reworked in Russia and, in its content, was somethir
of an Eastern counterpart to Dante's *Divine Comedy*. Russia
liked especially its spirit of compassion for sinners, shown by t
Holy Virgin's intercession on behalf of the souls condemned
perpetual torment. The Jobian theme of man's discontent wi
his fate was treated, in the form of a dialogue, in the apocryph
tale *Adam's Address to Lazarus in Hell*. This theme was take
up some six centuries later in an autobiographical *vita*
Monk Epiphany, a follower of the famous martyred Archprie
Avvakum.

A few works from Byzantine scholarly literature becam
known in Kievan and, later, in Muscovite Russia, such as t
historical chronicles of John Malalas and George Hamartol
and the *History of the Judaic War* by Joseph Flavius. The sty
and manner of these writers were followed by the early Russia
chroniclers.

Secular tales received by Russia from Byzantium included t
legends of *Barlaam* and *Josaphat* and *Digenis Arkritas*, as we
as the *Alexandria*. The first, of Indian origin, gives an accoui
of the life of Buddha, who is presented as Prince Josaphat,
fictitious Christian hero and saint. It was reworked in Byzantiu
and Russia many times, and in the sixteenth century a Russia
hymnologist, Markel Bezborody, composed a poetic church ser
ice in honor of this prince. The legend of *Digenis Akritas* orig
nated within the confines of Byzantium and Persia and relate
the heroic deeds of Christian knights fighting the infidels. A
though this Byzantine forerunner of the Spanish epic of El C
was almost the only knightly tale known to Kievan Russia, i
entire romantic element was expurgated from it by the auste:
Church authorities.

None of the great works of pre-Christian Greek poets, pla
wrights, and philosophers apparently found their way to O
Russian readers. It is true that Homer was known to them,
least by name, and some passages from his works were tran
lated, but it can not be definitely stated that larger portions
his writings were ever in the hands of the literate Kievan. A
most the same can be said of the writings of Plato and Aristotl
While occasional quotations and passages from the works
these philosophers can be found in some ancient collections, a
for instance, *The Bee*, none of their works was ever entire
translated into Church Slavonic.

5. Earliest Russian Sermons and Thought

In the cultural life of every newly converted land, the clergy
vays occupies a position of pre-eminence. Therefore there is
thing astonishing in the fact that the first Russian writers and
rned men were predominantly representatives of the Church.
Novgorod, soon after his elevation to the bishopric there in
36, Luka Zhidiata wrote his *Instruction*, which is usually con-
ered the oldest dated work in Russian literature. This is a
lactic, rather dry homily consisting of admonitions and re-
iders concerning Church ritual. It is written in very simple
guage and can hardly be considered an inspiring piece of
toric.

Of completely different intellectual and literary value are the
mons of Metropolitan Hilarion, the first Russian—not Greek—
id of the Russian Church, elevated to this position in 1051
Yaroslav the Wise. Hilarion was a well-trained theologian
l skillful writer who apparently knew Greek and was well
sed in Byzantine religious literature. His main work, the
mon on Law and Grace, is especially pointed and convincing,
l despite its elaborate allegorical language the thought is
ar and readily understandable. It begins with a treatment of
problem of the spiritual superiority of the New Testament
r the Old: of the teachings of Christ over the law of Moses.
arion then switches very astutely from this topic to the thesis
he equality of newly converted Russia with older Byzantium.
considers that Russia has gained an honorable position in the
ristian world because the religion of grace, ". . . the fount of
Gospel . . . overflowed upon our land . . . and, together with
Christians, we glorify the Holy Trinity." Hilarion presents the
tiny of Russia in the general framework of world history and
rprets it in the light of the divine plan for the general salva-
of mankind. Strangely enough, this earliest Russian metro-
itan is rather a philosopher of history than a preacher of
ely religious, moralistic truths, and the appearance of a
ker of such depth of historical vision in the first decades of
ssian Christian history is one of the most amazing phenomena
he early development of Russian culture.

While Hilarion is primarily anthropocentric, more concerned
his writings with the fate of man on earth or of the nation
n with purely theological problems, Cyril of Turov, a
acher of the mid-twelfth century, is entirely theocentric. A
nber of a rich noble family, Cyril preferred the life of a
1k to a military or court career. He subsequently became

bishop, but he always remained a man of contemplation, me
tating on the mystical relation between God and man. Of
numerous works, his sermons won the particular admiration
his contemporaries and of later generations. Their main conce
is the problem of salvation, which he treats with great eruditi
and oratorical skill. Perhaps he often exaggerates in the use
complex allegories and metaphors, but it is precisely this p
fect command of ornate Byzantine stylistics that lends
writing great charm and elegance. For long centuries his s
mons remained the best example of elevated rhetoric in Russi
literature, and Cyril can be called, without exaggerating, t
greatest preacher of medieval Russia.

A rather humanistic trend in the Russian sermon was rep
sented by the works of Metropolitan Clement, a native
Smolensk who was elected to the metropolitan see in Kiev
1147. His contemporaries accused him of quoting more oft
from Plato, Aristotle, and Homer than from the Bible or t
Church Fathers. The only fragment of his works which has be
preserved is an impressive example of early Russian scholarsh
in the best Byzantine tradition. Clement's knowledge of Byz
tine Greek learning seems to be very extensive, and there
reason to believe that he completed his education not in Rus
but in some Greek monastery or school.

Very close in his cultural background and spirit to the
prelates of the Russian Church was Prince Vladimir Monoma
(died 1125), grandson of Yaroslav the Wise. Monomakh had
fluent command of five foreign languages, was well read, a
left some significant writings. Among them, his *Instruction*,
dressed to his children, stands out for its penetrating moral a
spiritual portrayal of the author himself. The work of a w
layman, a stern though benevolent, indefatigable, and farsight
ruler, the *Instruction* was written for the practical purpose
advising his children. In his admonitions Vladimir shows hi
self to have a profound understanding of Christian teachi
and illustrates his advice with examples from his own life.
cording to Monomakh, humility, contemplation, and the exar
nation of one's own mind and life are the main instruments
the hard task of the self-perfection of a ruler. He follows t
general patterns of the instructions of Byzantine and ev
Anglo-Saxon rulers (it may be recalled that his wife was
Anglo-Saxon princess). His ideas concerning a prince's obli
tions to his people and to himself are, however, original,
appropriate to the general framework of the developing Russi
spirituality: a ruler should never forget the teaching of Chr

for humility is one of the outstanding qualities of a Christian man and prince.

Among the erudite men of Kievan Russia was also a certain Daniel, styled "the Exile," who was the author of a *Supplication* written circa 1200 and addressed to the prince of Suzdal, Yaroslav. More adroitly than any other stylist of the dawn of Russian writing, Daniel plays gracefully with quotations from the Bible and Greek writers, Russian folk sayings, and his own pointed witticisms. Apparently intended as a petition for patronage, Daniel's *Supplication* displays his superior command of literary Church Slavonic and contemporary learning.

6. CHRONICLES

The chronicle (*letopis*) forms the most important and sizable part of Russian literature of the Kievan Era. These chronicles— or, more precisely, annals, since they consist usually of annual entries organized chronologically—contain very heterogeneous material. Along with concise entries giving in one or several lines information on a ruler or an event in a city, there can be found various historical and diplomatic documents, treaties, and admonitions, as well as longer stories about the deeds, adventures, and campaigns of a prince or the prose recordings of heroic legends. The Russian chronicles were not the product of a single author but a complex and continuously maintained work that was copied, completed, and often re-edited by successive writers. The earliest Russian annals are the *Primary Chronicle*, or *The Tale of Bygone Years*—the most interesting and best written of them. There can be discerned various distinct layers in the *Primary Chronicle*, which was begun about 1040 and continued through 1118 by at least six different annalists, among whom the most remarkable were its first writer-editor, Monk Nikon, who worked on it in the 1060's, and Monk Nestor, one of its last editors and compilers, who practically completed the writing of this work. It is very difficult to determine now which of its various writers gave the chronicle its general tenor and main ideological line, but in any case this "collective" work, the compositional elements of which are so heterogeneous, still produces a very unified and sustained impression. The annalist, or annalists, consistently stress the necessity of preserving the unity of the Kievan state, appeal repeatedly to the princes to give up their fratricidal feuds and live in brotherly love because they are members of the same dynasty, "brothers who have the same father and the same mother," who are supposed to preserve, not destroy, the fruits "of the heavy labor" of their forefathers.

In the Prolegomenon to the *Primary Chronicle* the annalist studies the formation of different peoples and races, all of whom were the offspring of Noah, and succeeds in finding among them the Slavs, the descendants of Japhet, thus establishing an honorable biblical background for his own nation. Describing the legendary visit to Russia by the Apostle Andrew, the annalist does not fail to claim that this Disciple of Christ predicted the forthcoming blossoming of Christianity in Russia. Very cleverly interweaving the actual fabric of historical material with legendary accounts and reminiscences, the annalist succeeds in creating a religious and political tradition for his newly emerged country, and points out that Russia has won a respectable status among the other nations of the Christian world.

A considerable amount of historical information covering the centuries preceding the rise of Russia was evidently taken from Byzantine chronicles, but it is reworked stylistically and ideologically. The very structure of the Russian annals—their chronological yearly entries—is different from that of Byzantine historical works, which are usually organized into chapters covering the reigns of the emperors.

Stories and tales integrated into the historical entries convey considerable freshness and charm to the *Primary Chronicle*. Many of these accounts, as, for instance, of the death of Prince Oleg or the revenge of Princess Olga, have a clearly legendary background and were probably taken from the epic tradition. Others have the character of actual eyewitness accounts, as, notably, the dramatic story of the blinding of Vasilko, written by Priest Vassily, or the narratives about the life of the monks of the Kievan Crypt Monastery.

The *Primary Chronicle* was the earliest and most literary, but not the only, historical work of the Kievan period. Most leading cities, as well as certain branches of the Rurik dynasty, which then ruled Russia, maintained their own annals from the twelfth century. Among these, the *Galician-Volynian Chronicle* and the *Kievan Chronicle* (a continuation of the *Primary Chronicle*) are the more skillfully written, and contain many passages that were the work of gifted writers. Most of the chronicles were written by members of the clergy, mainly monks; only the *Galician-Volynian* and perhaps the twelfth-century *Kievan* chronicles, which emphasize details of army and court life, were composed probably by a member of the princes' retinue. The northern chronicles, on the other hand, especially those of the city of Novgorod, are much drier and more concise, and are characterized by their business-like, even abrupt, style.

The heroes of the chronicles are predominantly princes. Sometimes the chronicler mentions commanders, knights, or priests, but such characters are certainly secondary. The annalists of the Kievan Era gave simple yet impressive sculptural—even monumental, in the words of D. Likhachev—portrayals of their hero-princes, who are divided clearly into positive characters and villains. The portrayals are frequently stereotyped: a good prince is usually described as "a good man of war," "handsome of face," "mild of habits," or "detesting wrong and loving right." The main positive attributes are defense of the Russian land, protection of the Church, and generosity toward his subjects. Few feminine figures appear in the chronicles, indeed, in general, in all of early Russian literature. Those that do are either faithful wives or affectionate mothers, but never a participant in a romantic love intrigue. Contrary to the Western tradition, Russia's austere Middle Ages do not know any amorous or erotic themes such as can be found in the *chansons* of the troubadours, not to speak of such manuals on the art of love as *de Arte honesti amandi* (1170) or *La Clef d'Amour* (1250), which were completely unthinkable in Kievan and early Muscovite letters. No traces even of innocent romantic courtship can be found in Russian chronicles or tales until the seventeenth century. The only exception, the Tale of *Peter and Fevronia of Murom*, written in the fifteenth century, stands out strikingly in pre-seventeenth century Russian literature for its unusual love theme, but even here the motif is one of the affection and devotion between a husband and wife.

7. KIEVAN VITAE AND PATERICS

Narrative writing with extensive biographical, occasionally fictional or legendary, content can be found in Kievan literature in the *vitae* (*zhitie*, saints' lives or hagiography) and paterics (monk's lives). While these two genres, especially the *vitae*, adhered to strict compositional patterns, they were nevertheless often embellished with interesting details mirroring medieval psychology and the author's own imagination.

The tragic fate of the Princes Boris and Gleb, sons of Vladimir, Christianizer of Russia, who were killed in 1016 in a fratricidal feud by order of their elder brother, was described in *vita* form as well as in two other narratives. Written by Nestor, one of the authors of the *Primary Chronicle*, the *vita* version of the brothers' martyrdom is most detailed and realistic, and it places the fratricide within the framework of Russian religious history. In Nestor's eyes Boris and Gleb were martyrs for peace in Russia, preferring death to participation in internecine strife. Their pathos is heightened by the touching laments Nestor puts in their mouths in anticipation of their murder. The anonymous author of the *Legend* (*Skazanie*) about Boris and Gleb emphasizes less their desire to preserve peace in Russia than their voluntary acceptance of death after the example of Christ. Meditating just before his murder, Boris recalls, "The Lord resists the proud and gives his grace to the humble." In these lines, written toward the end of the eleventh century, appears for the first time one of the leading characteristics of Russian Christianity—humility and the acceptance of fate in imitation of the deeds of Christ. This idea can be traced through subsequent Russian literature even into the early twentieth century.

Another masterpiece of early Russian hagiography is the *Life of St. Theodosius*, co-founder of the Kievan Crypt Monastery. This work, also written by Nestor, is probably his best. He furnishes not only abundant material on the life of Abbot Theodosius, which makes the *vita* a vivid and realistic narrative, but also tries to convey the religious philosophy of this great Russian saint: simplicity in life, humility of attitude before God and people, and Theodosius' gentle, loving care toward the monks and his spiritual children.

The early *vitae* and stories of the paterics have many structural features in common, and usually consist of a number of episodes loosely woven into one continuous narrative. While both were intended as edifying religious literature for the Christian education of their readers, their final purposes are, however, different. The *vita* is the official biography of a saint, explaining his role in the development of Orthodox saintliness and the religious mind, and giving the reason for his canonization. It is always solemn, often begins and ends with a prayer or hymn, and, much more than the pateric narrative, stresses the spiritual aspect of its hero's life. The *vitae* were traditionally constructed according to a stereotyped pattern, with the ideal of sainthood outweighing an accurate presentation of the details of the saint's actual life, since the aim of the hagiographer was not to present the life story itself but rather the saintly example, for the edification of believers. The stories of the paterics, on the other hand, were simply instructive tales about the lives of monks, many of whom were never canonized. The pateric described the life and deeds of the monks of a given monastery, and consequently the name of the monastery was usually included in the title.

These two genres are not always clearly distinguishable, and some biographies of noncanonized monks are very similar to the hagiographic *vitae*. Toward the end of the Russian Middle Ages the *vita* lost its strict hagiographic purpose and developed into a new genre of secular biography. The narratives of the pateric, likewise, gradually assumed the form of a not strictly religious short story. Both the *vitae* and paterics were the most popular reading of medieval Russia, and innumerable versions of the lives of Russian saints were written and rewritten from the eleventh through the seventeenth centuries. Together with Byzantine paterics and hagiography, they formed the major part of the libraries of Russian monasteries and of private collections, since they were the medieval equivalent of modern short stories and novels and intermingled descriptions of everyday life, edification, and ebullient oriental phantasy.

8. THE EPOS

The greatest literary work of Kievan Russia is the *Lay of Igor's Campaign* (*Slovo o polku Igoreve*), which describes an unsuccessful raid by Russian princes against the nomadic Turkic tribe of Kumans, who, in the twelfth and thirteenth centuries, inhabited the plains north of the Black Sea. This raid, which took place in 1185 under the leadership of Igor, Prince of Novgorod-Seversk, became the subject of the only epic and purely poetic work of Kievan Russia, written probably within a year or two after Igor's return from Kuman captivity.

Against the rather uniform and undiversified background of the chronicles and religious literature of the Kievan period, the *Lay of Igor's Campaign* stands out as an exceptional specimen of strictly secular poetic letters. Its lyric pathos, rich imagery and symbolism, noble national spirit and pagan references contrast strikingly with the rest of the preserved wealth of early Russian literature. Literary historians usually classify the *Lay* as a typical example of epic poetry, but its loose structure, lyric and rhetorical digressions, and the author's addresses to his audience rather suggest its classification as a work of mixed genre in which the epic content is strongly diluted by lyric digressions and allusive admonitions.

The origins of the Russian epic tradition still remain in darkness despite decades of intensive research. Since the end of the eighteenth century a tremendous wealth of Russian epic songs, the *byliny*, have been discovered and collected. Much of this epic folklore deals with the time of Kievan Russia and the court of Prince Vladimir, "the bright sun," Christianizer of Russia, and his valorous knights—Ilia Muromets, Aliosha Popovich, Dobrynia

Nikitich, and many others—who formed around Vladimir a Russian counterpart of King Arthur's Round Table. Scholars, however, can not agree in their estimates of the actual age of the *byliny*. Indeed, Dobrynia was the real uncle of Vladimir, and is well known from the chronicles. The name of Ilia, "the Russian knight" or "cousin of Vladimir," can be found in Scandinavian and Lombardian epics penned as early as the eleventh and twelfth centuries. Moreover, while the oldest Russian work containing a reference to the *byliny* epics and their heroes dates only from the sixteenth century, the narrative parts of the *Primary Chronicle* itself, as well as such later works as, for instance, the *Tale of the Destruction of Riazan*, show very definite traces of the epic tradition. Hence, it is possible to assume that the Russian epic tradition goes back as far as the time of Kievan Russia, although their exact form and poetic devices can hardly be determined at the present stage of scholarship. It may only be surmised that at the time when the *Lay of Igor's Campaign* was written, the Russian poetic and epic tradition already had rather deep roots, especially since the *Lay* refers to the songs of a former bard, Boyan, who previously glorified the valor of Russian princes.

The subject and treatment of the *Lay* may be compared to some extent with the French *Chanson de Roland*. Both have for their topics a Christian army's fight for the honor of its country and its defeat by pagan warriors. Both treat nature as an almost animate participant in the military and national drama. Also, both use extensively fixed epithets in characterizing their heroes. A decade ago Roman Jakobson pointed out the *Lay*'s similarity to its contemporary Western counterpart in the use of pagan, pre-Christian motifs. He also showed the similarity of the poetic devices of the *Lay* to those studied and described by the Byzantine scholar Choiroboskos, whose treatise on poetic tropes and figures had been known in Russia since 1073. In view of these parallels with West European and Byzantine writings, it is possible to state that the *Lay* did not evolve exclusively from the Russian epic tradition but might also have been influenced by the general poetic environment of Western Europe and the Balkans, with which Russia was so closely connected at that time. In any event, the *Lay of Igor's Campaign* will probably continue to be an enigma for many more generations of scholars because it remains a unique specimen of unusually high quality in Kievan poetics.

The narrative part of the *Lay* is not very developed. Instead of reporting in detail the successive stages and episodes of the campaign, the author really only alludes to events and persons supposedly familiar to his audience or readers. Instead of communicating the minutiae of the battle, he impresses on his audience his own sorrow over the Russians' defeat and his desire to see Russia once again powerfully united in order to prevent further national calamity. The work strongly mirrors Russia's and the author's sorrow over the princes' feuds, their perpetual warring, and the political decline of Russian power.

The narrative structure given the *Lay* by its author, whose intent was apparently not so much to narrate as to warn his contemporaries of the perilous consequences of princely feuding, differs from that of most Western or later Russian epic works, whose usual purpose is to recall past deeds and glory. This might be explained by the fact that the *Lay* was composed almost immediately after Igor's stunning defeat, while the episodes of the campaign were still vividly preserved in the reader's memory.

The *Lay of Igor's Campaign* did not considerably influence Russian literature in the next decades and centuries. It was too different from the generally functional, didactic, and religious tenor of the other writings of the newly Christianized Russians. Its reference to the pagan Slavic gods, moreover, probably seemed to the clergy too hazardous to warrant any wide circulation, while the topic of defeat could not have been particularly popular among the princes, especially since in the very near future the relatively minor misfortunes of Igor's campaign were vastly overshadowed by a catastrophe of immensely greater magnitude. Therefore, it is not too surprising that the *Lay* was preserved only in a single manuscript and that only one other medieval Russian poetic work definitely reflects a strong stylistic and structural influence of the *Lay of Igor's Campaign*. This is *Zadonshchina*, written two hundred years later, on the occasion of the first major Russian victory, in 1380, over the nomads, Russia's historical enemy.

II. THE PERIOD OF THE TATAR YOKE AND FEUDAL DIVISION (1240–1478)

9. The Mongol Invasion

THE foreboding of the author of the *Lay of Igor's Campaign* and his apprehensions for Russia's future were soon justified by historical events. In 1223 the vanguards of Genghis Khan's

Mongol army, after a successful Caucasian campaign, unexpectedly crossed the Don River and inflicted a crushing defeat on regiments of the South Russian princes at the Kalka River. At this time the Mongols did not proceed to the conquest of Eastern Europe but crossed the Volga and disappeared into the Central Asian plains. In 1237, however, exactly half a century after the writing of the *Lay*, the Mongol hordes reappeared on the Volga, and in the following three years subjugated and devastated all of Russia.

It might be expected that the Mongol, or Tatar, Yoke ("Tatar" was the name of one of the Mongolian tribes of the Horde but became applied by the Russians to all of these Asian nomads) left a widespread influence on Russian culture and letters. Apart from the fact that Russian civilization was set back two centuries, however, this was not the case. Russian spiritual, artistic, and literary development remained entirely immune to the culture of these illiterate horsemen, while only a few political and military patterns of the Mongol Empire modified the previous Russian organizational forms. The Asian nomads—cattlemen and shepherds—did not settle in the Russian territories, but preferred the nearly uninhabited plains and grazing lands of the eastern and southern confines of present Russia to the forests and marshes of its central and northern parts, where most of the Slavic population lived. The tremendous differences in language, religon, and way of life between the sedentary Christian Slavs and the pagan (only subsequently Moslem) Asian nomads prevented the Russians from indulging in any widespread commerce with their conquerors, and there were few intermarriages between Russians and Tatars in the Middle Ages.

The century following the invasion was one of marked cultural decline but hardly of any perceptible changes in the basic features of Russian civilization. Monasteries and palaces had been burned, and the cultural elite decimated or abducted into slavery, but the surviving representatives of the Russian clergy and aristocracy tried to preserve the remnants of Russian civilization and literature although they were hardly able to develop them. The cultural decline was further intensified by the conquest of Western Russia by Poles and Lithuanians and the splitting up of Russian territories under the Mongols into innumerable small principalities that competed and fought among themselves. Only northern Russia, the republic of wealthy Novgorod, preserved the integrity of its immense territory, and the city itself became the center for burgeoning new forms in the arts, especially of architecture and painting.

10. MILITARY TALES

While no stylistic changes are perceptible in Russian writings of the first century after the Mongol conquest, their topics clearly evidence whether they were written before or after the collapse of Kievan Russia. One of the most popular subjects for thirteenth-century works was, of course, the Tatar invasion and therefore the military tale—already well known in Kievan literature, as seen from the *Lay of Igor's Campaign* and the chronicles—now became much more widespread. Of the new ones, two, the *Orison on the Downfall of Russia* and the *Tale of the Destruction of Riazan*, give an exceptionally artistic treatment of the invasion and the feelings of the survivors.

Still enigmatic in its origin, the *Orison on the Downfall of Russia* seems to be only an introduction to some now lost longer work. It speaks of the previous grandeur and glory of the realm founded by Vladimir and Yaroslav and is highly pathetic, but, unfortunately, the preserved fragments end exactly with the words that begin a description of the catastrophe.

Tales of the capture of various cities are poignant and numerous. Riazan, a city in the extreme southeast of Kievan territory, was the first to fall to the Tatar armies, and the description of its destruction is the most dramatic account of this type. The *Tale of the Destruction of Riazan* is a complex work in which four separate episodes and various genres are interwoven. The episode dealing with Evpaty Kolovrat, a *bogatyr* (knight) who challenged the Mongol army, has strong motifs of the oral epos, and is no less impressive than Western tales of heroic knightly deeds. Folklore elements can also be found in the laments of the princes. The narrative is considerably more vivid and dynamic than that of the *Lay of Igor's Campaign* or of earlier military tales. While some of the symbols and tropes have a close connection with those of the *Lay*, however, the *Tale* is far behind the *Lay* in its poetic and stylistic excellence. The dominant idea of the *Tale* is the juxtaposition of the Christian Russian army to the Tatar "infidels," and more than any other work of early Russian literature the *Tale* conveys the concept of Russia as the bulwark of Christian civilization against the hordes of pagan Central Asian nomads. Other military tales of the time deal with the conquest of Kiev and of other Russian cities that fell to the Tatars, as well as the first battle, in 1223, between Russians and Mongols on the Kalka River.

During these difficult years the Tatars were not the only conquerors of Russian lands. Poles and Lithuanians succeeded in occupying extensive regions in the west, from the Nemen to the Dniester rivers and from the Carpathian Mountains to Kiev and Smolensk. German knights of the Livonian Order took over present Latvia and Estonia and pushed against the ancient city of Pskov. Swedes appeared on the Neva River, attacking the confines of the territory of Novgorod. The defense of this northern border is the subject of many episodes of the *Life of Prince Alexander Nevsky* (called "Nevsky" for his defeat of the Swedes on the Neva River). In the manuscripts his *vita* usually follows the *Orison on the Downfall of Russia*, and some scholars even believe that the *Orison* was intended as an introduction to the life of this courageous prince who was so largely responsible for Russia's gradual rehabilitation after the Tatar conquest. Alexander, who died in 1263, was canonized primarily for his devotion to the cause of the Russian land and Church rather than for exceptional spirituality. Therefore, his *vita* is more a work of secular biography incorporating military tales than a piece of hagiography. The author widely used biblical portrayals and stylistics in Alexander's *Life*, and treated many events in the manner of the Byzantine chronicles and military stories. Alexander is compared to Roman emperors and biblical patriarchs The *Life* ends with a touching miracle: when, during Alexander's burial, the metropolitan wanted to put in Alexander's hand a parchment remitting his sins, in accordance with Church ritual the dead hero extended his hand to take it.

The defense of Pskov against the Lithuanians forms the background of the *Tale of Prince Dovmont*, written in the thirteenth century, while the miraculous deliverance of the city of Smolensk from the Tatars is related in the *Heroic Deeds of Mercurius of Smolensk*, written in the fourteenth, or even fifteenth, century In no other Russian military tale does the miraculous element play such importance as in this story, which is treated in the hagiographic manner: beheaded by the Tatars, Mercurius returns to the city he had saved, holding his severed head in his hands.

The great battle in 1380 at the Don River, where the Russians inflicted their first decisive defeat upon the Tatars toward the end of the Tatar Yoke, supplied rich material for several literary works. *Zadonshchina* (*The Deeds Beyond the Don*), the best known of these, written by Sofony of Riazan, is to a large extent an inversion of the *Lay of Igor's Campaign*. Indeed, Sofony appropriated many of the compositional patterns and poetic devices of the *Lay*, and in places *Zadonshchina* adheres almost literally to the figures of speech and symbolism of the *Lay of*

Igor's Campaign. Like the author of the *Lay*, Sofony had recourse to poetic generalization rather than to a minute description of the details of battle, and let the lyric laments of Russian women express the sorrow of the Russian land at the losses suffered by the Russian army. Still, the narrative of *Zadonshchina* is somewhat more detailed, realistic, and sustained in plot than the great twelfth-century Russian lay. Its spirit is entirely Christian, and it lacks the pagan tendencies of the former. While not so adept poetically, Sofony was no less skillful in expressing his ideas than was the anonymous bard of Kiev. Both gave voice to Russia's hopes, sorrows, and expectations: the *Lay* deplored the princes' disunity; *Zadonshchina* praised their successful united effort to cast off the foreign yoke.

Two other works that treat the same Russian victory, less poetic but more informative than *Zadonshchina*, are the *Tale of the Battle on the Don* in the Simon and Ermolinsky chronicles and the *Legend* (*Skazanie*) of the *Rout of Mamai* (khan of the Tatar Horde). In the latter are some beautiful, highly poetic descriptions of the Russian army and of the night preceding the battle.

With *Zadonshchina* the era of the Kievan tradition in Russian literature came to a close. During the cultural revival that ensued in Russia in the late fourteenth and fifteenth centuries, new problems, topics, and literary methods came to the fore.

11. THE VITA OF ORNAMENTAL FORMALISM

At the end of the fourteenth century Russian letters came under the influence of a new spiritual and literary movement that had arisen among the monks of Byzantium and of the Slavic Balkan states. The participants in this movement, who called themselves "Hesychasts" (from *Hesychia*—quietude, silence, indirectly, contemplation), taught self-perfection and domination of the passions. According to their views, a believer could achieve direct vision of the Divine Light, a visual contemplation of the Creator. This teaching, which to a large extent was conditioned by renunciation of the passions and the pleasures of this world and led its followers away from the realities of this life, resulted in the field of literature in the development of a highly artificial and rhetorical style. At first primarily influencing hagiography, in the fifteenth and sixteenth centuries this style spread to other types of writing. For a Hesychast writer, not the recorded biography but the ideal truth of the saints' lives was important. Their *vitae* depict not the everyday deeds of the heroes but rather the supreme truth and eternal significance of the saints' actions. Like the modern impressionist or even contemporary abstract painter, the writer conveyed a portrayal of the saint as he visualized it and not as it necessarily was.

In their search for a medium worthy of describing spiritual perfection, the Byzantine and Balkan-Slavic Hesychasts developed a highly ornate language. Its elements were bookish words, compounds (*composita*) consisting of two or three words, complex syntactical structure with a multitude of subordinate clauses, numerous epithets, repetition of the same sound at the beginning of each rhythmic unit of the sentence, and archaic grammatical forms. These devices conveyed to the *vita* an especially elevated and solemn tone.

Callistos (Patriarch of Constantinople from 1350 to 1363) was the first writer to apply widely this formal, sophisticated, and ornate style which, from Byzantium, spread to Serbia and Bulgaria and, at the beginning of the fifteenth century, to Russia. The Balkan-Slavic writers of this period considerably reformed their literary language by reviving outlived ancient grammatical forms of Church Slavonic. When the Hesychast literary vogue came to Russia, it also became instrumental there in restoring to the literary language the archaic Church Slavonic grammar and phonetics. This "neo-Byzantine" literary influence in Russia, whose duration is referred to as the second Balkan, or South Slavic, period in Russian literature, dislodged from Russian letters purely East Slavic vernacular forms, renewing the archaic Church Slavonic. The outstanding Russian representative of this new ornamental formalism, which Russians termed "weaving of words," was Epiphanius, called "the Wise" for his writings (died in 1422). His masterpieces were the well-known *Lives* of St. Sergius and St. Stephen, evangelizer of Perm, a Finnic region west of the Urals. Despite his rich stylistics, Epiphanius successfully conveys a realistic portrayal of the saints, adorned with prayers, eulogies, and laments, and his writings remained for some two centuries the most imitated specimens of the formal, ornamental style in Russia. In the mid-fifteenth century his work was continued by Pachomius the Serb, an emigré from the Balkans who reworked some of Epiphanius' *vitae* and composed numerous new ones.

Ornamental formalism reigned in Russian literature until the seventeenth century. Not all the literary works of these two centuries were written in this style, but it became almost compulsory in hagiography, sermons, and historical writings. The result was the transformation of the *vita* into a uniform enumer-

n of the saint's virtues, and lengthy eulogies that frequently
pletely overshadowed the actual story of his life. In the
-sixteenth century Metropolitan Macarius, tutor and adviser
he young Ivan IV, undertook a compilation (*Chetyi Minei*)
he finest in Russian spiritual literature, and at that time all
earlier *vitae* were reworked according to the exigencies of
amental formalism.

ide by side with the erudite writers of rhetorical *vitae* and
onicles, however, there were other literary works of the late
rteenth and fifteenth centuries whose authors used a simple,
ost vernacular, language without any particular embellish-
nt. A good example of such unsophistication and even naïve
ration are the early versions of the *vita* of St. Michael of
psko (its later versions were reworked by the Muscovite
ters of ornamental style) in which the hagiographer con-
trates rather on interesting episodes of the saint's life than on
thets and eulogies.

Also in the same unadorned, yet expressive, language is the
-tale of Prince Peter of Murom and his wife, Fevronia. This
he only medieval Russian literary work with some romantic
tent, and it supplies many everyday details from the life of
se saint-spouses. Fevronia, a peasant girl by origin, is
ced against the background of rural life. The composition of
narrative is complex, containing legendary folklore motifs
rwoven with the narrative. This charming story, which ends
h a description of the hero's and heroine's death and post-
nous miracles, may be considered a Russian counterpart of
Western legend of Tristan and Isolde.

12. CHRONICLES OF THE FOURTEENTH AND FIFTEENTH CENTURIES

The writing of annals was almost completely interrupted by
Mongol invasion. Kiev and Vladimir, Russia's northern capi-
were so thoroughly sacked by the invaders that cultural life
re was entirely suspended. Therefore the main chronicles of
thirteenth and fourteenth centuries are those of Novgorod,
er, and Rostov; in the fourteenth century, when Moscow
se as a new political rival, chronicle writing also commenced
re. The transfer of the Russian metropolitan see to Moscow
1325 made out of this previously insignificant princedom an
portant religious and cultural center. The Muscovite chroni-
s of the late fourteenth and early fifteenth centuries—the
on and *Trinity* (*Troitsky*) chronicles—include the ancient
mary Chronicle, and use widely the annals of such other

cities as Novgorod, Smolensk, Riazan, Tver, and others. T‌
cultivate insistently the idea of Russian reunification under
aegis of the Muscovite prince. The fact that they are only c
pilations necessarily deprives them of inner unity and of
stylistic uniformity that characterizes the *Primary, Kievan,*
Galician-Volynian chronicles, and they often grow into tren‌
dous codices, since they were supposed to contain ever-grow‌
new material beside the wealth of early historical informat‌
While the chronicler's task became increasingly difficult in th‌
centuries, he continued to work according to the origin‌
elaborated methods: yearly entries and the inclusion of het‌
geneous material. Among the codices of the era the most im‌
tant are the *Laurentian*, written in 1337 for Great Prince Dm‌
of Suzdal and Nizhny-Novgorod; the *Hypatian*, compiled in
early fifteenth century; and the *Radzivil*, or *Königsberg*, c‌
pleted in the late fifteenth century and given by Prince‌
Radzivil to the Königsberg library. All of these contain the
tire text of the *Primary Chronicle* and rich later material.

Since the late fifteenth century there developed in Russi‌
new type of historical work, the so-called chronograph, in wh‌
the material was organized into article-chapters in place of
customary yearly entries and in which surveys of world eve‌
were usually included along with events in Russian hist‌
They were written in the new ornamental style with he‌
panegyrics to the rulers and Church leaders, a style wh‌
spread to the chronicles themselves, whose compilation c
tinued into the late seventeenth century.

13. POLITICAL LEGENDS AND TALES

From the mid-fourteenth to the mid-fifteenth century †
principalities, Tver and Moscow, competed for supremacy .
attempted to unify around themselves the central regions‌
Russia on the upper Volga and Oka rivers. The victor ⸱
Moscow, which subjugated Tver and won leadership over
central Russia. The subsequent unification of all of Great Ru‌
was completed in 1478, when Ivan III (1462–1505), the foun‌
of Muscovite power, forced Novgorod also to accept the su‌
rainty of Moscow.

Eager to justify their claims to the political leadership
Russia, the Muscovite dynasty and its ideologists elaborated,
cording to the medieval tradition, a number of political lege‌
most of which had their origin in Byzantine and Western
torical myths. Among them, the *Legend of the Babylonian K*‌
dom and the *Legend of the Princes of Vladimir* propagated

a that only a powerful ruler could guarantee the security of
nation. The latter legend aimed, moreover, at providing the
scovite princes with a respectable genealogy: according to
; legend, the Muscovite dynasty descended not only from
f-mythical Rurik but had its origins much deeper in history—
founder was said to be Prus, a wholly imaginary brother of
Roman Emperor Augustus.

The narrow purpose of the Muscovite political legends—to
ablish the prestige of the Muscovite dynasty and gain support
its political claims—to a large extent limited their circula-
ı and popularity. More widely read was the Novgorodian
e of the White Cowl. Novgorod, Moscow's main adversary,
> sought historical tradition in defending its independence
l republican institutions against encroachment by the Mus-
ite princes. The central idea of this tale is Russia's selection
God as the defender of Orthodoxy: the final kingdom of the
ly Spirit, which will replace both the Old Testamentary
gdom of law and the New Testamentary kingdom of grace,
uld become manifest in the Russian land. Novgorod and its
hbishop are singled out in this legend as the heirs to one of
most sacred symbols of pure Christianity, the White Cowl,
possession of which endowed this old republican city with
ritual superiority and placed it on a level with Moscow in the
ere of Church tradition. The *Tale of the White Cowl* became
·ticularly popular in the seventeenth century and had a pro-
nd influence on the subsequent development of Russian
ology. In connection with this legend there arose in the early
:eenth century the theory of Moscow, the Third Rome. This
icept, however, differed considerably from that of the *Tale of*
· *White Cowl,* which taught that the entire people of Russia,
: only Moscow and its ruler, bore historical responsibility for
· guardianship of true Orthodoxy.

III. THE MUSCOVITE PERIOD
MUSCOVITE RUSSIA'S FIRST CENTURY (1478–1598)

1478 Ivan III, by annexing the tremendous territory of the
public of Novgorod, completed the main stage of the unifica-
n of Russia, which for centuries had remained divided into
all feudal principalities. Two years later the Russians shook
forever the Tatar Yoke, and the Golden Horde disintegrated.
ne seventy years later, in 1547, Ivan IV was crowned the
:t Tsar of Russia by the wise and erudite Metropolitan
ıcarius. Feudal Russia, with its endless fratricidal feuds and

princely warring, was replaced by one powerful, unified au
cratic state. This process of unification and the rise of autocr
required considerable military effort to preserve the new ur
and defend the young tsardom, as well as the further elaborat
of a new political philosophy justifying this newborn power
is therefore understandable that throughout the late fiftee
and sixteenth centuries, during the reigns of Ivan III (146
1505). Vassily III (1505–1533) and Ivan IV (1533–158
Russian literature was dominated by two basic genres: the m
tary tale and political polemics.

14. The New Military Tale

In the late fifteenth century there appeared a new type
military tale—narratives about the siege and defense of fortres
or cities. One of the first of these was the *Tale of the Taking
Constantinople*, which fell to the Turks in 1453. It was writ
by a certain Nestor Iskander, a professional Russian soldier w
had been captured by the Turks, forced to accept Islam, a
to join the Ottoman army. He was a writer of considera
talent, and described colorfully as an eyewitness the siege a
storming of the city. While he is highly rhetorical, he nonet
less conveys a realistic picture of the battles. His original nar
tive was apparently reworked by some Muscovite writer w
added an ideological introduction and conclusion: after the c
quest of the Balkans and the fall of the capital of Orthodo
Russia was to take over the role of protector of Orthodoxy a
become responsible for its fate.

The siege of the Tatar capital, Kazan, which was taken
1552 by Russian troops under Ivan IV, supplied the topic
two very different narratives on the subject. One, the *Kaz
History*, was written in the 1560's by an anonymous Russ
who, similarly to Nestor Iskander, became prisoner of the Tat
and spent two decades in Moslem captivity. He observed t
military operations from within the city, on the Tatar side, a
after the Russians' victory joined Ivan's army. His work, I
sides depicting the siege, covers an extensive period of tir
studies Russo-Tatar relations, the life of Russians in Tatar ca
tivity, and the preparations for war. His literary devices a
patterned considerably after Iskander's tale. Although he d
picts the heavy fighting and storming of Kazan in long a
ornate sentences, he provides very lively descriptions. Partic
larly impressive is his account of the tsar's return to Mosc
and the capital's jubilation. Another treatment of the sar
siege was given by Prince Andrew Kurbsky, one of Ivan's co

manders, in his *History of Tsar and Grand Prince Ivan Vassilie-vich*. Kurbsky is much more matter of fact, and uses the rich stylistics of his era with great taste and economy.

The *Story of Stephen Bathory's Campaign Against Pskov* exceeds all previous military tales in the extended employment of intricate, ornamented stylistics, allegory, metaphors, and epithets. The author belonged to a particularly sophisticated current in Russia letters, and had perfect command of all the subtleties of ornamental formalism. The use of compound words, figures of speech, and elaborate sentences makes this tale one of the best specimens of the heavy, embellished style of early Muscovite literature.

15. POLEMIC LITERATURE

Beginning in the early fifteenth century, polemics on theological and political problems form a prominent part of Russian letters of the early Muscovite era. The first polemic arose over the heresy of the Strigolniks, a movement for Church reform that denied the necessity of some sacraments and of an ordained clergy and that grew very strong in Pskov and Novgorod around 1400. A century later appeared the rationalistic Judaizers, who to some extent followed the teachings of the Strigolniks but also denied veneration of icons and the dogma of the Trinity, thus preceding by half a century the emergence of the West European Unitarianism of Servetus and Socinius. This movement spread to Moscow, and Ivan III himself was strongly suspected of being a secret sponsor of the sect. In any case, the main opponent of the Judaizers, Abbot Joseph of Volok, who finally won the struggle and succeeded in destroying the movement, clearly hinted at the "pernicious" role in Church affairs played by Ivan III, the founder of Russian political unity. The lively polemics for and against the heresy of the Judaizers lasted several decades and produced a number of important works.

The struggle against the Judaizers was not yet over when a new conflict arose between the supporters and opponents of monastic estates. Joseph of Volok once again came out forcefully in favor of the estates of the monasteries, which he called "the wealth of the poor" and which in his eyes were fundamental for maintaining and educating the clergy as well as for the Church's social work. In Joseph's opinion the Church was responsible for the souls and well-being of believers and was supposed to take the necessary action for preserving their spiritual condition. His adversaries were the contemplative hermit-elders from the hermitages of northern Russia beyond the Volga,

who taught that the Church's wealth leads to corruption of the
clergy and diverts the attention of the monks from their spiritual
tasks. They opposed Church intervention in the inner life of
believers, and considered that only a Christian's personal action
may lead to his salvation. Their leader, Nil Sorsky, a pupil of
the Greek Hesychasts, insisted that the way to God can be
found only through suppression of the passions, self-perfection,
and a believer's individual effort to understand and follow the
divine commandments. His teaching in some respects also had
certain points in common with later Western Protestantism, since
he was against adornment of the Church and excessive ritualism,
supporting a purely spiritual, nonsocial role for the clergy. The
polemics between the followers of Joseph, called the "Jose-
phites," and the Trans-Volga elders was largely a discussion of
the necessity for discipline and the enforcement of Church law
against spiritual freedom and an individual approach to God.

In the 1550's there arose in Moscow and northern Russia still
another religious movement, this time under the very definite
influence of the Western Reformation. Like the previous non-
conformist sects, its leader disputed the value of the sacraments
and the Church hierarchy. This new threat to Orthodoxy, however, was rapidly liquidated and did not leave many traces in
Russian spirituality. The controversies around these various
teachings led to the growth of a prolific polemic literature
which, while neither fictional nor even particularly artistically
written, is nonetheless an important witness to an intense spiritual and intellectual life in the first century of the Muscovite
Era.

Purely political polemics are best seen in the *Story of Sultan
Mehmed*, by Ivan Peresvetov, and in the correspondence between Ivan IV ("the Terrible") and Prince Andrew Kurbsky. In
his story, written about 1550, Peresvetov describes conditions
in Russia under the guise of those in the Ottoman Empire, and
argues against the excessive power of the boyar aristocracy. He
was a firm supporter of autocracy, in which he saw the best
instrument for consolidating national power: "When the Tsar is
gentle and weak, his Tsardom declines and his glory diminishes.
When the Tsar is dread and wise, his Tsardom grows and his
name is glorified on the earth," writes Peresvetov. It can be
considered that the autocratic rule of Ivan IV was to a certain
extent the result of Peresvetov's writings, in which the latter
suggested breaking the power of the feudal lords.

Prince Andrew Kurbsky represented a completely different
viewpoint. He defended the political role of princes, boyars,

d aristocracy in general, which he regarded as the bearer of
tional stability, conservatism, and wisdom. According to
urbsky, autocratic rule necessarily leads to excesses, and a
oud ruler becomes instrumental in the decline of his nation.
well-trained dialectician and writer, Kurbsky cleverly and
nvincingly presents his views in his correspondence with Ivan
'. He appeals to the tsar to cease persecuting the aristocracy
d to pardon the victims of his wrath. Ivan was hardly less
udite than the prince, but he did not command his passions
d pen as well, and exploded in vituperative replies to Kurbsky,
s former friend and commander in chief of the Russian armies.
an is sarcastic and biting, and does not shun using the most
fensive language in speaking of his enemies. The tsar's strong-
t argument is the boyars' misrule, which he describes in
collecting his childhood. While Kurbsky is always concise and
the point, Ivan is verbose, accumulating one argument after
other to prove his views. Very different in their respective
vles, Prince Kurbsky and Tsar Ivan are certainly the most
tstanding of Russian sixteenth-century polemists, and their
tters are the best example of the Muscovite epistolary art.

16. ENCYCLOPEDIC WORKS

The greatest literary undertaking of the reign of the dread
ar Ivan IV were the encyclopedic compilations of various
pes of Russian writings initiated and conducted under the
pervision of Macarius, Metropolitan of Moscow from 1543
1564. The most important of these works were the *Reading
eneae* (*Chetyi Minei*), a collection of *vitae* and other spiritu-
y edifying readings arranged for each calendar day. Alto-
ther, there are in these *Meneae* some thirteen thousand folio
.ges, the equivalent of thirty or forty modern volumes; most
the existing *vitae* were rewritten for this new compilation in
e official style of ornamental formalism.

The other encyclopedic work, written in the same ponderous
rmal manner, was the *Book of Grades* (*Stepennaia kniga*), an
tensive rewriting of the chronicles and chronographs in which
ecial attention was paid to the biographies of Russian rulers.
ie main literary interest presented by this historical work
nsists in the small stories and anecdotes incorporated in them
ften taken from oral folklore) which herald the nascence of
e fictional short story. Both of these works abound in neo-
gical compounds, epithets, and long rhetorical constructions.

The third important encyclopedic work of this time was the
kon Illustrated Codex of Chronicles*, a monumental historical

encyclopedia covering not only Russian but also world histor
as far as it was known to sixteenth-century Muscovites.
consists of twelve enormous volumes richly illustrated with ov
ten thousand miniatures.

The completion of these catenae apparently exhausted th
energies of Russian writers of the late Byzantine tradition ar
the talent of the ornamental formalists. After codifying ar
rewriting nearly all of previous Russian literature in these serie
it was difficult and almost purposeless to invent any ne
sophistications in the adorned and heavy style. Thus, the *Rea*
ing Meneae, Book of Grades, and *Illustrated Codex* became th
final monuments of the period of exclusive Byzantine domin
tion over Russian literature. While ornamental stylistics laste
into the seventeenth century, undergoing a final blossoming
1615–1630, new currents and literary genres began to appear.

This last century of the undisputed domination of Byzanti
stylistics over Russian writing was simultaneously the last ce
tury of the Rurik dynasty, which, according to legend, ha
ruled in Russia since 862. After the death of Ivan IV, his so
the last offspring of this dynasty—Tsar Theodore—reigned f
some fifteen years, but with his death in 1598, the Rurik dynas
was extinguished. During the following fifteen years (159
1613), called the "Time of Troubles" (*Smuta*), Russians wi
nessed four legitimate tsars from three new dynasties, two tsa
impostors, grave social disturbances, the breakdown of centr
government and foreign intervention, all of which brought th
nation to the verge of another complete catastrophe. Only
1613 was a new tsar, Michael (ruled 1613–1645), elected. Ts
Michael was the first of the Romanov dynasty, which reigne
for the next 304 years, disappearing only with the revolution
1917. His task was to rehabilitate the state, put an end to Poli
and Swedish intervention, and bring social order to the natio
These tasks were fairly soon accomplished and order restore
but Russian culture and letters survived this historical trial ve
considerably changed.

B. THE WANE OF MEDIEVAL RUSSIA (1598–1700)

 EROSION of the traditional Byzantine patterns in ancient Russi
literature becomes perceptible from the second part of th
sixteenth century. In historical works authors tend to prefer na
ration of the mythical legend in the manner of the Poli
chroniclers to the down-to-earth style of early Russian annalis
Prose becomes more and more frequently interspersed wi
fragments of rhymed couplets. Job, Russia's first patriarch (fro

1589 to 1605), included even in his *vita* of Tsarevich Dmitry long versified passages. One of the best, but now almost completely forgotten, medieval Russian hymnologists, Abbot Markel Bezborody, soon after his retirement in 1557, wrote a memorial church service to the saints Barlaam and Josaphat in the unusual form of a dramatic poem with vivid dialogues. Many hagiographers, especially those who did not belong to the official school of ornamental formalism but who wrote in a simple, unadorned manner, began to include the autobiographical reminiscences of their heroes, thus conveying a more realistic tenor to their *vitae*. Even the writers of these *vitae* began to lift the veil of anonymity, providing the reader with more information about themselves. Along with the steady growth of autobiographical elements in both the *vita* and in historical narratives, the Western picaresque tale and knightly novel became translated into Russian for the first time. Finally, fictional characters and a satirical portrayal of Russian life make their appearance, as in the short tale of *Shemiaka's Judgment,* written probably around the end of the sixteenth century.

This inauguration of new ways in Russian letters and the passing of the old literary tradition were accelerated by the events of the Time of Troubles, when large numbers of foreigners—Poles, Lithuanians, Swedes, and German and French mercenaries—came to Russia in the ranks of invading armies. At the same time many representatives of Russian society became closely acquainted with Western modes of life during their captivity in Poland, Lithuania, and Sweden. The reunion of "Little Russia"[1] with Muscovy in 1653 intensified Western, especially Polish, cultural influences. Moreover, the alienation from the hierarchy and the state of the conservative, Old Believer wing of the Church[2] considerably weakened the influence of traditionalists with the government and the cultural elite, and facilitated the further secularization and modernization of the Russian state, its culture, and letters.

To be sure, many Russian writers still continued until the middle of the seventeenth century to use the previously established literary manners, methods, and devices, but the more important and interesting part of literary production comes now from writers seeking new ways of expression. From the beginning of this century the *vita* was gradually replaced by secular biography, autobiography, and first-person confession. Ever-

---

[1] The southern part of Russia, with Kiev, now called "the Ukraine."
[2] For more detailed information on this movement, see the introduction to *The Life of Archpriest Avvakum by Himself* in this volume.

growing attention is given to the psychology of the heroes, and
purely fictional characters come into being. The occasional
rhymed couplets and versified fragments grow into larger poetic
works, and lyric and epic songs open a new era in the expression
of feelings and emotions.

17. HISTORICAL WORKS OF THE TIME OF TROUBLES

During the decades immediately following the Time of
Troubles, historical works describing the calamities of social
disturbance and foreign intervention played a dominant role in
Russian letters. Both old and new literary methods characterize
this transitional period. While some seventeenth-century writers
achieved a high perfection in the employment of ornate stylistics, behind their rhetorical facade can frequently be found
detailed portrayals of the character and psychology of their contemporaries as well as analyses of the reasons for the great
cataclysm. The best stylist of the time was the *dyak* (high
official) Ivan Timofeev, author of the well-known *Vremennik*
(*Book of the Times*). His sentences are often built of rhythmic
units with occasional rhyme, and are extremely rich in epithets,
compound words, and a symbolic interpretation of names: for
instance, artillery becomes "artifacts for the destruction of
walls"; boats—"transporters over the water"; Theodore—"the gift
of God"; John—"the Grace." The abundance of stylistic devices
and allegories makes a reading of this clever analytical work—
his study of the time of Ivan IV is particularly penetrating—
extremely difficult. Timofeev's ideology is strictly conservative,
the Time of Troubles being, in his mind, the result of the disappearance of the ancient dynasty and the rise of new social
groups. Still, his conservatism does not preclude a severe judgment of the boyars, the upper class of this semifeudal society,
whom Timofeev accuses of political irresponsibility and lack of
civic virtue.

Other authors of historical works on the Time of Troubles—
Palitsyn, Khvorostinin, Katyrev-Rostovsky, Shakhovskoy—use
predominantly the same literary devices but, being more modest
in displaying their stylistic ability, their works are more acces-
sible to contemporary readers and translators. The most distinguished of these works is the *Povest'* (*Story*) written by Prince
I. Katyrev-Rostovsky around 1626. Despite frequent rhetorical
digressions, effusions of sympathy and indignation, he provides
a well-organized, clear, and rather simply written account of
events of the Time of Troubles. His versified fragments are
skillfully rhymed, and refresh the prose recital of events. He

should be remembered as the first seventeenth-century writer to present physical and psychological depictions of his heroes, as well as descriptions of landscape. Palitsyn's *Skazanie* (*Narrative*), the main part of which deals with the siege of the Holy Trinity and St. Sergius Monastery near Moscow, is remarkable for its powerful and severe philippic against the ruling classes of Russia, which, in his eyes, neglected their Christian and patriotic duties and, instead of caring for the nation and Church, indulged in the accumulation of personal power and wealth. The works devoted to the Time of Troubles are so numerous that it is hardly possible even to enumerate them here, but at least one other such work should be mentioned, the *Tale on the Death of Prince Skopin-Shuysky*. It is notable for the touching laments uttered by the prince's relatives after his poisoning. The author made in these laments extended use of folklore motifs, cleverly weaving them into the fabric of his tale.

18. Late Muscovite Vitae and Autobiography

The drastic changes in the traditional genres are particularly visible in the seventeenth-century *vita*. One of the earliest of this century was written by K. Osoryin, who, soon after the death of his mother in 1604, Yuliania Lazarevskaia, wrote the story of her life. The matter-of-fact, simple, and realistic narrative style of this *vita* opened a new era in Russian hagiography. Yuliania, who later was canonized, is presented against a background of the everyday life of rural Russia. In place of the habitual eulogies and stereotyped enumeration of the saint's virtues, Osoryin supplies details of family relations, of his mother's daily household occupations, her generosity toward the poor and the sick, and her help to the peasants during the famine that struck Russia under Boris Godunov. Of course, there are in this *vita* some descriptions of miracles performed by St. Yuliania, but for the first time the heroine of a hagiographic work is neither a nun distinguished by her holy life nor a pious princess, but the simple and devout wife of a small nobleman. The story's language is simple and unadorned, very fitting for a description of the life of this charitable and unobtrusive woman.

Close to the realistic descriptions found in the *vita* of Yuliania Lazarevskaia are the *vitae* of St. Dionysius, Abbot of the Holy Trinity and St. Sergius Monastery, of Ivan Neronov, of Boyarina Morozova—the two latter being important leaders of the Old Believers—and of Theodore Rtischev, boyar and close friend of Tsar Alexis (1645–1676). Although they preserve some features of traditional hagiography, most of these works are secular biographies of people of exemplary religious life, particularly the last, the story of a boyar noted for his welfare work and his role in promoting enlightenment in Russia. These *vitae* are almost completely devoid of rhetorical stylistics, and frequently employ elements of the vernacular language.

In the 1670's leaders of the schismatic Old Believers wrote the first true Russian autobiographies. *The Life of Archpriest Avvakum by Himself* belongs among the most significant works of medieval Russian literature, and modern Russian literary historians are unanimous in considering Avvakum one of the greatest masters of the Russian tongue. Concise, expressive, biting, and sarcastic, Avvakum broke radically with the old formalist tradition and the centuries-long use of Church Slavonic as the written language of Russian letters. D. Mirsky feels that Avvakum was the only Russian writer to use satisfactorily a pure Great Russian vernacular (the spoken language of Muscovy, present central and northern Russia) for a literary purpose: "Avvakum molded it into a new form for his own purpose, revamped it, widened its use and gave to this language new, purely literary, importance. His style is active, original, literary, creative." Avvakum reduced the length of the sentence, renounced the use of subordinate clauses, participles and gerunds, multiple epithets and compounds. He saturated his short, dynamic phrases—usually some eight to twelve words in length —with nouns and verbs. This leader of the Old Believers was not only a consummate stylist and expressionist but also a master of psychological delineations, and from his pen issued concise, pointed characterizations of his contemporaries. When appropriate, however, Avvakum knew how to use rhetorical stylistics in descriptions of his co-believers, as, for instance, in that of Boyarina Morozova. While his *Life* was the best of his numerous works, in most of Avvakum's writings can be found his vivid, colorful, colloquial language and his unusual gift for observation.

Another outstanding autobiography, or, rather, confession, came from the pen of Avvakum's spiritual father, Monk Epiphanius, who recorded his martyrdom and spiritual experiences during the persecutions inflicted upon the Old Believers by the Church and government. While Avvakum's *Life* treats his sermons, tribulations, and struggle for the old faith, Epiphanius' *Confession* presents the powerful, moving story of the writer's inner life, his doubts and visions, mystical experiences, and spiritual recoveries. This "Jobian" monologue is the first instance in Russian literature of the "exposure of the soul," which later became so famous in the works of Dostoevsky and Tolstoy.

The emergence of secular biography, autobiography, and the literary confession signaled the end of the medieval literary patterns. With the secularization of life, literature turned away from purely religious-historical biography. New ways of life, together with freer cultural and spiritual criticism, demanded a new type of letters, greater realism, and a more penetrating portrayal of character and human psychology. A fictional hero replaced the historical or hagiographical one, and the novella and satirical tale made their appearance.

19. The Birth of Fiction

The rise of fiction was the most spectacular literary event of the last century of Muscovite Russia. Many literary historians classify all the fictional works of this time under the term *povest'* (tale, long story, or novella), but among these numerous works with fictional heroes and plots can be distinguished two different genres. One, of the novella type, centers upon the deeds of the main character. In the other, the satirical tale, the social aspect, and the criticism of conditions and mores, overshadow the narrative part and character delineation. Both of these types of *povest'* evidently arose under the influence of Western picaresque novels that were translated in the seventeenth century into Russian, as, for instance, *Peter of the Golden Keys, Brunswick, Prince Bova, Basil the Golden-Haired, Eruslan Lazarevich* (of Oriental origin), or the *History of Apollonius of Tyre*. The seventeenth-century Russian novella, however, has a simpler structure than Western picaresque novels. It is much more concise, contains fewer characters and adventures, and the narrative is provided a purely Russian socio-historical setting. The most interesting aspects of this new genre are its unexpectedly wide range of topics, its moral appraisals, linguistic facets, and manners of treatment.

The *Tale of Savva Grudtsyn*, which to some extent resembles the story of Dr. Faust's temptations, is probably the oldest Russian novella, the earliest version dating from the middle of the seventeenth century. Written in heavy Church Slavonic and interwoven with hagiographic motifs, the tale depicts Savva's amorous adventures, and its realistic, even naturalistic, depictions of the worlds of the merchant and soldier are strikingly novel. Savva's adventures are placed against an actual historical background, and even the name of this fictitious hero belongs to a well-known merchant family. The same theme—the down-

fall and moral recovery of a youth—is the basis of another
charming novella, this one in verse form, *Misery-Luckless-Plight*
which, for its choice use of the vernacular, the extensive inclu
sion of figures of folk speech, and its impeccable structure, can
be considered one of the finest works of late medieval literature

Shifting still further away from the earlier literary manner
is the *Tale of Frol Skobeev, the Rogue.* Any moral element i
entirely absent from this work, and the author obviously enjoy
relating the successful adventures of another new hero—a rogue
from the lower nobility whose swindles finally open for him the
door to the society of the upper aristocracy. While Savva
Grudtsyn is the victim of his own passions and of sorcery, Fro
Skobeev is simply an adroit, cynical scamp who cares nothing
for true love and for whom the seduction of aristocratic An
nushka is merely a means to social success. The tale's language
shows a new stage in the development of literary Russian: in
place of the heavy Church Slavonic of *Savva Grudtsyn,* the
author of *Frol Skobeev* uses the vernacular extensively and doe
not shun vulgarity.

An intermediate stage among these three novellas is repre
sented by the tale *Karp Sutulov,* the story of a merchant's virtu
ous wife who cleverly maintains her virtue during her husband's
absence on a business trip. A contrasting evolution of amorou
motifs can be found in a touching *Novel in Verse,* written prob
ably toward the very end of the century, about a young gir
whose father forces her to break with her true love and marry
another man. This tale is rich in colorful details of everyday life
during this culturally and socially transitional period. The *Tale
of Solomonia, the Possessed,* on the other hand, is the mos
striking Russian medieval horror novella because of its demono
logical scenes. In most of these novellas the plots and characters
are given a precise setting as to locale and time.

No less rich is seventeenth-century satire, often written in
rhymed verse. Its oldest specimen, *Shemiaka's Judgment,* men
tioned above, is charming for its naïve and abrupt style. The
judicial system of medieval Russia suffered strongly from the
partiality and graft of the judges, and supplied abundant mate
rial for satire. Shemiaka is the classic type of venal judge, and
this story, which became extremely popular in seventeenth- and
eighteenth-century Russia, is known in innumerable prose and
verse versions. A similar theme appears in the various prose
and verse versions of the satire *Yorsh Yorshovich (Ruff, Son of
Ruff): Proceedings of a Suit Brought by the Bream Against the
Ruff in the Case of the Lake and Rivers of Rostov.* This theme

of the partiality or impartiality of judges goes far back into history, to Buddhist, Tibetan, and Indian legends, Arabic tales, or ballads on the judgments of Charlemagne. Similar tales were certainly popular in oral form in Russia for centuries, but only now, with the relaxation of state and Church control over literature and the breakdown of a purely spiritually oriented culture, did they become available in written form. Other satirical poems and prose narratives have as their heroes drunkards, corrupt clerics and monks (as, for instance, in the *Supplication of Kaliazin* and the *Novella of Priest Savva*); the virtuous man and the sinner (as in the *Legend of the Rooster and the Fox*, the rooster being the symbol of polygamic man); or the debauched aristocracy, a jealous husband, and inefficient administrators. The number of novellas and satires penned in the seventeenth century is extremely large, and they clearly reflect the secularization of Old Muscovy and the collapse of its traditional mode of life and mentality.

20. POETRY

In the nineteenth century the beginning of Russian poetry was usually ascribed to Simeon Polotsky (1629–1680), a West Russian scholar and poet of Polish training and culture who, after coming to Moscow in 1664, became the writer of odes to the court and tutor to Tsar Alexis' children. Later research has discarded Polotsky not only as the initiator of Russian poetry but even as the first poet of the syllabic school of versification. As early as 1608 a nobleman, Ivanets Frunikov, wrote an ironical versified epistle, full of puns and folk witticisms, the *Letter of a Nobleman to a Nobleman*. With this oldest dated Russian work in verse not only Russian rhymed poetry began, but also its satirical and ironic ramifications—which later, after the middle of the century, produced verse versions of such satirical tales as *Shemiaka's Judgment*, *Yorsh Yorshovich*, or *Foma and Erema*. All of them use the vernacular, folk witticisms, and the rhymed couplet of the *skomorokhs*, folk jesters and entertainers. As every product of folk poetics, which abound in rhymed puns, colloquial sayings and vulgarisms, such works, unfortunately, are hardly fitted for translation.

At the same time, also in the beginning of the seventeenth century, there appeared the so-called "presyllabic" versification, of a more formal type, which was characterized by a regular use of rhymed couplets in a line of undetermined length, vacillating usually between eight and sixteen syllables, but with no specific meter. Patriarch Job in his *vita* of Tsarevich Dmitry, mentioned above, used a wealth of such couplets for the first time in a hagiographic work. Numerous similarly versified fragments can be found in the historical writings of the Time of Troubles, especially those of I. Katyrev-Rostovsky and G. Shakhovskoy, as well as in *The New Story About the Glorious Muscovite Tsardom* (*Novaya povest*) written around 1610. One of these earliest poets was Prince Ivan A. Khvorostinin, who in 1624 wrote the first large, formal poetic work, *Epistle Against Blaspheming Heretics,* a monumental theological poem abounding in autobiographical digressions. Directed against the propagation in Russia of Western religious beliefs, Khvorostinin's *Epistle* numbers over three thousand versified lines. The vogue for versification (*stikhobesie*) spread rapidly to various genres of Muscovite letters, and Khvorostinin's example was followed by scores of Russian versifiers who complied their theological and political treatises in rhymed form. Even many of the Old Believers, usually the staunch enemies of all new spiritual and cultural currents, succumbed to the temptations of this new vogue and also wrote some of their protests in verse form.

An attractive aspect of seventeenth-century Russian poetry can be found in lyric verses in which writers gave expression to their feelings, hopes, and sorrows. The earliest of these were recorded, surprisingly enough, by an English traveler in Russia in 1619, a certain Richard James, in whose transcriptions have been preserved the oldest known specimens of Russian lyric verse. The above-mentioned *Novel in Verse,* a huge work organized in alphabetic form with each chapter beginning with a consecutive letter of the alphabet, is partially a novella, partially a love poem. To the same transitional type also belongs *Misery-Luckless-Plight.* Toward the end of the century some remarkable lyric songs were written or recorded by Peter Kvashnin, S. Pazukhin, and other poets of this new Muscovite school. Most of them show the strong influence of folklore and are in the meter of folk lyrics, although some use the rhymed endings that developed under Western poetic influence, and a rather novel and sophisticated vocabulary.

The final stage of seventeenth-century Russian poetry is represented by the appearance of "syllabic" versification, which had come into ascendance in Polish poetry and made its way to Russia. The prosodic foundations of syllabic verse were a fixed number of syllables in each line, exclusively feminine rhyme, and a *caesura,* or break, in the middle of each line. This method of versification, so perfectly suited to the Polish language because of its constant accent on the penultimate syllable, was

dly appropriate for Russian, with its unstable stress. There-
e syllabic verse lasted only a short time in Russia, and syllabic
etry completely disappeared from Russian letters in the
ond quarter of the eighteenth century leaving very few traces
Russia's further poetic development. It was important, how-
er, for acquainting Russians with the formal techniques of
sody.

This syllabic versification came to Muscovy from western and
thern Russia (the Ukraine), where scholars and poets dur-
the century of Polish domination were strongly influenced
Polish culture. The earliest syllabic poems appeared in
ssian as early as the 1650's, but the first significant Russian
abic poet was S. Polotsky, mentioned above, who was also
first Russian poet whose poems were printed during his life-
e. An erudite scholar and accomplished technician of *ars
tica,* Polotsky was not a man of real poetic inspiration. His
ious work falls into two categories: odes written in his capac-
as court panegyrist, and didactic poems revealing to Musco-
s either ancient mythology or some achievement of Western
olarship. Skillfully constructed and often formed in geometric
pes and figures, in accordance with the mode of the time,
verses are dry and uninspiring, and should be classified
her as the writings of a leader of the enlightenment than of
enuine poet.

From the point of view of the development of the Russian
rary language, Polotsky's verses—written in an artificial ad-
ture of the Muscovite and Kievan versions of Church Sla-
ic—were a step backward, away from the increasingly simple,
nacular language of the novellas, satires, and autobiographies.
otsky's importance in Russian literature is primarily historical
ause his work, which belongs more to baroque than to
dieval literature, in the periodization suggested by D. Chizh-
ky, brought Russia entirely into the literary sphere of the
st. In the baroque period of the late seventeenth century,
ich signaled the end of the centuries-long medieval tradition,
rominent literary role was played by Polotsky's Muscovite
owers, K. Istomin, S. Medvedev, and K. Khonykov, and later
the eighteenth century by A. Kantemir. Their language is
newhat easier than that of Polotsky, and they reveal more
uine poetic inspiration than did their teacher, but they do
excel him in erudition and poetic techniques.

The emergence of poetry was one of the most obvious mani-
tations of the profound changes in Russian literature. Western
des of life and culture rapidly won a place in Russia, and

Muscovy, in the second half of the seventeenth century, v
very different not only from what it had been in the sixteer
century, but even in the *first* half of the seventeenth. 1
reunion of southern, formerly Kievan, Russia with Muscovy
1653, as well as the Russian-Polish War of 1653–1668, were be
instrumental in effecting these changes, since thousands
Kievan and West Russian scholars, noblemen, and mercha
moved to Moscow or to the northern and eastern cities of
empire, carrying new Polish and Western modes with the
The Russian court was quick to adopt them, and in 1673
first theatrical troupe performed in the palace of the tsar. Fo
teen years later, in 1687, the first institution of higher educati
the Muscovite Slavo-Greco-Latin Academy, was founded, a
when, at the beginning of the eighteenth century, Peter I int
duced his reforms—many of which only continued further
trends that had been taking place in preceding years—he,
effect, merely legalized the transformation of medieval Mus
vite Russia into a Westernized empire and European power.

Blinded Prince Vasilko asks for water.
A miniature from the *Radzivil Chronicle* of the fourteenth century.

12. *Metropolitan Hilarion*
Sermon on Law and Grace

THE *Sermon on Law and Grace* is arranged in two distinc
parts: "The Sermon on the Law of Moses Given to Him by God
and on the Grace and Truth Brought to the Earth by Jesus
Christ," and "The Eulogy to Our Kagan, Vladimir."

This famous sermon by Metropolitan Hilarion is one of the
oldest Russian literary-philosophical works and is the earliest
Russian sermon preserved. It was written several decades be
fore the *Primary Chronicle* and the most ancient Russian *vitae*
probably between 1037 and 1050. Its author, Hilarion, became
in 1051 the first Russian (non-Greek) head of the Russian
Church and Metropolitan of the city of Kiev. He was one of the
most erudite and brilliant Russian preachers and writers of the
Kievan age. Despite his clearly Byzantine cultural background
he manifests the Russian national spirit.

Besides the *Sermon on Law and Grace*, there has also been
preserved Hilarion's *Confession of Faith*, in which he emphasizes
the Trinitarian foundation of Christian dogma and the dual nature of Jesus Christ. In this work he wrote, "He suffered for me
as a man. . . . He revived as God, . . . and after three days he
arose from the dead, as a victor, Christ, my King."

In his *Sermon on Law and Grace* Metropolitan Hilarion reveals himself to be an astute preacher. The central idea of the
sermon is the juxtaposition of the faith of the Old Testament
with that of the New Testament. For a biblical comparison, he
uses the story of the two sons of Abraham: the first, Ishmael,
who was not free, but the son of Hagar, Sarah's handmaid; the
second, who was free, being the son of Abraham by his wife,
Sarah. For Hilarion, Christianity is the faith of freedom and
liberation, while the religion of the Old Testament was one of
law, compulsion and strict obedience.

Hilarion's attitude toward the problem of salvation is very
characteristic of early Eastern Christianity: salvation through
"baptism and good deeds," through Christian mercy and charity.
This is remote from Luther's and Calvin's teachings of salvation
solely through faith and, concomitantly, moral behavior.

This sermon, despite its clear tendency to raise the prestige of the Russian nation and the Russian Church, was composed in a typical Byzantine style, and is saturated with repeated parallels between Hagar and the Old Testament, and between Sarah and the New Testament. When Hilarion wrote that "Divine Grace announced to God" and that "the Father did as he was told by Divine Grace," he apparently referred to "Holy Sophia," that is, the Divine Omniscience of the three hypostases of the Trinity. The teaching of "Holy Wisdom," or "Holy Sophia," was widespread throughout Byzantium and Russia at that time, and is attested to by the fact that cathedrals in Kiev, Constantinople, and Novgorod were dedicated to "Holy Sophia."

Having adroitly presented his point, which is the supreme nature of the Christian faith, Hilarion turned to the destiny of the Russian people. In his eyes, when the Russians adopted Christianity they became the equal of all Christian peoples, including the Greeks. He regarded the Russian Church as having the same dignity, status, and rights as the Byzantine Church. It must be remembered that both Yaroslav and Hilarion attempted to liberate the Russian Church from Byzantine supervision and that Hilarion was the first native Russian to head the Russian Church and to defend its autonomy from Constantinople.

Hilarion ends his sermon with a highly rhetorical panegyric to Prince Vladimir, whom Russians consider a saint for having Christianized Russia. Optimistic, bright, even triumphant notes can easily be discerned in Hilarion's treatment of history. Russia had become enlightened by the Christian faith, and therefore its future would lie in Christ's hands.

The following translation is based upon the text of Metropolitan Hilarion's sermon published by A. B. Gorskii in *Pamiatniki dukhovnoi literatury vremeni velikogo kniazia Yaroslava I-ogo*, Moscow, 1844.

◆ ◆ ◆

THE SERMON OF THE LAW OF MOSES GIVEN TO HIM BY GOD, AND OF THE GRACE AND TRUTH BROUGHT TO EARTH BY JESUS CHRIST

Blessed be the God of Israel, the God of Christianity who visited his people and brought them salvation. He did not disdain his creation which was for ages possessed by pagan darkness and by worship of the devil, but he enlightened the Children of Abraham by giving them his Law tablets, and later he saved all nations, sending them his Son, his Gospel, and his baptism, and by giving them resurrection to eternal life.

Law was the precursor and the servant of Grace and Truth.
Grace and Truth were the servants of the future life and immortal life. Law led its people of the Old Testament toward the
blessing of baptism, and baptism led its sons to the life eternal.
Moses and the prophets announced the coming of Christ, but
Christ and the Apostles announced resurrection and the future
age.

And what could the Law achieve? And what could Grace
achieve? First was the Law and then Grace. Hagar and Sarah
are the pictures of Law and Grace: Hagar was a handmaid and
Sarah was free. First comes the handmaiden and then the free
woman may come. And he who reads (the Bible) must understand this. Abraham, since his youth, had Sarah for his wife and
she was free and not a slave, and so God decided before all ages
to send his Son into the world that Grace might appear through
him (but sent him to man only later). But Sarah was restrained
from bearing children, since she was unfruitful. But she was not
actually unfruitful, but was chosen by divine Providence to bear
in her old age. The wisdom of God was not revealed to anyone,
but concealed from both angels and men. This wisdom was not
shown, but was concealed to be revealed at the end of the age.
    It was Sarah who said unto Abraham:
        "Behold now, the Lord has prevented me from bearing
        children; go in to my maid; it may be that I shall obtain
        children by her."
And so the divine Grace (of the Son) announced to God, the
Father:
        "It is not yet my time for descending to the earth and to
        save the world. Descend to Mount Sinai and give them the
        Law."
And, just as Abraham did as Sarah told him and went into
Hagar, so God, the Father, did as he was told by the divine
Grace and descended to Mount Sinai.
    And Hagar, the handmaid, bore from Abraham a servant (not
a truly free man), and Abraham gave him the name Ishmael.
And Moses brought from Mount Sinai the Law and not the
Grace, the shade and not the Truth.
    When Abraham and Sarah were old, God appeared to Abra-
ham by the oaks of Mamre, as he sat at the door of his tent in
the heat of the day. And he ran to meet him, and bowing lowly
to the earth, he hastened into the tent (to Sarah). And so,
when the end of the age was nearing, God appeared to the
humankind, descended to the earth, and blessed the womb of

the Virgin. And he was received by the Immaculate Virgin into the tent of the flesh. And the Virgin said to the angel:

"Behold I am the handmaid of the Lord; let it be to me according to your word."

Once the Lord gave Sarah to bear a child, and she begat Isaac, and the free woman begat a free son. And, when once more our Lord visited the humankind, he appeared unknown and hidden from men and then was born Grace and Truth, but not the Law. And now it was the Son and not the servant.

And the child grew up and was weaned; and Abraham made a great feast on the day that Isaac was weaned. And when Christ was upon the earth Grace did not reveal Itself and Christ was hiding himself until he was thirty. And when he had grown and was weaned, then there, in the river Jordan, Grace was revealed by a man. And our Lord invited many and made a great feast and offered up the fatted calf of the age, His beloved Son, Jesus Christ, and God then called to this feast many of heaven and earth and they the angels and men into one (Church).

This blessed faith spreads now over the entire earth, and finally it reached the Russian nation. And, whereas the lake of the Law dried up, the fount of the Gospel became rich in water and overflowed upon our land and reached us. And now, together with all Christians, we glorify the Holy Trinity, while Judea remains silent.

THE EULOGY TO OUR KAGAN VLADIMIR

Rome, with voices panegyrical, praises Peter and Paul through whom they came to believe in Jesus Christ, the Son of God:

Asia, Ephesus, and Patmus praise John the Theologian;

India praises Thomas;

Egypt, Mark.

All lands, cities, and men honor and glorify their teacher who brought them the Orthodox Faith. Thus, let us, through our own strength, humbly praise our teacher and mentor, the great Kagan of our land Vladimir, the grandson of Igor of yore and son of glorious Sviatoslav, who ruled in their day with courage and valor, becoming famed in many lands for their victories and fortitude. And they did not reign in a poor and unknown land, but in Russia, which is known and celebrated by all to the ends of the earth.

A good attestation of your devotion, blessed one, is the Holy Church of the Blessed Virgin, the Mother of God, which you

build on the orthodox foundation and where your valorous body
now lays at rest and awaits the archangel's trumpet.

A good and certain attestation is your son, George [Yaroslav's
Christian name], whom God has made the heir to your throne,

who does not destroy your laws, but confirms them,

who does not diminish works of piety, but extends them,

who does not undo, but strengthens,

who finishes that which you have left unfinished

even as Solomon finished the works begun by David;

who has built a great and holy temple to God's omniscience

that it may hallow your city;

who has embellished with all manner of things beautiful,

with gold and silver and precious stones

and with sacred vessels;

so that the church is a wonder to all surrounding lands

and so that the like cannot be found in all the northern
land,

nor in the east nor the west;

who has given your famous city of Kiev the crown of glory,

who has turned your city and its people

to all-glorious Mother of God,

who is always ready to succor Christians

and for whom he has built a church with doors of gold

in the name of the first holy day of the Lord of the
Annunciation,

that the veneration, which the archangel will offer to the
Virgin,

may also be upon this city.

To her he speaks, saying:

"Rejoice, Blessed One, the Lord is with you!"

And to the city he speaks, saying:

"Rejoice, faithful city, the Lord is with you!"

Arise from your grave, venerated prince,

Arise and shake off your sleep.

You are not dead,

but only sleep until the day of resurrection of all.

Arise! You are not dead,

for it is not right that you should die,

for you have believed in Christ,

the Sustainer of the whole world.

Shake off your deep sleep

and lift up your eyes

that you might see what honor the Lord has granted you,

and you still live upon this earth,
unforgotten through your sons.
Arise! Behold your child George,
Look upon your beloved one,
whom God has brought forth from your loins.
Behold him embellishing the throne of your land.
Rejoice and be of good cheer!
Behold the pious wife of your son, Irina.
Behold your grandchildren
and your great-grandchildren.
Behold how they live and how they are cared for by God.
Behold how they preserve devotion in your tradition,
how they partake of the Sacraments of the Holy Church,
how they glorify Christ,
how they venerate before his Holy Name.
Behold your city radiant with grandeur.
Behold your blossoming churches,
Behold Christianity flourishing.
Behold your city gleaming,
adorned with holy icons and
fragrant with thyme,
praising God and filling the air with sacred songs.
   And beholding all this, rejoice and be of good cheer, and
praise the Lord, the Creator of all which you have seen.

13. Cyril of Turov
Sermon on the First Sunday After Easter

AMONG Russian writers of the Kievan period, Cyril, Bishop of
Turov, was probably the most accomplished master of Orthodox
theology and the Byzantine style of writing. He had an excellent
command of Greek and his literary achievements surpass those
of any other Russian man of letters of that era. He wrote
numerous epistles, prayers, and sermons, all of which are distinguished by their elegant and elaborate style. They show
clearly the author's gift for composition and his extensive knowledge of the Bible and early Church history. In his works he
quotes the patriarchs and prophets of the Old Testament with
unusual adroitness for that time. Though full of symbolism and
allegory, his writings are nonetheless lucid and fully comprehensible, and they gained the admiration of endless generations
of Russians. Even as late as the seventeenth century, many of
Cyril's stylistic patterns were still popular with writers of the

conservative literary tradition. Of all his works, Cyril's trium
phant description of spring as the symbol of the resurrection i
the most popular.

Very little is known of the author's life except that he live
in the middle of the twelfth century and was Bishop of Turov
His best-known works are eight sermons delivered on the oc
casion of the eight Sundays beginning with Palm Sunday. Th
Sermon on the First Sunday after Easter, perhaps his mos
famous single composition, is offered here in a translation b
Leo Wiener.

◆ ◆ ◆

The Church needs a great teacher and a wise orator to cele
brate the holiday properly, but we are poor in words and din
in mind, not having the fire of the Holy Ghost—the enjoymen
of words useful to the soul; yet for the love of my brethren wh
are with me, we shall say something about the renewal of th
Lord's resurrection. In the past week of the Easter there wer
joy in heaven and terror in the nethermost regions, a renewal o
life and liberation of the world, a destruction of hell and victory
over death, a resurrection of the dead, and annihilation of th
enticing power of the devil; a salvation of the human race b
the resurrection of Christ; an impoverishment of the Old Testa
ment and enslavement of the Sabbath; an enrichment of th
Church of Christ, and enthronement of the Sunday.

Last week there was a change of all things, for the earth
was opened up by heaven, having been purified from its satani
impurities, and the angels with their wives humbly served a
the resurrection. All creation was renewed, for no longer are th
air, the sun, the fire, the springs, the trees, thought to be gods
no longer does hell receive its due of infants sacrificed by thei
fathers, nor death its honors, for idolatry has come to an end
and the satanic power has been vanquished by the mystery o
the cross. The Old Testament has become impoverished by th
rejection of the blood of calves and sacrifices of goats, for Chris
has given himself to the Lord as a sacrifice for all. And with
this, Sunday ceased to be a holiday, but the Sunday was sanc
tified on account of the resurrection, and Sunday is now su
preme, for Christ arose from the dead on that day. . . .

Today the heavens have been cleared from the dark cloud
that enshrouded them as with a heavy veil, and they proclaim
the glory of God with a clear atmosphere. . . .

Today the sun rises and beams on high, and rejoicing warm
the earth, for there has arisen for us from the grave the rea

un, Christ, and he saves all who believe in him. Today the noon descends from its high place and gives honor to the greater lights. The Old Testament, as had been prophesied, has topped with its Sabbath, and with its prophets gives honor to the Testament of Christ with its Sunday. Today the winter of in has stopped in repentance, and the ice of unbelief is melted y wisdom. Today spring appears spruce, and enlivens all arthly existence; the stormy winds blow gently and generate ruits, and the earth, giving nurture to the seed, brings forth reen grass. For spring is the beautiful faith in Christ which, hrough baptism, produces a regeneration of man, and the tormy winds are the evil, sinful thoughts that, being changed o virtue through repentance, generate soul-saving fruits; but ne earth of our being, having received the Word of God like a eed, and, passing through an ecstatic labor, through the fear of im, brings forth a spirit of salvation.

Today the newborn lambs and calves frisk and leap about oyfully and returning to their mothers gambol about, so that the nepherds, playing on their reeds, praise Christ in joy. The ambs, I say, are the gentle people from among the pagans, and ne calves—the idolaters of the unbelieving countries who, hav- ng accepted the Law through Christ's incarnation and the eachings of the Apostles and miracles, and having returned to ne holy Church, suck the milk of its teachings; and the teachers f Christ's flock, praying for all, praise Christ, the Lord, who ad collected all the wolves and sheep into one herd.

Today the trees send forth buds and the fragrant flowers loom, and behold, the gardens already emit a sweet odor, and ne workers laboring in hope acclaim Christ the giver of fruits. Ve were before like the trees of the forest that bear no fruit, ut today the faith of Christ has been grafted on our unbelief, nd those who already held to the roots of Jesse have burgeoned rith the flowers of virtue and expect through Christ a regenera- on in heaven, and the saints who labor for the Church expect reward from Christ. Today the plowman of the Word leads ne oxen of the Word to the spiritual yoke, sinks the plow of aptism into the furrows of thought and deepening them to arrows of repentance plants in them the spiritual seed and ejoices in the hope of future returns. Today everything old has aken an end, and all is new for the sake of the resurrection. oday the apostolic rivers are full, and the pagan fish let out neir broods, and the fishermen, having examined the depth of ne divine incarnation, drag in full nets into the Church. . . . oday the industrious bees of the monastic order show their

wisdom and set all to wonder, for living in the wilderness and
providing for themselves, they astonish both angels and men
just as the bee flies upon the flowers and forms combs of honey
in order to furnish sweetness to man and what is needed in the
Church. . . .

Today there is a feast of regeneration for the people who are
made new by the resurrection of Christ, and all new things are
brought to God: from heathens, faith; from good Christians
offerings; from the clergy, holy sacrifies; from the civil authorities, God-pleasing charity; from the noble, care for the Church;
from the righteous, humility; from the sinners, true repentance;
from the unhallowed, a turning to God; from the hating,
spiritual love.

THE LIVES OF SAINTS AND MONKS

14. *Nestor: The Martyrdom of Boris and Gleb*

ᴬᶠᵀᴱᴿ the death of Vladimir, a fratricidal struggle broke out among his sons. The eldest, Sviatopolk, seized power and began plotting the elimination of his brothers, Boris, Gleb and Yaroslav. The murder of Boris and Gleb is described in a touching manner by the chronicler: the two refused to take up arms against their elder brother in order to prevent further bloodshed. They decided to accept their fate passively, following the example of Christ. This was the earliest imitation in the Middle Ages of Christ as a humble martyr dying for the sins of man. In both Western and Byzantine Christianity at that time, Christ's image was that of a pantocrat: an awe-inspiring, omnipotent ruler of the universe, to be dreaded. The humble aspect of Christ was stressed neither in Byzantine nor in Western Christianity until the time of St. Francis, some two hundred years after the martyrdom of Boris and Gleb.

The text presented here is the Samuel H. Cross translation.

❖ ❖ ❖

Sviatopolk settled in Kiev after his father's death, and after calling together all the inhabitants of Kiev, he began to distribute largess among them. They accepted it, but their hearts were not with him, because their brethren were with Boris. When Boris returned with the army, after meeting the Pechenegs, he received the news that his father was dead. He mourned deeply for him, for he was beloved of his father before the rest.

When he came to the Alta, he halted. His father's retainers then urged him to take his place in Kiev on his father's throne, since he had at his disposal the latter's retainers and troops. But Boris protested: "Be it not for me to raise my hand against my elder brother. Now that my father has passed away, let him take the place of my father in my heart." When the soldiery heard these words, they departed from him, and Boris remained with his servants.

But Sviatopolk was filled with lawlessness. Adopting the device of Cain, he sent messages to Boris that he desired to live in peace with him, and would increase the territory he had

received from his father. But he plotted against him how
might kill him. So Sviatopolk came by night to Vyshegoro
After secretly summoning to his presence Putsha and the boya
of the town, he inquired of them whether they were who
heartedly devoted to him. Putsha and the men of Vyshegor
replied, "We are ready to lay down our lives for you." He th
commanded them to say nothing to any man, but to go and k
his brother Boris. They straightway promised to execute l
order. Of such men Solomon has well said: "They make has
to shed blood unjustly. For they promise blood, and gather ev
Their path runneth to evil, for they possess their souls in d
honor" (Proverbs, i. 16–19).

These emissaries came to the Alta, and when they a
proached, they heard the sainted Boris singing vespers. For
was already known to him that they intended to take his lif
Then he arose and began to chant, saying: "O Lord, how a
they increased who come against me! Many are they that ri
up against me" (Psalms, iii, 1). And also, "Thy arrows ha
pierced me, for I am ready for wounds and my pain is befo
me continually" (Psalms, xxxviii, 2, 17). And he also utter
this prayer: "Lord, hear my prayer, and enter not into judgme
with thy servant, for no living man shall be just before the
For the enemy hath crushed my soul" (Psalms, cxl, 1–3). Aft
ending the six psalms, when he saw how men were sent out
kill him, he began to chant the Psalter, saying, "Strong bu
encompassed me, and the assemblage of the evil beset me.
Lord my God, I have hoped in thee; save me and deliver n
from my pursuers" (Psalms, xxii, 12, 16, vii, 1). Then he beg
to sing the canon. After finishing vespers, he prayed, gazi
upon the icon, the image of the Lord, with these words: "Lo
Jesus Christ, who in this image hast appeared on earth for o
salvation, and who, having voluntarily suffered thy hands to
nailed to the cross, didst endure thy passion for our sins, so he
me now to endure my passion. For I accept it not from tho
who are my enemies, but from the hand of my own brothe
Hold it not against him as a sin, O Lord!"

After offering this prayer, he lay down upon his couch. The
they fell upon him like wild beasts about the tent, and ove
came him by piercing him with lances. They also overpower
his servant, who cast himself upon his body. For he was belove
of Boris. He was a servant of Hungarian race, George by nam
to whom Boris was greatly attached. The prince had given hi
a large gold necklace which he wore while serving him. The
also killed many other servants of Boris. But since they cou

t quickly take the necklace from George's neck, they cut off
s head, and thus obtained it. For this reason his body was not
cognized later among the corpses.

The desperadoes, after attacking Boris, wrapped him in a
nvas, loaded him upon a wagon, and dragged him off, though
was still alive. When the impious Sviatopolk saw that he was
ll breathing, he sent two Varangians to finish him. When
ey came and saw that he was still alive, one of them drew
s sword and plunged it into his heart. Thus died the blessed
ris, receiving from the hand of Christ our God the crown
nong the righteous. He shall be numbered with the prophets
d the Apostles, as he joins with the choirs of martyrs, rests in
e lap of Abraham, beholds joy ineffable, chants with the
gels, and rejoices in company with the choirs of saints. After
s body had been carried in secret to Vyshegorod, it was buried
the Church of St. Basil.

The impious Sviatopolk then reflected, "Behold, I have killed
ris; now how can I kill Gleb?" Adopting once more Cain's
vice, he craftily sent messages to Gleb to the effect that he
ould come quickly, because his father was very ill and
sired his presence. Gleb quickly mounted his horse, and set
t with a small company, for he was obedient to his father.
hen he came to the Volga, his horse stumbled in a ditch on
e plain, and broke his leg. He arrived at Smolensk, and setting
t thence at dawn, he embarked in a boat on the Smiadyn.
this time, Yaroslav received from Predslava the tidings of
eir father's death, and he sent word to Gleb that he should not
t out, because his father was dead and his brother had been
urdered by Sviatopolk. Upon receiving these tidings, Gleb
rst into tears, and mourned for his father, but still more
eply for his brother. He wept and prayed with the lament,
Woe is me, O Lord! It were better for me to die with my
other than to live on in this world. O my brother, had I but
en thy angelic countenance, I should have died with thee.
hy am I now left alone? Where are thy words that thou didst
y to me, my brother? No longer do I hear thy sweet counsel.
thou hast received affliction from God, pray for me that I
ay endure the same passion. For it were better for me to dwell
th thee than in this deceitful world."

While he was thus praying amid his tears, there suddenly
rived those sent by Sviatopolk for Gleb's destruction. These
issaries seized Gleb's boat, and drew their weapons. The
rvants of Gleb were terrified, and the impious messenger,

Goriaser, gave orders that they should slay Gleb with dispat[c]
Then Gleb's cook, Torchin by name, seized a knife, and stabb[ed]
Gleb. He was offered up as a sacrifice to God like an innoc[ent]
lamb, a glorious offering amid the perfume of incense, and [he]
received the crown of glory. Entering the heavenly mansio[n]
he beheld his long-desired brother, and rejoiced with him [in]
the joy ineffable which they had attained through their brothe[rly]
love.

"How good and fair it is for brethren to live togethe[r]
(Psalms, cxxxiii, 1). But the impious ones returned again, ev[en]
as David said, "Let the sinners return to hell" (Psalms, ix, 1[7]).
When they returned to Sviatopolk, they reported that his co[m]
mand had been executed. On hearing these tidings, he w[as]
puffed up with pride, since he knew not the words of Dav[id]
"Why art thou proud of thy evildoing, O mighty one? T[hy]
tongue hath considered lawlessness all the day long" (Psal[m]
lii, 1).

After Gleb had been slain, his body was thrown upon t[he]
shore between two tree trunks, but afterward they took him a[nd]
carried him away, to bury him beside his brother Boris in t[he]
Church of St. Basil. United thus in body and still more in so[ul]
ye dwell with the Lord and King of all, in eternal joy, ineffa[ble]
light, bestowing salutary gifts upon the land of Russia. Ye g[ive]
healing to other strangers who draw near with faith, making t[he]
lame to walk, giving sight to the blind, to the sick health, [to]
captives freedom, to prisoners liberty, to the sorrowful conso[la]
tion, and to the oppressed relief. Ye are the protectors of t[he]
land of Russia, shining forever like beacons and praying to t[he]
Lord in behalf of your countrymen. Therefore must we worth[ily]
magnify these martyrs in Christ, praying fervently to them a[nd]
saying: "Rejoice, martyrs in Christ from the land of Russia, w[ho]
gave healing to them who draw near to you in faith and lo[ve]
Rejoice, dwellers in heaven. In the body ye were angels, serva[nts]
in the same thought, comrades in the same image, of one he[art]
with the saints. To all that suffer ye give relief. Rejoice, B[oris]
and Gleb, wise in God. Like streams ye spring from the fou[nt]
of life-giving water which flow for the redemption of the rig[ht]
eous. Rejoice, ye who have trampled the serpent of evil bene[ath]
your feet. Ye have appeared amid bright rays, enlightening l[ike]
beacons the whole land of Russia. Appearing in faith immu[ta]
ble, ye have ever driven away the darkness. Rejoice, ye w[ho]
have won an unslumbering eye, ye blessed ones who ha[ve]
received in your hearts the zeal to fulfill God's only comma[nd]
ments. Rejoice, brethren united in the realms of golden light,

he heavenly abodes, in glory unfading, which ye through your merits have attained. Rejoice, ye who are brightly irradiate with the luminance of God, and travel throughout the world expelling devils and healing diseases. Like beacons supernal and zealous guardians, ye dwell with God, illumined forever with light divine, and in your courageous martyrdom ye enlighten the souls of the faithful. The light-bringing heavenly love has exalted you, wherefore ye have inherited all fair things in the heavenly life: glory, celestial sustenance, the light of wisdom, and beauteous joys. Rejoice, ye who refresh our hearts, driving out pain and sickness and curing evil passions. Ye glorious ones, with the sacred drops of your blood ye have dyed a robe of purple which ye wear in beauty, and reign forevermore with Christ, interceding with him for his new Christian nation and for your fellows, for our land is hallowed by your blood. By virtue of your relics deposited in the church, ye illumine it with the Holy Spirit, for there in heavenly bliss, as martyrs among the army of martyrs, ye intercede for our nation. Rejoice, bright daysprings, our Christ-loving martyrs and intercessors! Subject the pagans to our princes, beseeching our Lord God that they may live in concord and in health, freed from intestine war and the crafts of the devil. Help us therefore who sing and recite your sacred praise forever unto our life's end."

15. *Nestor*

The Narratives of the Kievan Crypt Monastery

THE Crypt Monastery, located on the hilly banks of the Dnieper River on the outskirts of the city of Kiev since its foundation in the eleventh century, became the main spiritual and cultural center of early Russia. Its founders, Sts. Antonius and Theodosius, were remarkable religious leaders whose lives and teachings inspired endless generations of the Russian people. Until the revolution of 1917, the Crypt Monastery remained the principal place for Russian devotional pilgrimages, and even now its churches and crypts attract numerous pilgrims.

Works describing life in the monastery are collected either in the *Primary Chronicle*, their author apparently being Nestor, a monk of this monastery, or in the *Kievan Crypt (Monastery) Paterikon* (the Greek word *paterikon* means a collection of lives of saints or stories about the life of monastery inhabitants). The *Kievan Crypt (Monastery) Paterikon* was written in the first

quarter of the thirteenth century by Bishop Simon and Mon
Polycarpe, both having been monks of this monastery. Later
more stories were added to the *Paterikon* by other writers
Despite the fact that Simon and Polycarpe lived some hundred
and fifty years after Nestor, the style of their work differs ver
little from his. In both collections can be found historical ac
counts of life in the monastery, edifying tales about its inhab
itants, some half-legendary stories with considerable mystic o
fantastic elements, and finally demonological narratives describ
ing the struggles of the monks with the devil.

The stories of the Kievan Crypt Monastery were entered b
Nestor under the years 1051 and 1074. However, as ofter
happens in the *Primary Chronicle*, these tales were not neces
sarily connected with the given year but describe life in th
monastery over most of the second half of the eleventh century
Nestor himself belonged to the monastery, and witnessed man
of the events described by him.

The text of this work is that of Samuel H. Cross as translate
by him in the *Primary Chronicle*.

◆ ◆ ◆

THE FOUNDING OF THE CRYPT MONASTERY AND
THE LIFE OF ST. ANTONIUS

1051 (6559)   Yaroslav, after assembling the bishops, ap
pointed Hilarion Metropolitan of Russia in St. Sophia.

Let us now relate why the Monastery of the Crypts bears thi
name. Prince Yaroslav was fond of Berestovoe and the Churc
of the Holy Apostles there situated. He gathered a large com
pany of priests, among whom was a presbyter named Hilarior
a virtuous man, learned and ascetic. Hilarion used often to wal
from Berestovoe toward the Dnieper to a certain hill, where th
old Crypt Monastery now is, and made his orisons there. H
dug a little crypt two yards deep, and often went thither from
Berestovoe to chant the hours and offer his prayer to God i
secret. Then God inspired the prince to appoint him Metro
politan in St. Sophia; and the crypt remained as it was.

Not many days afterward, there was a certain man, a layma
from the city of Liubech, in whose heart God inspired th
desire to go on pilgrimage. He made his way to Mount Athos
beheld the monasteries there, and upon examining them an

[1] Mount Athos, or the "Holy Mount," has long been the most im
portant monastic center of Eastern Christianity. It is located in Greec
in the vicinity of the city of Saloniki.

being charmed by the monastic life, he entered one of the local monasteries, and begged the prior to confer upon him the monastic habit. The latter complied with his request and made him a monk, calling him Antonius, and after he had admonished him and instructed him in his monastic obligations, he bade him return to Russia accompanied by the blessing of the Holy Mount, that many other monks might spring from his example. The prior blessed him and dismissed him, saying, "Go in peace." Antonius returned to Kiev, and reflected where he should live. He went about among the monasteries and liked none of them, since God did not so will, and subsequently wandered about among the hills and valleys seeking the place which God should show him. He finally came to the hill where Hilarion had dug the crypt, and liked this site, and rejoiced in it. He then lifted up his voice in prayer to God, saying amid his tears, "O Lord, strengthen me in this place, and may there rest upon it the blessing of the Holy Mount and of the prior who tonsured me." Thus he took up his abode there, praying to God, eating dry bread all the day long, drinking water in peace, and digging the crypt. He gave himself rest neither day nor night, but endured in his labors, in vigil, and in prayer. Afterward good men noticed his conduct, and supplied him according to his necessities. Thus he acquired distinction as the great Antonius, and those who drew near to him besought his blessing.

When the Great Prince Yaroslav died, Iziaslav his son inherited his domain and settled in Kiev, while Antonius was celebrated throughout Russia. Iziaslav observed his manner of life, and came with his retainers to request his blessing and prayers. The great Antonius was thus remarked and revered by everyone. Brothers joined him, and he welcomed and tonsured them. Brethren thus gathered about him to the number of twelve. They dug a great crypt and a church, and cells, which exist to this day in the crypt under the old monastery. When the brethren had thus assembled, Antonius said to them, "God has gathered you together, my brethren, and ye are under the blessing of the Holy Mount, through which the prior at the Holy Mount tonsured me, and I have tonsured you also. May there be upon you first the blessing of God and second that of the Holy Mount." And he added this injunction: "Live apart by yourselves, and I shall appoint you a prior; for I prefer to go alone to yonder hill, as I formerly was wont when I dwelt in solitude." So he appointed Barlaam as their prior, and betook himself to the hill, where he dug a grotto, which is under the new monastery, and in which he ended his life, enduring in

virtue, and for the space of forty years never issuing forth from
the crypt in which his bones lie to the present day.

The brethren thus abode with their prior, and as the number
of monks in the crypt increased, they considered the establish-
ment of a monastery outside the original crypt. Thus the prior
and the brethren approached Antonius and said to him, "Father,
the brethren have increased in numbers, and we can no longer
find room in the crypt. If God and thy prayers so direct us, we
might build a small church outside the crypt." Antonius then
bade them so to do. They obeyed him, and built a little chapel
over the crypt and dedicated it to the Assumption of the Holy
Virgin.

God continued to augment the number of the brotherhood
through the intercession of the Holy Virgin, and the brethren
took counsel with the prior as to constructing a monastery. The
friars again visited Antonius, and said, "Father, our brethren
increase in numbers, and we are desirous of building a monastery." Antonius rejoiced, and replied, "Blessed be God for all
things, and may the prayers of the Holy Virgin and of the
fathers of the Holy Mount be with you." Having thus spoken
he sent one of the brotherhood to Prince Iziaslav with the
message, "My Prince! Behold, God strengthens the brotherhood,
but their abode is small; give us therefore the hill which is
above the crypt." When Iziaslav heard these words, he rejoiced
and sent his servant, and gave to them the hill. The prior and
the brethren founded there a great church, and fenced in the
monastery with a palisade. They constructed many cells, completed the church, and adorned it with icons. Such was the
origin of the Crypt Monastery, which was so named because
the brethren first lived in the crypt. The Crypt Monastery thus
issued from the benediction of the Holy Mount.

ST. THEODOSIUS, ABBOT OF THE CRYPT MONASTERY

Now, when the monastery was completed during the priorate
of Barlaam, Iziaslav founded the Monastery of St. Demetrius,
and appointed Barlaam prior therein, since he intended, by
virtue of his material wealth, to make it superior to the ancient
monastery. Many monasteries have indeed been founded by
emperors and nobles and magnates, but they are not such as
those founded by tears, fasting, prayer, and vigil. Antonius had
neither silver nor gold, but accomplished his purpose through
tears and fasting, as I have recounted.

When Barlaam had departed to St. Demetrius', the brethren
held a council, and then once more visited the ancient Antonius

with the request that he should designate them a new prior. He inquired whom they desired. They replied that they desired only the one designated by God and by his own selection. Then he inquired of them, "Who among you is more obedient, more modest, and more mild than Theodosius? Let him be your prior." The brethren rejoiced, and made their reverence before the old man. Being twenty in number, they thus appointed Theodosius to be their prior. When Theodosius took over in the monastery, he began to practice abstinence, fasting, and tearful prayer. He undertook to assemble many monks, and thus gathered together brethren to the number of one hundred.

He also interested himself in searching out the monastic rules. There was in Kiev at the time a monk from the Studion Monastery named Michael, who had come from Greece with the Metropolitan George, and Theodosius inquired of him concerning the practices of the Studion monks. He obtained their rule from him, copied it out, and established it in his own monastery to govern the singing of monastic hymns, the making of reverences, the reading of the lessons, behavior in church, the whole ritual, conduct at table, proper food for special days, and to regulate all else according to prescription. After obtaining all this information, Theodosius thus transmitted it to his monastery, and from the latter all others adopted the same institutions. Therefore the Crypt Monastery is honored as the oldest of all.

While Theodosius lived in the monastery, following a virtuous life and the monastic rule, and receiving everyone who presented himself, I, a poor and unworthy servant, came to him, and he accepted me in my seventeenth year. Hence I have set down and certified what year the monastery came into being, and why it is named the Crypt Monastery; but to Theodosius' life we shall recur later.

1074 (6582) In this year the Church of the Crypts was founded by the Prior Theodosius and the Bishop Michael, while George the Metropolitan was absent in Greece and Sviatoslav was reigning in Kiev.

Theodosius, the Prior of the Crypt Monastery, passed away. We shall therefore supply a brief account of his assumption. When the Lenten season approached, upon the eve of Quinquagesima Sunday, Theodosius was accustomed, after he had embraced the brethren according to his practice, to instruct them how to pass the Lenten period in prayer by night and by day, and how to guard against evil thoughts and the temptations of the devil. "For," said he, "demons incite in monks evil thoughts and desires, and inflame their fancy so that their prayers are impaired. One must combat such thoughts when they come by using the sign of the cross and by saying, 'Lord Jesus Christ our God, have mercy on us, Amen!' With this end in view, we must practice abstinence from many foods, for evil desires develop out of excessive eating and immoderate drinking, and by the growth of such thoughts sin is caused. By this means," said he, "oppose yourselves to the influence of the demons and their malice, guard against laziness and too much sleep, be zealous in churchly song, in the traditions of the fathers, and in the reading of the Scriptures. For it befits monks above all things to have upon their lips the Psalter of David, and thereby to expel the weaknesses caused by the devil. It befits all young persons to show toward their elders love, obedience, and attention, and it behooves all older persons to offer the younger brethren their love and admonition, and to be an example by their continence and vigil, their self-restraint and humility, to counsel and console the youthful, and to spend Lent in such pursuits."

"For," he added, "God has given us these forty days in which to purify our souls. This is a tithe given to God by the body. For the days of the year are three hundred and sixty-five, and giving to God each tenth day as a tithe makes a fast of forty days, during which the soul is cleansed and happily celebrates the resurrection of the Lord as it rejoices in God. For the Lenten season purifies the heart of man. In the beginning, fasting was first imposed upon Adam, so that he should not taste of one tree. Moses fasted forty days to prepare himself to receive the law upon Mount Sinai, and then he beheld the glory of God. During a fast, Samuel's mother bore him. Through their fasting, the Ninevites averted the wrath of God. By his fasting, Daniel prepared himself for great visions. After his fast, Elijah was taken up to heaven to receive celestial sustenance. Through their fasting, the Three Children quenched the violence of the fire. And our Lord, by fasting forty days, made known to us the Lenten season. By means of their fasting, the Apostles rooted out the teaching of the devil. By virtue of their fasts, our fathers appeared to the world as beacons that continue to shine after their decease. They exhibited great labors and continence; for example, the great Antonius, Euthymius, Savva, and the other fathers. Let us imitate them, my brethren."

After thus instructing the brotherhood, he kissed them, calling each by name, and then left the monastery, taking with him but a few loaves of bread. He entered a crypt, closed the door behind him, and covered himself with dust. He spoke to no one, unless some object was needful to him, and in any case he conversed only on Saturday and on Sunday through a small window. Upon other days, he remained in fasting and in prayer, maintaining strict abstinence. He returned to the monastery on the eve of Friday, St. Lazarus' day. For on this day ends the forty days' fast, which opens on the first Monday after the week of St. Theodore and concludes on Friday, the feast of St. Lazarus. Holy Week is then observed as a fast on account of our Lord's passion. Theodosius thus returned according to his custom, embraced the brethren, and with them celebrated Palm Sunday.

When Easter Day came, he celebrated it brilliantly as usual, and then fell ill. When he was taken ill, and had been sick for five days, he bade them carry him in the evening down into the courtyard. The brethren laid him upon a sled and set him before the church. He then desired that the whole brotherhood should be summoned, so the brethren struck upon the bell, and all assembled together. Theodosius then said to them, "My brethren, my fathers, and my children! I now depart from you, for God made known to me, while I was in the crypt during the Lenten season, that I must now quit this world. Whom do you desire for your prior, that I may confer my blessing upon him?"

They made answer, "You have been a father to us all. Whomsoever you yourself select shall be our father and our prior, and we shall obey him even as we obey you." Then our father Theodosius said, "Go apart from me and designate him whom you desire, except the two brothers Nicholas and Ignatius: but choose from the rest whomever you prefer, from the eldest down to the youngest."

They obeyed his behest, and upon withdrawing a short distance in the direction of the church, they took counsel together, and then sent two of the brethren back to Theodosius to beg him to designate the one chosen by God and his own holy prayer, and who should be agreeable to Theodosius himself. Theodosius then made answer, "If you desire to receive your prior from me, then I will appoint him not so much from my own choice as by divine disposition," and he designated the presbyter James. This nomination did not meet with the approval of the brotherhood, who objected that James had not taken orders in the monastery, since he had come thither from Letetz with his brother Paul. They demanded rather Stephen the Cantor, who was then a pupil of Theodosius, and therefore said, "He has grown up under your hand and has served with you; appoint him as our prior."

Then Theodosius said, "By the commandment of God, I designated James, but you prefer that the appointment should coincide with your own wishes." He gave way to their desire, however, and appointed Stephen to be their prior, and blessed him, saying: "My son! I give over to you this monastery. Guard it with care, and maintain what I have ordained in its observances. Change not the traditions and the institutions of the monastery, but follow in all things the law and our monastic rule."

The brethren then raised him up, carried him to his cell, and laid him upon his bed. At the beginning of the sixth day, while he was seriously ill, Prince Sviatoslav came to visit him with his son Gleb. While the prince was sitting beside him, Theodosius said: "I depart from this world and entrust this monastery to your guardianship in the event that some disorder arises in it. I confer the priorate upon Stephen; desert him not in his hour of need."

The prince embraced him, and after promising to care for the monastery, departed from him. When the seventh day was come, while Theodosius was steadily growing weaker, he summoned Stephen and the brotherhood, and spoke to them these words: "Upon my departure from this world, if I have found favor with God and he has accepted me, then this monastery, after my decease, will grow and prosper through his help. In that event, know that God has accepted me. But if, after my death, the monastery begins to lose in membership and income, be assured that I shall not have found favor in the sight of God."

When he had spoken thus, the brethren wept, saying, "Father, intercede with God for us, for we know that he will not scorn your labors." They thus sat out the night with him, and at the beginning of the eighth day, being the second Saturday after Easter, in the second hour of the day, he commended his soul into the hands of God, upon May 3rd, in the eleventh year of the indiction. The brethren thus mourned for him.

Theodosius had given command that he should be buried in the crypt where he had performed many good works. He had also directed that his body should be buried by night, and they followed his injunction in this respect. When evening was come, the brethren took up his body and laid it in the crypt, after conducting it thither in all honor with hymns and candles to the glory of our God Jesus Christ.

BROTHER ISAAC AND THE DEMONS

There was also another monk, named Isaac. While still in

the world, he was very rich, since in the secular life he was by birth a merchant of Toropetz. But he resolved to become a monk, and distributed his fortune to the needy and to the monasteries. He then approached the great Antonius in the crypt, and besought him to receive him into the order. Antonius accepted him, and put upon him the monastic habit, calling him Isaac, for his secular name was Chern. Isaac adopted an ascetic mode of life. He wrapped himself in a hair shirt, then caused a goat to be bought, flayed it, and put on the skin over his hair shirt, so that the fresh hide dried upon him. He shut himself up in a lonely gallery of the crypt in a narrow cell only four ells across, and there lamented and prayed to God. His sustenance was one wafer, and that only once a day, and he drank but moderately of water. The great Antonius carried it to him, and passed it in to him by a little window through which he inserted his arm. Thus Isaac received his food. He subsisted thus for seven years without seeing the light of day or even lying down upon his side, for he snatched what sleep he could in a sitting posture.

Once, when evening had fallen, he had knelt till midnight singing psalms, as was his wont, and when he was wearied, he sat down upon his stool. As he sat there, and had as usual extinguished his candle, a light suddenly blazed forth in the crypt as if it shone from the sun, and strong enough to take away man's vision. Two fair youths then approached him. Their faces were radiant like the sun, and they said to him: "Isaac, we are angels; Christ is drawing near to you. Fall down and worship him."

He did not understand their devilish artifice nor remember to cross himself, but knelt before the work of the demons as if to Christ himself. The demons then cried out and said, "Now, Isaac, you belong to us."

They led him back into his cell and set him down. They then seated themselves around him, and both the cell and the aisle of the crypt was filled with them. One of the devils, who called himself Christ, bade them take flutes and lyres and lutes and play, so that Isaac could dance before them. So they struck up with flutes, lutes, and lyres, and began to make sport of him. After they had tormented him, they left him half alive, and went away when they had beaten him.

The next day at dawn, when it was time to break bread, Antonius came to the window according to his custom and said, "May the Lord bless you, Father Isaac." But there was no answer. Then Antonius said, "He has already passed away," so he sent into the monastery in search of Theodosius and the brethren. After digging out the entrance where it had been walled up, they entered and lifted him up, thinking him dead, and carried him out in front of the crypt. They then perceived that he was still alive, and Theodosius the prior said, "This comes from the devil's artifice." They laid him upon a bier, and Antonius cared for him.

About this same time it happened that Iziaslav returned from Poland, and was angry with Antonius on account of Vseslav, so that Sviatoslav caused Antonius to escape by night to Chernigov. When Antonius arrived there, he was attracted by the Boldiny hills, and after digging another crypt, he settled there. At that spot in the Boldiny hills, there is a monastery dedicated to the Virgin even to this day. When Theodosius learned that Antonius had fled to Chernigov, he came with his brethren, took Isaac, and bore him to his own cell, where he cared for him. For Isaac was so weakened in body that he could not turn from one side to the other, nor rise up, nor sit down, but he lay always upon one side, and relieved himself as he lay, so that numerous worms were caused under his back by his excrement. Theodosius washed and dressed him with his own hands, and for two years cared for him thus. It is wondrous and strange that he lay thus for two years, tasting neither bread nor water nor any other food nor fruit, nor did he speak with his tongue, but lay deaf and dumb for the whole two years.

Theodosius prayed to God in his behalf, and offered supplications over him by day and by night, until in the third year he spoke and heard, rose upon his feet like a babe, and began to walk. He would not go faithfully to church, but the brethren carried him thither by force; they also taught him to go to the refectory, but seated him apart from the rest of the brethren. They set bread before him, but he would not take it unless they placed it in his hand.

Theodosius then said, "Leave the bread before him, but do not put it in his hand, so that he can eat of his own volition."

For a week he ate nothing, but gradually he became aware of the bread, and tasted it. Thus he began to eat, and by this means Theodosius freed him from the craft of the devil.

Isaac then assumed severe abstinence. When Theodosius was dead and Stephen was prior in his stead, Isaac said: "Demon, you deceived me once when I sat in a lonely spot. I must not confine myself in the crypt, but must vanquish you while I frequent the monastery." He then clad himself in a hair shirt, and put on over this a sackcloth coat, and began to act strangely. He undertook to help the cooks in the preparation of food for the brotherhood. He went to matins earlier than the others, and stood firm and immovable. When winter came with its heavy frosts, he stood in shoes so worn that his feet froze to the pavement, but he would not move his feet till matins were over. After matins, he went to the kitchen, and made ready the fire, the water, and the wood before the other cooks came from the brotherhood.

There was one cook who was also named Isaac, who mocked at Isaac and said, "There sits a black crow; go and catch it." Isaac bowed to the ground before him, then went and caught the crow, and brought it back to him in the presence of all the cooks. They were frightened, and reported it to the prior and the brotherhood, who began to respect him. But not being desirous of human glory, he began to act strangely, and to play tricks, now on the prior, now on the brethren, and now on laymen, so that others dealt him blows. Then he began to wander through the country, acting like an idiot. He settled in the crypt where he had formerly lived, for Antonius was already dead. He gathered young men about him and laid upon them the monastic habit, so that he suffered blows from the Prior Nikon as well as from the parents of these youths. But he suffered these hardships, and willingly endured blows and nakedness and cold by day and by night.

One night he lit the stove in a cabin by the crypt. When the stove was heated, fire began to issue forth from the crevices, for it was old and cracked. Since he had nothing to put over the stove, he braced his bare feet against the flame till the stove burned out, and then left it. Many other stories were told about him, and I myself witnessed some such occurrences.

Thus he won his victory over the demons, holding their terrors and apparitions of as little account as flies. For he said to them: "You did indeed deceive me the first time in the crypt, since I did not perceive your craft and cunning. But now that I have on my side the Lord Jesus Christ and my God and the prayers of my father Theodosius, I hope to vanquish you." Many times the demons harassed him, and said, "You belong to us, for you have worshiped us and our leader." But he replied, "Your chief is Antichrist and you are demons," and signed his countenance with the cross. At this they disappeared. Sometimes, however, they came upon him again by night, and frightened him in his dreams, appearing like a great company with mattocks and spades, and saying, "We will undermine the crypt, and bury this man within it," while others exclaimed, "Fly, Isaac, they intend to bury you alive." But he made answer, "If you were men, you would have come by day; but you are darkness and come in darkness, and the darkness shall swallow you up." Then he made the sign of the cross against them, and they vanished.

On other occasions, they endeavored to terrify him in the form of a bear, sometimes as a wild beast and sometimes as a bull. Now snakes beset him, and now toads, mice, and every other reptile. But they could not harm him, and said to him, "Isaac, you have vanquished us!" He replied, "You conquered me in the image of Jesus Christ and his angels, of whose sight you are unworthy. But now you rightly appear in the guise of beasts and cattle or as the snakes and reptiles that you are, repulsive and evil to behold." Thereupon the demons left him, and he suffered no more evil at their hands. As he himself related, his struggle against them lasted for three years. Then he began to live still more strictly, and to practice abstinence, fasting, and vigil.

After thus living out his life, he finally came to his end. He fell sick in his crypt, and was carried in his illness to the monastery, where he died in the Lord upon the eighth day. The Prior John and the brethren clothed his body and buried him.

Such were the monks of the monastery of Theodosius, who shine forth like radiant beacons since their decease, and intercede with God in behalf of the brethren here below, as well as for the lay brotherhood and for those who contribute to the monastery in which to this day the brotherhood abides together in virtuous life amid hymns, prayers, and obedience, to the glory of Almighty God, and protected by the intercession of Theodosius, to whom be glory, Amen.

16. *Bishop Simon and Monk Polycarpe*
The Kievan Crypt Paterikon

THE narratives of this *Paterikon* come from the pen of Simon, Bishop of Vladimir and Suzdal, who apparently began his ecclesiastical career in the Crypt Monastery; and from the pen of Polycarpe, a monk of the same monastery. Simon, who became bishop in 1214 and died in 1226, wrote his narratives as an appendix to his epistle to Polycarpe. In this epistle Simon endeavors to reconcile Polycarpe, who was dissatisfied with his life in the monastery, with his brethren and abbot, and to convince him that the monastery was the spiritual center of the land

pparently Polycarpe wanted to become a bishop and his rela-
ns with the other monks were rather strained. That portion of
e *Paterikon* written by Polycarpe was done some years later,
hen he had become reconciled with the monastery. It is ad-
essed to Abbot Akindin, and has about the same structure as
e first part—that is, an epistle with eleven tales about the
ves of the monks, but is in a style less personal than the work
Simon. It was written for wide circulation both within and
ithout the monastery, whereas the work of Simon was meant
be read only by Polycarpe.

In the thirteenth century both works were made into one,
d to them was added the story of "The Brethren of the Crypt
onastery" (Damian, Jeremy, and Matthew) and "Isaac and
e Demons" from the *Primary Chronicle* by Nestor. Later,
ore narratives were added to this *Paterikon,* and it became one
the most popular collections of this genre in Russia.

Bishop Simon wrote the first four stories of this collection,
hile the last one, "Marko the Gravedigger Who Was Obeyed
the Dead," is the work of Polycarpe. The translations here
esented are based on the text published by D. Abramovich,
ievo-Pecherskii paterik, Kiev, 1931.

◆ ◆ ◆

Bishop Simon

PRINCE SVIATOSHA OF CHERNIGOV

This blessed and faithful Prince Sviatosha, called Nicholas
ter he became a monk, was the son of Prince David and the
andson of Prince Sviatoslav. This prince came to the conclu-
on that all things in this vain life are illusive and that every-
ing on the earth comes to its end and passes away, but that
e blessings of the future life are eternal and everlasting and
at the Kingdom of Heaven, which God has prepared for those
ho love him, is unending. And he relinquished his princedom
gether with all his honor, glory and power, seeing no worth
all these things. And he came to the Crypt Monastery and
came a monk. This happened in 1106 (6614) on the 17th day
February. All the monks who were living in the monastery at
at time are witnesses to his virtuous life and his fulfillment of
e vows of obedience.

For three years he remained in the kitchen working with his
ethren. With his own hands he chopped wood for the prepa-
tion of meals, carrying it on his shoulders, often from the river

Dnieper. And his brothers, Iziaslav and Vladimir, were hard]
able to keep him from such heavy labor. However, he aske
and begged that they permit him to work at least one more yea
in the kitchen with his brethren. Thereafter, he was placed i
charge of the monastery gates, for in every type of work he wa
skillful and diligent. He remained there, at the gates, for thre
years, never leaving except to attend church services. Fron
there he was told to go and serve in the refectory. Finall
according to the will of the abbot and all the brethren, he wa
permitted to have his own cell, which he himself built. Th
cell is called Sviatosha's cell to this very day, and the vegetab]
garden, which he planted with his own hands, is also calle
after his name still. People say of him that no one has ever see
him idle. He was always occupied with some kind of work, an
thus he earned his keep. On his lips permanently was a praye
to Jesus: "Jesus Christ, have mercy upon us." He never ate any
thing more than the monastery meals. He had considerab]
wealth, but he gave everything away to pilgrims and the poo
and for the building of churches. Up to now there are man
books given by him to your monastery. When he was still rulin
this blessed Sviatosha had a very skilled physician, Peter, wh
was from Syria. This Peter came with him to the monaster
but, seeing that the prince voluntarily accepted poverty an
worked in the kitchen and at the gate, he left him and, settlin
in Kiev, became a doctor for many citizens of this city. Th
physician used to come often to Prince Sviatosha at the mona
tery and, seeing his bitter sufferings and endless fasting, tried t
convince him to change his way of living, saying: "Prince, yo
should care for your health and not ruin your body with endles
labor and abstinence. You will become so ill, that you will not b
able to carry the burden which, for God's sake, you have volun
tarily accepted. God does not desire unbearable fasting an
labor, but only a humble and contrite heart. You are not ac
customed to hardships such as you, working like a slave, mu
now endure. Your pious brothers, Iziaslav and Vladimir, fee
that your poverty is a reproach to them. How could you tur
away from such glory and honor to such wretchedness and ho
can you exhaust your body with such food? I wonder abou
your stomach; once sweet meals were too heavy for it, and no
it accepts and endures simple herbs and dry bread. Beware, fc
sometime all your maladies will attack you at once, and you
deprived of resistance, will succumb, and I will not be able t
help you. You will leave your inconsolable brothers to moun
after you. Also, your boyars, who once served you, hoped to be

ome powerful and glorious with your help. Now they are de-
rived of your love, and they complain about you. They have
uilt large houses for themselves, but they remain in them in
reat grief. You yourself have not even a place to lay your head,
emaining in this backyard. They consider that you have become
sane. Who among the princes has done anything of this
ature? Did your blessed father, David, or your grandfather,
viatoslav, do so? Or who among the boyars has acted in this
ay? Or who even intended to do anything similar, excepting
arlaam, who was the abbot here? And if you don't follow my
dvice, you will meet an untimely death."

So he used to talk with Prince Sviatosha, now Monk Nicholas,
tting with him in the kitchen or at the gate. And he was
structed to do so by Prince Sviatosha's brothers. But Prince
viatosha answered him, saying: "Brother Peter, I have thought
r a long time and I have decided not to spare my flesh so as
prevent it from arousing in me a new struggle. It is better
keep it submissive under the burden of heavy labor, for it is
id: 'Strength is achieved through weakness,' and, 'These
resent temporary passions are nothing worse in comparison
ith the glory which will be revealed in us.' I thank God for
e has liberated me from the slavedom of this world and made
e the servant of his servants, these blessed monks. And my
others had better look after themselves, for each man must
ear his cross alone. They should be satisfied with having my
atrimony—all of what I had: my wife and children, the house
d power, brethren and friends, serfs and estates, I gave up
r Christ's sake so as to inherit eternal life. I became poor for
e sake of God, so that I might gain God's favor.

"And even yourself, when you treat people, don't you pre-
ribe refraining from excessive eating? To die for Christ would
a real acquisition of fortune for me. And sitting here in the
ackyard next to the refuse heap is the winning of a real
ngdom. It may be that no prince has done as I do now. Then
will be the first example for them. Perhaps one of them will
ant to imitate my example and follow in my footsteps. As far
my life is concerned, it should not be of concern to you, nor
those who have asked you to come to me."

When the blessed prince was sick, his physician, Peter, usu-
ly prepared some medicine for the illness, such as severe
eartburn or other pains that had occurred to the prince. But
efore the physician could reach the prince, the prince was
ready cured. And he never permitted himself to be treated by
physician. And so it happened many times. Once, when the

physician himself became ill, Prince Sviatosha sent him a me⊥
senger to say: "Don't take your medicine and you will be cure⊥
And if you don't obey me, you will suffer bitterly."

But the latter, relying on his medical skills, drank the med⊥
cine, hoping to be cured of his illness; but instead of bei⊥
cured, he almost died. And only the prayer of the blessed prin⊥
helped and cured him.

Another time the physician again became ill, and the blesse⊥
prince sent his messenger once more to say, "If you do⊥
attempt to cure yourself, you will be completely recovered ⊥
three days."

The Syrian obeyed him, and on the third day he recovere⊥
according to the words of the blessed prince. As soon as he h⊥
recovered, the blessed one asked him to come to the monaster⊥
and there he enjoined the physician to become a monk, sayin⊥
"In three months from now, we shall part." With these wor⊥
Prince Sviatosha predicted the death of the physician.

The Syrian misunderstood the prince's words, thinking th⊥
not his own death but that of the prince was nearing. He f⊥
before the prince's feet and tearfully implored him, saying:

"Alas, woe is me, my lord and benefactor!
Who will help me, a foreigner?
Who will feed so many people who are hungry?
Who will be the intercessor of the offended?
Who will be merciful with the poor?
Have I not told you, my prince,
that you will be mourned by all your inconsolable brother⊥
You cured me not only through the words and power ⊥
    God,
but also with the help of your prayers.
Where will you depart to, my good pastor?
Tell me what fatal illness you have,
and I will cure you.
And, if I cannot,
then my head shall be given for your head,
and my soul for your soul.
Oh, my lord, don't leave me
without telling me how you learned of your death.
I would give my life for you.
If God has announced your passing away to you,
please pray to him that I might die in your place.
Where would I be able to mourn my loss,
if you leave me?

Should I do it here, at this refuse heap,
or at the gate where you live?
And what can you leave me if you die?
You yourself are almost naked, and when you die
you will be buried in your patched and tattered garments.
Help me through your prayers
as once Prophet Elijah gave Elisha his mantle
to get through paradise
under the shelter of the wonderful house of the Lord.
Even the beast knows where the sun will rise
before it goes to its lair.
And the bird knows how to find its abode
and the turtledove knows how to find the nest
where it raises its fledglings."

But the blessed one answered him: "It is better to place one's hopes in the Lord than to rely upon many; God knows how to feed his creatures and how to protect and save his poor. My brothers should not worry about me, but about themselves and their children. I never wanted any treatment by a physician during my life, because when the hour of death has come the physician cannot help." And the prince went with the physician down into the crypt and dug a grave for himself, and he asked the Syrian, "Which of us wants this grave the more?"

And the Syrian replied: "It should come to pass as each of us desires. But you should live, and I should be buried here."

And then the blessed prince told him, "Let it be as you do desire."

The Syrian physician became a monk, and passed three months weeping incessantly both day and night. The blessed one consoled him, saying, "Brother Peter, do you wish that I should take you with me?"

And the physician answered tearfully: "I want you to release me and let me die in your place. Please, pray for me."

And the blessed prince told the physician, "Prepare for death, my son, and in three days you will depart to the lord."

And after three days the physician took Holy Communion, lay down on his bed, adjusted his robes, stretched out his legs, and gave up his soul into the hands of the Lord, as it was predicted by Blessed Prince Sviatosha.

Prince Sviatosha lived after this for another thirty years, never leaving the monastery again. And when he died, almost the entire city of Kiev came to his burial. Learning of Blessed Sviatosha's death, his brother, Prince Iziaslav, sent a messenger

to the abbot, asking that he be given the crucifix of Prince
Sviatosha, his pillow, and the board upon which he had knelt.

The abbot gave them to the prince, saying, "It will renew
your faith."

The prince accepted them and carefully preserved them at
home. And he gave the abbot three pieces of gold so as not to
receive this blessing of the abbot for nothing.

Once, this prince became so ill that all his family lost hope
and, seeing that he was about to die, his wife, children, and
boyars went to his chambers and remained with him. He raised
up slightly and asked for some water from the well of the Crypt
Monastery, and then he became mute.

In the meantime a messenger went to the monastery for the
water. The abbot took Sviatosha's hair shirt,[1] put it first on the
grave of St. Theodosius, and then gave it to the prince's messenger, telling him to put this shirt on Prince Iziaslav. Before
the messenger had returned with the water and hair shirt, the
ill prince suddenly uttered the words, "Go beyond the gates of
the city and meet St. Theodosius and St. Nicholas."

And when the messenger returned with the water and the
hair shirt, the prince exclaimed, "Nicholas—Nicholas Sviatosha!"

And the prince was given the water, and the hair shirt was
placed on his body, and he recovered immediately. And everyone glorified God and his saints. And each time Iziaslav became
ill, he would put on this hair shirt, and he always recovered.
And in all battles he wore this hair shirt, and he remained unharmed. But once, a poor sinner, he dared not put on the hair
shirt, and he was slain in battle. And he was buried in this hair
shirt, as he had requested. And the brethren still remember
other great deeds of the saint. Until this day the monks of the
Crypt Monastery still hold Blessed Prince Sviatosha in their
memory.

Bishop Simon

VIKING SHIMON AND ST. THEODOSIUS

THE BUILDING OF THE CHURCH OF THE HOLY VIRGIN
OF THE CRYPT MONASTERY

And now I will come to other stories. Everyone should know
how, according to the will of God and the prayers and desires
of the Holy Virgin, the beautiful and great Church of the Crypt

---

[1] Hair shirt—a shirt made of horsehair, and worn as a penance.

Monastery, dedicated to the Holy Virgin, was founded and built. This is the church of the great abbey of all the Russian land, the monastery of St. Theodosius.

There was in the land of the Vikings[2] a certain prince whose name was Africanus, the brother of Yakun, who, when he and Prince Yaroslav were fighting against evil Prince Mstislav, lost his gold-embroidered mantle when he was fleeing from battle. This Prince Africanus had two sons, Friand and Shimon. After Prince Africanus' death, his brother, Yakun, drove his nephews from their patrimonies. And thus Shimon came to our faithful Prince Yaroslav. And Yaroslav received him with honor and sent him to his son, Vsevolod, appointing him to be the senior counselor to Vsevolod. And through this position Shimon gained great influence. The reason for Shimon's devotion to the Holy Crypt Monastery is explained in the following narrative.

During the reign of Prince Iziaslav in Kiev, the Kumans came to the Russian land, this being in 1068 (6576). And the sons of Yaroslav, Princes Iziaslav, Sviatoslav, and Vsevolod, decided to attack them. And Shimon went with Prince Vsevolod. When they came to the great and holy Father Antonius and asked him for his blessing and prayers, the abbot opened his lips, which had been sealed for a very long time, and clearly foretold of their forthcoming demise. Then Shimon the Viking fell at the abbot's feet and begged him to tell how he, Shimon, might escape this fate.

And the blessed abbot told him: "My son, many of you will fall in battle, pierced by swords. And when many of you attempt to escape from the enemy, you will be pursued and struck down by weapons or drowned in the river. But you, my son, will escape, and later you will be buried in the church that you will build."

And the Russian regiments engaged in battle on the river Leta, and because of God's wrath the Christians were defeated and routed. And many *voevodas*[3] and warriors fell in battle. Among those who had fallen in battle lay Shimon, who was wounded. He raised his eyes to the heavens and there saw a great church, the same that he had seen once at sea. And, remembering the words of the Savior, he said, "Lord! Deliver me from bitter death through the prayers of your most holy Mother and the reverend fathers Antonius and Theodosius."

And at that moment a certain power took him from the

[2] Apparently Shimon came to Russia from Sweden.
[3] Military commanders.

clutches of death. He became cured of his wounds and soor found that all his family was safe and in good health.

And then he returned to the great Antonius and told him o this wonderful miracle, saying: "My father, Africanus, onc(made a cross on which was the figure of Christ with pieces o gold that weighed fifty grivnas.[4] And on his head he placed ; golden crown. When my uncle, Yakun, drove me from my patri mony, I took with me the girdle and the crown from this image of Jesus. And when I did so, I heard coming from the cross ; voice that was directed to me, and it said:

> " 'Man, never put this crown on your own head, but take it to the place that I have chosen. And there the Reverenc Father Theodosius will erect a church in honor of my Mother. Place this crown in his hands and tell him to hang it over my altar.'

"And I fell to the ground, seized with awe, and I lay there motionless, as if dead, for a long time. Then I got up and wen to a ship. When we were crossing the sea, there occurred a grea storm, and we all feared for our lives. And I began to pray 'Lord! Forgive me, for I am perishing because of the crown I took from your revered and holy image.'

"And I saw in the heavens a church, and I began to wonder what this vision meant. And then there came from above a voice that announced:

> " 'This is the church that should be built by the Reverenc Father Theodosius in the name of the Mother of God. And in this church you are to be buried.'

"And I saw the size and the height, and I measured it with the golden girdle and found it to be twenty feet wide and thirty feet high, and the walls and the roof were fifty feet. And we all glori fied God and, becoming consoled, we experienced great joy at having escaped a bitter death. Until now, I did not realize where the church, shown me both at sea and at the river Leta where I was lying at death's door, was to be built. And then I heard from your revered tongue that I will be buried here in the church that will be erected."

And Shimon took out the golden girdle, and said, "Here are the measurements and the plan, and here is the crown that should be hung above the holy altar."

And Abbot Antonius glorified God, and told the Viking, "My child, from this day on you will never be called Shimon, but Simon."

---

[4] Old Russian unit of money.

And Antonius invited Blessed Father Theodosius to come to him, and he told him, "Here is Simon who wants to build such a church." And Antonius gave Theodosius the girdle, crown, and plans. And from that day Simon loved holy Theodosius very much, and he gave him his wealth and estate for the needs of the monastery.

Once Simon came to Blessed Theodosius, and after the usual talk he told the holy one, "Father, I ask you to give me a gift."

And Theodosius answered, "Oh, my child, what can you, a powerful man, ask from me, a humble one?"

And Simon answered, "The gift I ask of you is most important, and beyond my power to obtain."

And Theodosius replied: "My child, you know how poor we are and that often we don't even have enough bread for the daily meal. And I know not what else we may have."

But Simon said: "If you want to give me this gift, you can do so, thanks to the grace that you have received from God, who called you a 'Reverend Father.' When I had taken the crown from the head of Jesus, he told me:

> "'Take it to the place that I have chosen. And there the Reverend Father Theodosius will erect a church in honor of my Mother.'

And so I now ask you to give me your word that your soul will bless me both during our lives and after our deaths."

And the saintly father answered: "What you ask me is beyond my power, but if the church is built, and if after my passing the rituals and traditions are preserved in this church, then know that I shall dare to ask God. But now I know not whether my prayers would be acceptable."

And Simon said: "God is my witness that I was told about you by the purest lips of his holy image. Therefore, I beg you, pray for me, for my son, George, and for his descendants, in the same way in which you pray for your monks."

The saint promised this to Simon the Viking, and then added: "I don't pray for my monks only, but for everyone who for my sake loves this holy monastery."

Then Simon bowed deeply to the earth, and spoke: "My father, I won't leave you until you have confirmed in writing what you have said."

Theodosius felt compelled to do so, since Simon loved him. And he wrote, "In the name of the Father, and of the Son, and of the Holy Ghost. . . ." And these words became the prayer which, from that time to this, is always placed in the hands of

the dead. And since that time it has become the custom to put
such letters in the coffins of the dead. No one did this before.
And the following was written in the prayer:

"Remember, me, O Lord, when thou comest into thy kingdom, and when thou judgest everyone according to his deeds,
then permit, O Lord, that thy servants Simon and George remain on the right side of thy glory, and hear thy blessed voice
saying, 'Come, O blessed of my Father, and inherit the kingdom
that has been prepared for you since time immemorial.'"

And Simon asked, "My father, please ask the Lord also to
absolve the sins of my father and my relatives."

And Theodosius raised his hands to the heavens and said,
"Be blessed by the God of Zion, and you, and everyone to the
last of your line, shall view the beauty of Jerusalem."

Simon received this holy blessing and this prayer as a price-
less gift. Once he was a Viking, and now, thanks to the grace
of God, he became an Orthodox Christian. He was instructed
by our holy father Theodosius, and, for the sake of the miracles
performed by holy Antonius and Theodosius, he gave up his
Western heresy and became a believer of the one true faith.
And this he did with all his household and all his priests, and
they numbered about three thousand. And Simon was the first
to be buried in the church of the Crypt Monastery. Since that
time Simon's son, George, also loved this holy place exceedingly.
Prince Vladimir Monomakh sent George, the son of Simon, to
the land of Suzdal, and entrusted to him his son, Yury. Many
years later this Prince Yury became the ruler of Kiev, and he
entrusted to George the land of Suzdal as if George were his
own father.

Bishop Simon

THE COMING OF THE GREEK ICONOGRAPHERS
FROM CONSTANTINOPLE TO ABBOT NIKON

Once, several Greek iconographers from Constantinople came
to Abbot Nikon of the Crypt Monastery and began to complain,
saying: "Bring before us the men who hired us. We wish to have
a trial. They hired us to embellish a small church, and we made
the agreement in front of witnesses, but this church is very
large. Take back your gold (which we received as payment),
and we'll return to Constantinople."

Abbot Nikon (not understanding of what they were speaking)

asked them, "Who were the people who made this agreement with you?"

And the Greeks described these people and gave their names as being Antonius and Theodosius.

But the abbot answered them, saying: "My children, we cannot bring them before you, for they departed this world ten years ago. But they still continue to pray incessantly for us; they steadily safeguard this church; they care for this monastery; and they protect all those who live in it."

Hearing these words, the Greeks were awestruck. However, they brought before the abbot numerous merchants, Greeks and Abkhasians,[1] who had traveled with them from Constantinople to Kiev. And the iconographers declared: "We made the agreement and accepted gold for payment from those who hired us in the presence of these merchants. But since you, Abbot, do not wish to bring to us those who commissioned us, or are unable to bring them here, then show us their images so that our witnesses can see them."

When the abbot brought them the icons of Sts. Antonius and Theodosius, the Greeks and Abkhasians, upon seeing them, bowed deeply and said: "Verily, they are their image! And we believe that even after death they still live and can protect, save, and succor those who turn to them for aid." And they decided to give the mosaic, which they had brought with them from Constantinople to sell, for the embellishment of the altar.

And the iconographers began to confess their sins: "When we arrived in our boats at the city of Kanev on the river Dnieper, we had the vision of a mountain on which was a large church. And we asked other travelers, 'What church is this?' and they answered, 'It is the church of the Crypt Monastery in which you are to paint the icons.'

"And, becoming angry,[2] we decided to go back, and started down the river. But that same night there occurred a severe storm on the river, and when we awoke the next morning we found that we were at the village of Tripole, farther up the river, and that a certain power was pulling us always up river. And only with great difficulty were we able to stop our boat. And we remained there the whole day, contemplating the meaning of this event, since in one night, and without any rowing,

[1] Abkhasians: a tribe in the western Caucasus.
[2] They were upset because having seen the size of the church they realized that their work would have to be much more extensive than they had expected.

we went up the river for a distance that usually requires three days of travel.

"The next night we again had the same vision of the church, and in the church was an icon of the Holy Virgin, and from this icon there came a voice announcing: 'Men! Why do you worry? Why do you not submit yourself to my will and that of my Son? If you do not obey, but try to escape, you, together with your boat, will be taken from this place and placed in the church. And know that you will never leave the monastery, but will there receive the tonsure, and will there end your days. But you will be granted mercy in the life eternal for the sake of the builders of the monastery, Abbots Antonius and Theodosius.'

"And the next day, when we awoke, we once more attempted to escape, and made a great effort to row downstream; but the boat moved continually upstream. And soon it landed at the shore under the monastery, and of its own accord."

After the Greeks had finished their narration, they and the monks glorified God, the miraculous holy icon of his most pure mother, and the holy fathers Antonius and Theodosius. And actually, having become monks, the iconographers and builders did end their days in the Crypt Monastery. And they were buried near the altar, and their robes still hang there and their books are preserved in the monastery for the commemoration of this miracle.

Bishop Simon

JOHN AND SERGIUS

There were two men from this great city (of Kiev) who were very close friends, and their names were John and Sergius. Once, both of them went into the Church of the Crypt Monastery, which was built by the will of God. And there they saw that from the icon of the Holy Virgin there emanated a bright light, even brighter than the rays of the sun. And so they decided to pledge themselves to become spiritual brothers.

Many years later John became very ill and was on his death-bed, leaving a son, Zacharias, who was only five years old. Before his death John called for the abbot of the Crypt Monastery, and gave him all his personal wealth for distribution to the poor. The part that belonged to his young son, which consisted of one thousand *grivnas* of silver, and one hundred *grivnas* of gold, he left in trust with his spiritual brother, Sergius. John also asked

is spiritual brother to care for his son, Zacharias, telling
Sergius, "Give this gold and silver to my son when he comes
of age."

When Zacharias was fifteen years old, he wanted to obtain
his gold and silver from Sergius. But Sergius, incited by the
devil, decided to keep the money for himself, and in so doing to
lose his soul. Therefore he told the youth: "Your father gave
his entire estate to God, and you should ask God for your gold
and silver. He owes it to you, and, being merciful, perhaps he
will return it to you. But I don't owe your father even a single
gold coin, for he, having lost his mind, gave away all his wealth
and left you in poverty."

Hearing these words, the youth became sad and once more
he begged Sergius for his money, but this time asking for only
one-half of his money, letting Sergius keep the second half. But
Sergius began to reproach the son and the son's father in strong
words.

Zacharias then attempted to obtain from Sergius at least one-
quarter or even one-tenth of his money; but seeing that he
would not receive anything from Sergius, he spoke to him,
saying, "Come and avow in the Church of the Crypt Monastery,
before the miraculous icon of the Virgin, the same icon before
which you pledged to be my father's spiritual brother, that
you received no money from my father."

And Sergius promised to avow before the icon that he had
received neither one thousand *grivnas* of silver nor one hundred
grivnas of gold from John. But as Sergius approached the icon
to avow, an invisible power prevented him from nearing it. And
suddenly he began to shout: "Holy Angels and St. Theodosius!
Enjoin this merciless angel not to slay me. Pray to the Holy
Virgin to drive away the devils who attack me! Take your
gold and silver! It is in a sealed vessel in my house!"

Everyone was seized with awe. And from that day it was
forbidden to pronounce avowals on this icon. Men were sent to
Sergius' house, and there they found the sealed vessel, and in it
were two thousand *grivnas* of silver and two hundred *grivnas*
of gold, for God had miraculously increased the fortune of the
poor, knowing that Zacharias would give his fortune to the
abbot of the Crypt Monastery. Zacharias remained at the monastery to the end of his days, and his fortune was used to erect
the Church of St. John the Baptist. This church was dedicated
to the memories of John and Zacharias, since their gold and
silver had erected it.

Monk Polycarpe

MARKO THE GRAVEDIGGER WHO
WAS OBEYED BY THE DEAD

We sinners imitate the ancient writings on the saints. But the ancient writers, with great difficulties, sought the saints in the wilderness, in the mountains, and in the abysses. Some of these authors have themselves seen these saints, while of other saints they have heard stories of their lives, works, miracles, and deeds, and have composed the *Paterikon*, which we read and in which we enjoy spiritual narrations. I, an unworthy one, have not yet been able to comprehend the truth of reason, and I have seen nothing of this kind. I tell only what I have heard. This narration was told to me by Bishop Simon, and I wrote it down for you, my reverend father. I have never been in holy places nor have I seen Jerusalem nor Mount Sinai. Therefore I am unable to add anything to this narration for the purpose of embellishment, as is the habit of those who are clever with words. I do not want to praise anything but this Holy Crypt Monastery, the monks who live therein, and the lives and miracles of the latter. I shall rejoice when I remember them, for I, a sinner, hope that the saintly fathers will pray for me. And here I shall begin the narration concerning the gravedigger Marko.

St. Marko used to live in the crypt, and during his life there the body of our father, Theodosius, was taken from the crypt into the great holy church. This Marko dug graves in the crypt with his own hands, and carried the earth away on his shoulders. He worked hard all day and all night to do these pious deeds. Though he dug many graves for the burial of his brethren, he never accepted payment for doing so. If someone gave him money, he would take it and distribute it among the poor and crippled.

Once, according to his custom, he dug a grave and, laboring very much, became tired. However, the grave was not sufficiently wide. It so happened that this very day one of the brothers passed to God, and there was no grave available except this narrow one. The dead man was brought to the crypt, but because the grave was so very narrow he could not be placed in it. And the brethren began to grumble at Marko, for it was neither possible to adjust the dead man's robes nor to anoint him with holy oil. Marko, the monk of the cave, bowed to everyone with humility and said, "Forgive me, my fathers, but I could not finish the grave because of my poor health."

But the monks continued to reproach him still more. Then Marko addressed the dead man: "Brother, your grave is so narrow we cannot even anoint you with holy oil. Take the oil and anoint yourself."

The dead man raised up slightly, extended his hand, took the oil, and anointed his face and chest, making the sign of the cross. He then returned the vessel, adjusted his robes, lay down, and once more died. Awe and trembling seized everyone because of the miracle.

Some time later, after a long illness, another brother died. One of his friends cleansed the body with a sponge and went to the crypt to view the grave where his friend was supposed to lie. He asked Marko about the grave, and Marko answered, "Go to the dead brother and tell him, 'Wait until tomorrow, until I dig your grave, and then you can enter into rest.' "

But the brother, who had come to the crypt, said: "Brother Marko, I have already cleansed the dead man's body with a sponge. How can you now ask me to speak to him?"

Marko once again spoke to him: "You can see for yourself that the grave is not finished. I enjoin you to go and tell the dead man that sinful Marko tells him: 'Brother, live one more day, and then tomorrow you will pass to God in peace. When I have prepared a place for you, I will send for you.' "

The brother who had come to Blessed Marko obeyed. When he returned to the monastery, all the brothers were standing around the dead man and were singing the usual hymns. The monk stood before the dead brother, and said, "Brother Marko has told me to tell you that your grave is not ready and that you should wait until tomorrow."

Everyone was astounded by these words. But as soon as they were spoken by the monk who had returned from Marko, the dead brother's soul returned to his body. The whole day and night he remained with his eyes open, but talked with no one at all.

The next day his friends once more returned to the cave to find out if the place was ready. And Blessed Marko told them: "Go and tell the following to one who has become alive: 'Abandon this provisional life and pass into the life eternal. Here the place is ready for your body. Give your soul to God, and your body will be buried here with many holy brothers.' "

The brothers came and told all this to the dead one who had come alive. Immediately the latter, in the presence of all who had come to visit him, closed his eyes and passed away. And

he was placed with honors in the new place in the cave. And
everyone wondered about this miracle. How could it be that
with just one word from Blessed Marko, the dead would become alive, and then die once more after Marko ordered it?

Two other brethren in this great Crypt Monastery had since
their youth been united by the great love in their hearts. They
had the same thoughts and the same desires, which were directed to God. And they begged Blessed Marko to prepare them
a common grave where they would be able to lie together when
God should order them to do so. Many years later the elder
brother, Theophile, left the monastery on business. In the meantime the younger brother became ill and died and was laid in
the grave prepared for him. Theophile returned only some days
after the burial. Having learned of the death of his brother, he
became very sad and, taking some other monks, went to the
cave to see in which place the deceased was laid.

Having noticed that his brother was buried in a place that
was higher than the place reserved for himself, he was seized
by wrath, and began to complain to Marko, saying: "Why did
you put him there? I am the older, and therefore should be put
in the higher place. But you have buried him in my place."

Marko, the monk of the cave, being a humble man, bowed
to Theophile, and said, "Excuse me, my brother, I have sinned
before you." Then he said to the deceased, "Brother, give your
place to your elder brother and lie down in the lower place."
And immediately after these words of Blessed Marko, the dead
man got up in the presence of all the monks and lay down in
the lower place. Everyone saw this terrible and awe-inspiring
miracle.

Then brother Theophile, who had reproached Marko, fell to
his knees and said: "Brother Marko, I have sinned by moving
my brother from his place. Tell him to return to the original
place."

But Blessed Marko told Theophile: "God ended the enmity
between us. He did so because you complained and so that you
might be prevented from lasting enmity and evil feelings toward me. Even this soulless body has demonstrated its love to
you, respecting your seniority even after death. I should like you
to make use of your seniority by not leaving this crypt, but by
lying down in this place. But you are not ready for passing
away. Therefore, go and care for your soul. In some days from
now you will be brought to this place. The resurrection of the
dead is the work of God, whereas I am only a miserable sinner.

ok on your dead brother, who was not able to bear the
roaches with which you covered me. And he left you a half
the place that was prepared for both of you. God can raise
e dead, but I cannot say, 'Go down and lie in the lower
ce,' and then say, 'Go up and lie in the higher place.' If you
nt him to go back to his former place, order it, and perhaps
will go back to the place he left before."

Having heard these words, Theophile became saddened, and
thought that he would be unable to walk back to the mon-
ery. When he returned to his cell, he began to cry discon-
ately. He distributed everything he had, and kept only his
ntle and robe. From that time forth, he was in permanent
pectation of death, and no one could bring an end to his bitter
ving and no one could convince him to eat well.

At the beginning of the day he would say to himself, "I don't
ow whether I shall live till evening." When evening was ap-
aching, he would cry and say: "What should I do? Shall I be
le to live till morning? Many people who arose this morning
re not able to live until evening, but were obliged to lie down
d were unable to get up again. And what of me? For I was
d by Blessed Marko that my end was very near." And he
ent each day mortifying his flesh with fasting, praying, and
essant weeping, expecting each day that his final hour was
proaching. The expectation that his soul would soon be sepa-
ed from his body exhausted him to such an extent that it
came possible to count his ribs. Many people wished to con-
le him, but this made him weep only the more. Finally, be-
use of his incessant tears, he became blind. And so Theophile
ent his days in great abstinence, thereby winning the grace
God by his exemplary life.

When Marko learned the hour of his own passing to God, he
ked Theophile to come, and he told him: "Brother Theophile,
rgive me for having caused you great sadness, lo! these many
ars. Now I leave this world. Pray for me. If I receive God's
ercy, I shall not forget you. Let us pray that we may see each
her with our fathers, Antonius and Theodosius, in the next
e."

And Theodosius answered tearfully: "Father Marko, why do
u leave me here? Why don't you return my sight to me?"

Marko told him: "Brother, don't grieve. Thanks to God you
ve lost your physical sight, but you have won the insight for
derstanding him with your spiritual eyes. My brother, I was
sponsible for your blindness, for I prophesied your death. But
did so for the sake of your soul, for I wanted to turn your

pride into humility, and God rejects neither the contrite he
nor the humble man."

And Theophile answered him, saying: "I know, my fath
that I should have fallen dead for my sins when you raised
dead brother. But, because of prayers, the Lord gave me n
life, hoping for my repentance. Now I beg you, please, eit
take me with you to the Lord or return my sight to me."

Marko replied: "There is no need for you to see this transit
world. Pray to the Lord that you may see his glory in the n
world. Your hour will come, even if you do not wish it
Nevertheless, I shall give you a foretoken of your passing. Th
days before your death, you will regain your sight. And, pass
to God, you will there see endless light and unspoken glor
And Blessed Marko passed to God, being buried in the crypt
a grave he himself had dug.

This separation from Brother Marko added greatly to Th
phile's suffering and increased his weeping. He shed whole t
rents of tears, and the tears continually increased. He had
special vessel, and because his tears would always reappe
when he began praying, he would put this vessel before hims
so that his tears would fall into it. Some days this vessel wo
be full of tears, since every day Theophile expected the end
his life as Blessed Marko had predicted. When Theophile ∫
that his day of passing to God was drawing near, he began
pray zealously, saying: "Our Lord who loves man, my God, ∶
most holy King, you do not want the death of a sinner; y
anticipate their conversion to righteousness. You know our we∶
nesses, our gracious Comforter. You are health to the ill a
salvation for the sinner. You are succor for the exhausted a
an uplifting for the fallen. O Lord, I, an unworthy one, pray
you in this hour to show me your amazing grace and to reve
to me the unfathomable depths of your mercy. Deliver me fr∢
temptation. Do not permit the enemy to overcome me in ☨
ordeal, but give me strength for the sake of the prayers of y∢
saints and our great fathers, Antonius and Theodosius, and
the sake of the prayers of all saints who have served you sin
the beginning of time."

And in this moment a beautiful youth appeared before hi
and said, "You pray well, but why are you so saddened by t
vanity of your tears?" And the youth, taking a vessel mu
larger than that which Theophile had, and which was filled w
the fragrance of myrrh, said: "Here are the tears that ha
poured forth from your contrite heart during your prayers

l. All your tears that you dried neither with your hand nor
h your robe nor with a cloth fell from your eyes to the
:h. All of them, at the command of the Creator, I gathered
. preserved in this vessel. Now I have been sent to you to
ounce tidings of joy. With joy will you go to the one who
l, 'Blessed are they that mourn, for they shall be comforted.'
ring spoken these words, the youth disappeared.

After this, Blessed Theophile asked the abbot to come to his
, and he told him of the appearance of the angel and of the
el's words. He showed the abbot both vessels, one of which
; filled with tears and the other with a fragrance that could
be compared to any other. And Blessed Theophile asked that
contents of both vessels be poured over his body after his
th.

Three days later, Blessed Theophile passed to the Lord and
; buried in the crypt near the grave of Marko the grave-
ger. And when the contents of the angel's vessel were spread
r his body, the entire crypt was filled with a wondrous sweet
grance. And the monks also poured the contents of the vessel
tears over him, doing this so that he who had shed these
rs might harvest the fruits of his labor.

APOCRYPHA

17. The Descent of the Virgin into Hell

AFTER the Christianization of Russia under Prince Vladin
canonical books,· such as the Bible, liturgic texts, and the wo
of the early Church Fathers, circulated through the Russ
land. In addition to these, a considerable number of apocryp
or noncanonical writings came to Russia. Patterned after
Bible and written at the time of the New Testament, they w
never recognized by the Church. Among such works, *The I
scent of the Virgin Into Hell*, or, as it was called by Russia
The Visitation to the Torments by the Mother of God, is
most distinguished owing to its concept of divine mercy and
originality of its composition. "A visit to hell" was a subj
common to both Eastern and Western Christianity, its m
famous version being, of course, Dante's great poem *The Div
Comedy*.

The juxtaposition of eschatological concepts with the conc
of divine mercy, as presented in this work, greatly influenc
the Russian religious mind and was reflected in medieval R
sian *vitae*, spiritual songs, and icons.

This translation is based on the text of a seventeenth-cent
manuscript that was revised and corrected by Professor N.
Gudzy according to a twelfth-century manuscript, and it
peared in his *Khrestomatiia po drevnei russkoi literature*, M
cow, 1955, pages 92–98. Some portions of this translation foll
that of Professor L. Wiener.

◆ ◆ ◆

The Holy Virgin wished to see the torments of the souls, a
so she said to the archangel, Michael, "I ask that you tell
all things which are upon the earth." And the archangel
swered, "I shall tell you all things which are upon the ear
Blessed One, as you would have it." And the Holy Virgin ask
him, "How many torments does the Christian race suffer?" A
the archangel said, "Innumerable are those torments." And th
the Holy Virgin replied, "Show me what is in heaven and up
the earth."

Then the archangel ordered the angels to come from
south, and Hell was opened. And she saw those that were s

fering in Hell, and there were a great number of them and there was much weeping. And the Blessed Virgin asked the archangel: "Who are these that they suffer so?"

And the archangel answered: "These are those who did not believe in the Father, the Son, and the Holy Ghost, but forgot God and believed in those things which God created for our sakes. They called the sun and the moon, beast and reptiles, earth and water God. And they made gods out of the devils Troyan, Khors, Veles, and Perun, and they worshiped these evil devils. And even now they are possessed by evil darkness, and therefore they suffer such torments."

And the Holy Virgin saw great darkness in another place. And she asked, "What is this darkness and who are those who dwell therein?" And the archangel answered, saying, "Many souls dwell in this place." And the Holy Virgin said, "Let the darkness be dispersed that I may see the torment." And the angels who watched over the torment answered, "We have been enjoined not to let them see light until the coming of your blessed Son, who is brighter than seven suns." And the Holy Virgin was saddened, and she raised her eyes to the angels and looked at the invisible throne of her father and said: "In the name of the Father, and the Son, and the Holy Ghost! Let this darkness be dispersed that I may see this torment."

And the darkness was dispersed and seven heavens appeared and there was a great multitude of men and women. And there were loud weeping and wailing in this place. And seeing them, the Holy Virgin said, weeping: "What have you done, wretched and unworthy people? What has brought you here?" But there was no voice nor any answer from them. And the watching angels spoke, "Wherefore do you not speak?" And one who was tormented replied, "Blessed One! For ages we have seen no light and we cannot look up." The Holy Virgin, looking on them, wept bitterly.

And a tormented one, seeing her, said: "How is it, Holy Virgin, that you have visited us? Your blessed Son came upon the earth and did not ask us, nor did Abraham the Patriarch, nor Moses the Prophet, nor John the Baptist, nor Paul the Apostle, the favorite of the Lord. But you, most Holy Virgin, are an intercessor and protector for the Christian people. You have prayed to God for us, but how did it come to pass that you have visited us, wretched as we be?"

Then the Holy Virgin inquired what was the sin of these tormented ones, and Michael answered: "These are they who did not believe in the Father, the Son, and the Holy Ghost, nor in you, Holy Virgin! They did not want to proclaim your name, nor that from you was born our Lord Jesus Christ who, having come in the flesh, has sanctified the earth through baptism. It is for this that they are tormented in this place."

Weeping, the Holy Virgin spoke to them. "Wherefore do you live in error? Do you not know that all creation honors my name?" And when the Holy Virgin finished speaking, darkness once more fell upon them.

And Michael said to her: "Whither, Blessed One, do you wish to go now: to the south or to the north?" And when the Virgin replied that she would go to the south, there appeared cherubim and seraphim and four hundred angels who took the Holy Virgin to the south. And there the Holy Virgin saw a river of fire. There was a multitude of men and women who stood in this fiery river. Some stood in the river to their waists, some to their shoulders, some to their necks, and some above their necks. Seeing this, the Holy Virgin exclaimed in a loud voice, "Who are they that stand in the fire up to their waists?" And the Archangel answered, "They are those that have been cursed by their fathers and mothers, and being so cursed, they are tormented here." And when the Holy Virgin inquired who were those who stood in the fire to their shoulders, Michael replied, "They are those who have cursed and indulged in lechery, and therefore are tormented in this place." And the Virgin asked, "Who are those that are in the fiery flame up to their necks?" And Michael answered, saying: "They are those who have eaten human flesh. For this they are tormented here." And the Holy Virgin then asked, "Those who are immersed in the fiery flame above their heads, who are they?" Michael the Archangel replied: "They are those, Lady, who, holding the cross, have sworn falsely. Such is the power of the cross that it is worshiped with awe by the angels and they tremble before it. And so, when a man swears by the cross and then lies, he is punished by such a torment."

And then the Holy Virgin saw a man who was hanging by his heels, and worms were devouring him. And she asked the archangel who he was and what were his sins. And the archangel answered, "They are those who took interest on their silver and gold, and therefore they are tormented in this place."

And then she saw a woman who was hanging by one tooth, and various serpents came from her mouth and were devouring her. The Holy Virgin, seeing this, asked Michael: "Who is this woman? What is her sin?" And the archangel answered, "Lady, this one is she who used to say evil words and gossiped, which

d to evil discourse among her neighbors, and therefore she is
mned." And the Holy Virgin replied, "Blessed be the woman
ho does not give birth to such a sinner."

And then Michael said, "Holy Virgin, you have not yet seen
e greatest torments." And the Holy Virgin replied: "Let us go
d visit so that I may see all torments." And, when Michael
quired where she should like to go, the Holy Virgin asked to
to the north. And then seraphim and cherubim and four hun-
ed angels took the Blessed One to the north where there was
great fiery cloud, and in this fiery cloud there were fiery
aces to lie down. In these places were a great many men and
omen. And the Holy Virgin, weeping, asked who these men
d women were and what were their sins. And the archangel
plied: "Lady, those are the ones who, during holy weeks, did
t get up to attend the Easter Midnight Service, but lay in bed
zily as if dead. Therefore, they are tormented in this place."
d the Holy Virgin asked, "And those who were not able to
t up, are they also condemned as sinners?" And Michael an-
vered, "Holy Lady, only those who cannot get up even when
eir house be in flame on all four sides do not sin when they do
t go to church."

And the Holy Virgin saw a big iron tree with branches of
n on which there were iron barbs. On these barbs hung a
eat many men and women by their tongues. Seeing them, the
oly Virgin began to sob, and asked Michael who these people
ere and what was their sin. And the archangel replied, "These
ople are calumniators and gossipers who separate brother from
other and husband from wife."

And she saw women hanging by their fingernails, and fire
me from their mouths and burned them. And serpents came
t of the flames and tormented them. And they cried out, say-
g, "Be merciful unto us, for we are tormented beyond all
her torments." And the Holy Virgin asked what were their
s. And Michael answered, "These are the widows of priests
ho did not revere the office of the priesthood, but married
her men after the death of their priestly husbands."

And the Virgin saw other women who were lying in fire and
ere devoured by various serpents, and Michael said, "These
e nuns from convents who sold their bodies for lechery, and
erefore they are tormented."

And the archangel said to the Blessed Virgin, "Come hither,
oly Virgin, and I will show you the place where many sinners
e tormented." And the Holy Virgin saw the river of flames.
d the river appeared as if it were flowing blood and it covered

the whole earth. In the middle of this river were a great man
sinners. Seeing these, the Virgin wept, and asked, "What
their sin?" And the archangel Michael answered, "These are t
whores and the adulterers, those who listen to gossip, the matc
makers and calumniators, the drunkards, merciless princes, bis
ops, and archbishops, tsars who did not fulfill the will of Go
the usurers, who collected interest, and the lawbreakers." Hea
ing this, the Blessed Virgin wept, and said, "Oh, these evil si
ners, it would have been better if they had never been born

And Michael asked her: "Wherefore do you weep, Holy On
Have you never seen such great torments before?" And th
Blessed Virgin answered, "Take me farther, that I may see a
torments that are." And Michael asked, "Where do you wish
go, Blessed One, to the east or to the west, to the right in
paradise or to the left where are the greatest torments?" And
soon as the Virgin replied that she wished to go to the left, the
appeared seraphim and cherubim and four hundred angels an
they took the Most Holy One to the east, to the left. And in th
vicinity of the river there was a great darkness, and in th
river there came many men and women, and it appeared as
the water were boiling. And great waves broke upon the si
ners, and when the waves rose they drowned the sinners in
thousand feet of water, so that they were not even able to utte
"Righteous Judge, be merciful unto us!" And there was muc
gnashing of teeth in this place, since the sinners were devoure
by the worms.

And seeing the Holy Virgin, the host of angels that watche
over the sinners exclaimed in unison: "Holy, Holy, Holy! Ho
God and you, Holy Virgin, we bless you and the Son of Go
born of you. For ages we have not seen light, but now, praise b
to you, we have seen the light." And once more all of the
exclaimed: "Rejoice, Blessed Virgin. Rejoice, Source of Lig
Eternal. Rejoice, Holy Archangel Michael and pray to our Lo
for the entire world, for we have seen the sinners who are to
mented, and we are very saddened."

The Holy Virgin, seeing the angels saddened and filled wit
sorrow because of the torments of the sinners, began to wee
And all exclaimed in unison, saying: "It is good that you hav
come to this darkness, for now you have seen their torment
Most Holy Lady and Archangel Michael, pray for them." An
she heard the sobs and voices of the sinners who raised the
laments, saying, "God have mercy upon us!" And the Virg
said, "God have mercy upon them." And as soon as she ha
said this, the tempest on the river of fiery waves ceased. An

the sinners gained the hope in a tiny mustard seed. And the Holy Virgin, seeing this, wept and said, "What is this river and of what are its waves?" And Michael answered: "This river is a river of hot pitch, and its waves are of flame. And the Jews are tormented here because they tormented our Lord, Jesus Christ. And those who were baptized in the name of the Father, the Son, and Holy Ghost and still believed in demons and rejected God and baptism are also tormented in this place. And those who committed lechery with their mothers and daughters, and those who murdered with poisons or who killed with weapons, or who strangled their children are tormented in this place. Because of such deeds they are tormented. And the Holy Virgin said, "They deserve this for their sins." And when she had said these words the fiery waves once again enveloped the sinners, and darkness betook them. And Michael said to the Holy Virgin, "There is no thought of God for those who are lost in darkness." And the Most Holy One said: "O evil sinners, the flame of this fire shall never become extinguished."

And then the Holy Virgin spoke, saying: "I have only one request. Let me also enter, that I may suffer together with the Christians, for they have called themselves the children of my Son." And the archangel said, "Rest yourself in paradise!" And the Holy Virgin replied, "I beg you, move the host of the angels that we may pray for the sinners, and God may accept our prayer and have mercy upon them."

The archangel replied, saying: "Great is the name of our Lord God. Seven times in the day and seven times in the night do we bring praises and worship our Lady for the sake of the sinners. And we hope that our Lord will listen to our prayers." And the Holy Virgin answered, "I beg you, order that the angelic host carry me to the heavenly height and take me before the invisible Father."

And the archangel so ordered, and there appeared cherubim and seraphim, and they carried the Blessed One to the heavenly height, and put her down at the throne of the invisible Father. She raised her hands to her Blessed Son and said: "Have mercy, O Lord, upon the sinners, for I have seen them, and I could not endure. Let me be tormented together with the Christians." And there came a voice to her which said: "I see nails in my Son's hands. How can I have mercy upon them?" And she said: "I do pray for the infidel Jews, but for the Christians I ask thy mercy." And a voice again came to her, saying: "I see how they have had no mercy upon my brethren, so I can have no mercy upon them."

And the Holy Virgin again spoke, saying: "Have mercy, O Lord, upon the sinners, the creation of thine own hands, who proclaim thy name over the whole earth and even in their torments, and who in all places say, 'Most Holy Lady, Mother of God, intercede for us.' And when a child is born people say, 'Most Holy Virgin, help us.'"

Then the Lord spoke to her: "Hear, Holy Virgin! There is not a human being who does not praise thy name. I will not abandon them, neither in heaven nor upon the earth." Then the Holy Virgin asked: "Where is Moses the Prophet? Where are all the prophets? And you, Fathers, who have never committed a sin? Where is Paul, God's favorite? Where is Sunday, the pride of the Christian? And where is the power of the pure cross through which Adam and Eve were delivered from their curse?"

Then the Archangel Michael and all the angels cried, "Have mercy, O Lord, upon the sinners!" And Moses wept aloud and said, "Have mercy upon them, O Lord, for I have given them thy Law!" And John wept and cried out, "Have mercy, O Lord, for I have preached thy Gospel to them." And Paul wept and said: "Have mercy, O Lord, for I carried thine epistles to the churches." [Here a fragment is missing, but it is apparent from the text that follows that God did not concede to the prayers of the Holy Virgin and the saints.] And the saints, hearing the voice of the Lord, did not dare to answer.

The Most Holy Virgin, seeing that she could not intercede and that God would neither listen to their pleas nor take mercy on the sinners, said: "Where is the Archangel Gabriel who announced to me, 'Rejoice, because you have heard the Father before all ages and he will take away his reproach among men?' . . . [fragment missing]. And where are the servants of the throne and where is St. John the Theologian? Wherefore did they not appear with us to pray for these Christian sinners? Don't you see that I shed tears for the sinners? Come, all angels which are in the heavens. Come, all righteous people acquitted by God, since you are given the right to pray for sinners. And come you, Michael, for you are the first incorporeal one and are next to the throne. Let us all pray to the invisible Father for mercy, and let us not move away as long as he will not have mercy unto the sinners."

And Michael bowed to the ground before the throne, and with him bowed all those who are in heaven and all the incorporeal angels. Then the Lord, seeing the intercession of the saints, became merciful for his Son's sake, and said, "Come down, my beloved Son, and listen to the prayers of the saints and appear before the sinners."

And the Lord came down from the invisible throne, and all sinners who were in the darkness exclaimed in unison, "Have mercy upon us, King of All Ages! Have mercy upon us, Son of God!"

And the Lord then said: "Hear all! I have planted paradise, and have created man in my own image, and made him lord over paradise, and gave him life eternal. But they have disobeyed me and sinned in their selfishness and delivered themselves unto death. And since I did not want to see deeds done by hands which were forced by the devil, I came to earth and became incarnate through the Virgin. And I was raised to the cross to free them from slavery and the original curse. And I asked for water, but I was given gall mixed with vinegar. My hand created man and man put me into the grave. I descended to Hell and defeated the enemy and raised the selected ones. And I blessed the river Jordan to save you from original sin, but you did not care to repent for your sins. You became Christians only in words, and did not keep my commandments. For this you find yourselves in the fire everlasting, and I ought not to have mercy upon you! But today, by the mercy of my Father who sent me to you, and through the intercession of my Mother who has wept much for you, and through Michael, the archangel of the Gospel, and through the multitude of martyrs who have labored much in your behalf, I give you from Good Thursday to Holy Pentecost, day and night, for rest and for praising the Father, and the Son, and the Holy Ghost!"

And they all answered, "Glory be to thy mercy!" Glory to the Father, and to the Son, and to the Holy Ghost, now and forever. Amen.

18. Adam's Address to Lazarus in Hell

AMONG early Russian writings that cannot be dated with certitude a very prominent place is occupied by *Adam's Address to Lazarus in Hell.* Its style and content indicate that this work was written in the Kievan era and probably in the same century as the *Lay of Igor's Campaign*, with which it has many parallels. Its content is definitely apocryphal, but it is still difficult to

determine whether the original text is Byzantine or Russian.
The topic of this work is Adam's address to Lazarus in hell before he had been raised from the dead by Jesus. The address
consists of two rather different parts, the first being poetic and
original, while the second is composed of quotations from the
Gospel, and apparently has been corrupted by the scribes.

The final text has been established by M. Hruchevsky, who
divided the work into poetic lines. The translation offered here
was published anonymously in *The Slavonic Review*, Volume
X, 1931, pages 246–252. Several stylistic corrections have been
made by the present editor.

◆ ◆ ◆

Hear, heaven, attend, earth,
  how speaks the Lord.
"I bore sons and exalted them,
  and they have rejected me.
The ass recognizes his master's manger,
But my people have not recognized me.
And behold I will not give my glory to another
  but will send my Word on earth
  that I may save my people from the meshes of Satan."

"Brethren, let us today sing songs,
  let us cast aside grief, and be full of joy,"
spoke David, seated in infernal Hell,
setting his eyed fingers on the live strings.
And he struck the lute and said:
"For now has come a joyful time,
  for now has come the day of salvation.
For I hear shepherds
  playing the reed in the cave,
And their voice passes the gates of Hell
  and enters my ears.
And I hear the trampling of feet of Persian horses,
  that carry the Magi with their gifts for him,
  from their kings to the King of Heaven,
  who has today been born on earth.
And him, brethren,
  we have been awaiting for many days,
  whose throne is heaven
  and whose feet rest on the earth.
The maiden mother
  wraps him in swaddling cloths

who wraps the heavens in clouds
and the earth in darkness.
And she speaks bending over him:
"O great and heavenly king,
how hast thou willed
to descend to us on the earth in poverty?
Hast thou desired this cave,
and this manger,
in which thou liest now?
And lo, how soon does the furious Herod
shake as he sharpens his sword against thee,
wishing to kill thee,
whose throne is heaven
and whose feet rest on the earth."
And Adam spoke,
to those that were with him in Hell:
"Come, ye prophets
and all ye just men,
let us send a message to the Lord,
into the living world,
to the Lord Christ
asking him with tears
whether he wishes
to release us
from these torments?"
And Isaiah and Jeremiah,
upbraiding Hell
and his impotent power,
said to David:
"But who can carry the message
from us to him?
Gates of brass,
posts of iron,
locks of stone,
solidly sealed."
Then David spake to them clearly:
"Isaiah, Jeremiah, Aaron,
Ezekiel, Solomon,
Adam, Abraham, Isaac,
Jacob, Samuel, Daniel,
and all the seventeen prophets
attend to my voice:
Tomorrow will go from us
Lazarus the four-dayed,

friend of Christ.
He from us
will carry the message."

And hearing this, Adam,
first-created of men,
began beating his face
with his hands.
Groaning heavily,
he exclaimed and said:
"Tell the Lord about me,
Lazarus, glorious friend of Christ:
Thus cries to thee
thy first-created Adam:
Was it for this, Lord, thou createdst me
to be on this earth
for but a short age
only to condemn me
to be tormented in Hell for many years?
Was it for this, O Lord, that thou madest the earth full?
For now thy beloved ones,
my grandchildren, lie in darkness
in the pit of Hell—tormented by pain
and finding their joy in their grief.
They wash their eyes with tears
and gladden their hearts with grief
and are downcast exceedingly.
For on this earth
but a short while did we know prosperity,
and now in this sorrow
many years are we in duress.

For a short while was I king
of all God's creatures,
and now for many days
am I slave to Hell
and captive to devils.

For a short while did I see thy light,
and now it is many a year
that I do not see thy bright sun
nor hear the stormy winds,
O Lord.

If I have sinned
worse than any man,

it is according to my deserts
thou hast assigned to me these torments,
I do not complain, O Lord.

But this is what fills me with pity—
I was created in thine image,
and now I am upbraided,
cruelly tormented by the devil,
who oppresses me, O Lord.

If I, Adam,
while I lived in nature,
broke thy divine commandment,
behold, O Lord,
Abraham, first patriarch,
and thy friend
who for thy sake was ready
to sacrifice his son,
his beloved Isaac,
but thou saidst:
Through thee, Abraham, all the generation on earth
    shall be blessed.
In what way has he sinned
that he should be tormented here in Hell
and sigh heavily?
Descend, O Lord, for the sake of Abraham,
or has Abraham, too, sinned unto thee, O Lord?

And behold thy servants
Isaac and Jacob his son
lying in thraldom in the infernal Hell.

And behold Noah, the just,
whom thou, O Lord,
deliveredst from fierce deluge,
and canst thou not deliver him from Hell?
Or maybe he too has sinned
like myself?

And behold thy great prophet Moses,
who led the Jews through the Red Sea,
and spoke with thee on the Mountain of Sinai
and in the burning bush face to face,
in what way, O Lord, has he sinned
that he too should lie with us in the darkness of Hell?
Or maybe, Moses, too, O Lord, has sinned unto thee?

And David, O Lord,
whom thyself exaltedst on earth
and gave him to reign over many men,
and he did make the psalter and lute,
in what way has he sinned, Lord?
But he too is tormented together with us in this Hell,
and sighs, as he groans frequently,
or maybe he too has sinned
in the same way as myself?

And here, O Lord, is thy prophet Isaiah,
who from his mother's womb was lifted to heaven
and then returned into his mother's womb,
like as thou too, O Lord, didst descend into the womb
    of a maiden,
and he too, O Lord, is with us in Hell,
or maybe Isaiah, too, has sinned, O Lord?

And here is thy great prophet Daniel,
son of Ezekiel the prophet,
who carried about a wooden rack in a frame,
who prefigured thy divine passion,
who smote the golden body in Babylon
and was cast into the lions' den,
and he, Lord, is with us in Hell
or maybe Isaiah, too, has sinned, O Lord?

And here, Lord, is Solomon son of David
who erected for thee a house in Jerusalem
and cast two eagles of gold
like unto cherubim and seraphim,
and spake: If God is on earth,
the Holy Ghost will descend on the two eagles.
And the two eagles flew round the church
and ascended to heaven.

And here is John, great among prophets,
The Lord's Precursor, the Baptist,
who was born from the annunciation of Gabriel,
who from youth grew up in the wilderness,
eating wild honey.
In what way has he sinned, O Lord?
On earth he was dishonored by Herod,
and now together with us he is tormented in Hell.

And here thy prophets complain,
Elijah and Enoch who pleased thee
more than all just men on earth.
No longer, O Lord, do we see
Thy resplendent sun
nor thy gratifying light,
but instead are possessed by sorrow
and downcast with grief.
Or maybe the prophets too have sinned unto thee?

Is it for the sake of our sins that thou wilt not release
    us?
or art thou biding thy time?
If thou willst descend thyself,
thou alone knowest it,
But we are yearning men
and thou art longsuffering and without malice.
Come to us soon,
release us from Hell and bind the devil,
that the mutinous Jews may know thee,
and we all may worship thee."

And hearing this the Lord went to Bethany, to Mary the
ster of Lazarus and of Martha; and Mary and Martha, as soon
s they heard that he was coming, hastened forth and falling at
s feet and wiping his feet with their hair said, "Lord, if thou
adst been here, our brother Lazarus had not died." And the
ord said to Martha and Mary, "Your brother shall rise again."
And Hell spake to the devil:

"I hear.
My soul is sad at having to release Lazarus,
and I am sore pressed to cast forth Adam."

And the Lord said to Mary and Martha: Where have ye laid
m? And they came to the grave, and the Lord told them to
ke away the stone from the entrance of the grave. And Mary
d Martha said: Lord, by this time he stinketh, for he hath
en dead four days. And the Lord said: If ye would believe,
should see the glory of God. And he lifted up his eyes and
id, Lazarus, come forth. And Lazarus rose at once, bound with
ave clothes, and the Lord said, Loose him.

And when Lazarus had risen from Hell, he spake to the Lord:
Lord, thy prophets in Hell cry unto thee, Adam the first-
eated and Abraham the patriarch with Isaac his son and Jacob

his grandson. David cries unto thee on behalf of Solomon [1] son, 'Lead us out of Hell.'"

And the Lord spake to Lazarus: "Had it not been for David my beloved servant, I would have destroyed Solomon in Hell. And the Lord descended to Hell in person, and a multitude heavenly warriors with him, Semiel, and Raguel, and Ismael and Nanael, Tartarus, Gabriel, Michael, and all the angels advanced with the cross against Hell, saying, "Lift the gates eternity and let the gates of sorrow be taken, that the King Glory may enter."

And the angels and the prophets spake: "The Lord is strong and terrible in battle, for he is the King of Glory. Let them taken."

And the great king David spake: "When I was alive . . . that the gates of brass be overthrown and the posts of iron broken.

And then will the Lord overthrow the gates of brass and break the posts of iron."

And the Lord spake to Adam: "This hand created thee from the beginning of time, and the same will lead thee out of corruption."

And then Jesus arose and said to his apostles: "Go Forth preach to all lands, baptising in the name of the Father, the Son, and the Holy Ghost, teaching to obey them . . ." And the Lord himself ascended to heaven and was seated on the right hand of the Father, and all over the earth is his glory, of Christ Jesus our Lord.

[1] An apparent lacuna.

MILITARY TALES

19. *The Lay of Igor's Campaign*

WRITTEN on the occasion of Prince Igor's unfortunate campaign against the Kumans in 1185, the *Lay of Igor's Campaign* (*Slovo o polku Igoreve*) is unanimously acclaimed as the highest achievement in Russian literature of the Kievan era.

Igor was himself a well-known historical personality, a prince of Novgorod-Seversk (not to be confused with Novgorod "the Great," the metropolis of northern Russia). Novgorod-Seversk, now a small city on the border between the Russian and Ukrainian S.S.R.'s, was at that time one of the Russian strongholds against the Kumans, nomads of Turkic origin who inhabited the prairie of southern Russia. Prince Igor (1151–1202), one of the leaders of Russian political and military activities of that region, began his campaign in 1185 to drive out these nomadic invaders, who, every year, would raid Russian territories, burn the cities and take the inhabitants as slaves. Relying only on his own military forces and those of his relatives, Igor moved into the prairie with no support from the other Russian leaders. This campaign ended in defeat and in Igor's capture by the Kumans, although he later escaped from them.

Though much is known about Igor, practically nothing is known about the author of the *Lay of Igor's Campaign*. One can only presume that he belonged to Igor's court, was a warrior, and, as is evident from his *Lay*, was very familiar with the life and environment of the prairie. Even less can be said of the literary antecedents of the work and of the epic tradition previous to it. It is true that the writer of the *Lay* often mentions Boyan, a bard who apparently lived in the eleventh century, but no details are known either of his life or of his poetic works. The *Lay* is a poetic masterpiece and a highly sophisticated literary work. The word "poetic" should not be understood here in its narrower sense, since the *Lay* is neither rhymed nor organized in verses, nor does it follow any metrical pattern. The rhythm and the length of the sentences to some extent replace verse organization. Beside rhythm, the poetic elements of the *Lay* comprise an extremely rich imagery constructed primarily on parallels with nature, symbolism, poetic address, and lyric

137

lamentation. Among other devices, the author of the *Lay* e
ploys the repetition of characteristic images, stylized descr
tions of military action, assonance and alliteration. Unfor
nately, the latter are impossible to reproduce in translation. T
structure of the *Lay* is by no means that of a narrative poe
and rather than being an epic tale, per se, it is much more
lament over the feudal discord in medieval Russia, a ste
admonition to the princes responsible for the fratricidal feu
The writer's forebodings of impending disaster in the Russi
land proved to be true, for only fifty years after Igor's def
and the writing of the *Lay*, Russia was subjugated by t
Mongol-Tatars and lost her independence for two hundred yea

Three distinct structural planes can be discerned in the *L*
The first concerns the destiny of Prince Igor, his campaign, c
feat, and escape from the Kumans. This plane, the narrat
core of the work, is somewhat clouded by invocations to the la
bard, Boyan, reminiscences of past glory, and the allusive atm
phere of foreboding. The second plane consists of portents a
lamentations over the outcome of the campaign and Russi
fate, such as the dream of Prince Sviatoslav of Kiev and t
lament of Yaroslavna, the wife of Igor. The final plane consi
of the author's admonitions to the princes to unite, and
censure of their feuding.

Unfortunately, the *Lay* was preserved in only one copy, c
covered at the end of the eighteenth century and first printed
1800. This single copy, which was subsequently destroyed ir
fire in Moscow during the Napoleonic invasion in 1812, was
self defective, and so the first edition of the *Lay* was an unsa
factory one reflecting the low standard of scholarship and int
pretation of ancient manuscripts of that time. Many porti
were apparently misread or misinterpreted, and in some pla
inadequately deciphered. Despite the efforts of generations
scholars and voluminous research, several passages in the *L*
still remain incomprehensible, and have lent themselves to c
tradictory interpretations. In the present translation such p
sages have been placed in brackets.

The text that was used for the present translation of the *L*
of Igor's Campaign is that revised by S. D. Likhachev and pu
lished in the series *Literaturnye pamiatniki*, Moscow-Leningr
1950. However, the present translator has made wide use of t
text and interpretations of Professor Roman Jakobson of Harva
University, who offers numerous and extremely ingenious exp
nations of certain unclear passages, while others have be

interpreted in the light of such research as that on nature symbolism by N. V. Charlemagne.

The *Lay's* complex symbolism, structure, imagery, and philosophy require a more detailed commentary than any other medieval Russian work. Notes on the symbolism of the *Lay* and on Russian literary tradition appear at the bottom of each page, as well as comments pertaining to historical and geographical names specific to the work. Finally, references of a more general type can be found in the Introduction and in the Glossary.

The typographical arrangement and the chapter and stanza form given here are in agreement with authoritative publications of the *Lay* and also reflect this editor's feeling that they contribute to readability. For the sake of better understanding, some explanatory words have been added in parentheses and proper names have been preceded by the words "prince," "river," or "city."

❖ ❖ ❖

I. Invocation

Might it not behoove us, brethren
to commence in ancient strains
the stern lay of Igor's campaign,
    Igor, son of Sviatoslav?
Then let this begin
according to the events of our time,
and not according to the cunning of Boyan.[1]
For he, Boyan the Seer,
when composing a song to someone,
soared in his thoughts over the tree (of wisdom[2]),
ran as a gray wolf over the land,
flew below the clouds as a blue-gray eagle.

When he recalled the feuds of former times
he would let loose ten falcons upon a flock of swans.
    And the first swan overtaken
    was the first to sing a song
    to old Yaroslav,[3]

[1] Apparently a bard who lived in the eleventh century and who composed songs in honor of the Russian princes.

[2] Apparently this refers to the tree of wisdom or thought, a common symbol of Eastern mythology.

[3] Prince of Kiev from 1019 through 1054. He is considered the greatest ruler of Russia during the Kievan era.

to brave Mstislav,[4]
who slew Rededia[5] before the Kasog regiments,
and to handsome Roman,[6] son of Sviatoslav.

Boyan, however, did not let loose ten falcons
upon the flock of swans.
But rather he lay his wise fingers
    upon the living strings
    and they sounded lauds to the princes.
Let us begin this narration, brethren,
from the old times of Vladimir[7] to this present time of Igor,
    who strengthened his mind with courage,
    who quickened his heart with valor
    and, thus imbued with martial spirit,
    led his valiant regiments
    against the Kuman land
    in defense of the Russian land.

II. PRINCE IGOR PREPARES HIS CAMPAIGN

Igor looked up at the bright sun,
and saw that all his warriors
became enveloped in darkness.[8]
And Igor spoke to his army:
    "Brethren and warriors!
    It is better to be killed in battle,
    than to become a captive.
    Let us mount our swift steeds, brethren!
    Let us view the blue river Don."

And the prince's mind was seized by ambition.
And the desire to drink from the great river Don
concealed the evil omens from him.
And he spoke:
    "I want to break a lance at the Kuman frontier.
    I want, oh, my Russians,

[4] Mstislav the Brave, the brother of Yaroslav the Wise and Prince of Tmutorakan, a principality located on the Caucasian shore between the Black and Azov seas.

[5] A prince of the Kasogs, now called the Cherkess, who was slain by Mstislav.

[6] Roman the Handsome, a prince of Tmutorakan who was killed by the Kumans in 1079.

[7] Apparently Vladimir the Saint, the Christianizer of Russia.

[8] The author probably meant that the sun was eclipsed. An eclipse of the sun occurred on May 1, 1185.

either to drink with you Don (water) from my helmet,
    or to leave my head there."
Oh, Boyan, the nightingale of yore!
If you were to sing the glory of the (Russian) campaign,
like a nightingale would you soar over the tree (of wisdom),
soaring in your mind up under the clouds
and singing the glory of both these ages.[9]
You would race along the trail of Trojan,[10]
over the prairies and the mountains.
And the god Veles' grandson
would sing Igor's song (thusly),
    "It is not a storm that has driven
    the falcons over the wide prairies.
    It is a flock of jackdaws
    racing toward the great river Don."

Or you, Boyan the Seer, grandson of god Veles, would sing:
    "Steeds neigh beyond the river Sula.
    Glory resounds in the city of Kiev.
    Trumpets blare in the city of Novgorod.
    Banners fly over the city of Putivl."[11]
Igor awaits his dear brother, Vsevolod.
This fierce auroch, Vsevolod,[12] (comes to him and) speaks:
    "My only brother, Igor,
    you are my only bright light.
    We are both the sons of Sviatoslav.
    Brother, order the saddling of your swift steeds,
    as my (swift steeds) are ready.
    They were already saddled at the city of Kursk.
    And my men of Kursk are famed as warriors.
    They were swaddled under trumpets.
    They were brought up under helmets.
    They were fed at lance point.
    The roads are known to them.
    The ravines are familiar to them.
    Their bows are taut,

[9] The glorious age of Vladimir and this age of Igor. (See "Invocation.")
[10] Trojan: the meaning of this word is not clear. It may refer to Trajan, Emperor of Rome (98–117),who campaigned in southern Russia, to a Slavic and Balkan deity, or the city of Troy.
[11] Novgorod-Seversk and Putivl: important cities in Igor's principality.
[12] Fierce auroch Vsevolod: Igor's brother, who died in 1196, was prince of Trubchevsk and Kursk.

their quivers are open,
their sabers have been sharpened.
They race into the prairie like gray wolves,
seeking honor for themselves
and glory for their prince."

III. The Omens

Then Prince Igor set his foot in the golden stirrup
and rode into the open prairie.
The sun barred his way with darkness[13]
and night, moaning with tempest, awoke the birds.
The whistling of the beasts arose.
And the Div[14] arose and from the treetops it cried,
enjoying unknown lands to listen:
   the land of the Volga,
   the land on the Azov Sea,
   the land at the river Sula,[15]
   the city of Surozh,
   the city of Kherson,[16]
   and you, the idol of the city of Tmutorakan.[17]

The Kumans hastened by untrodden ways
to the great river Don.
Their carts squeak at midnight,
one may say, as dispersed swans.
Igor leads his warriors to the river Don.
The birds in the forests of oak portend his misfortune.
The wolves conjure the tempest in the ravines.
The screeching eagles call the beasts to the feast of bones.
Foxes bark at crimson shields.

O Russian land! You are already far beyond the hills.

IV. The First Day of Battle: The Russians Are Victoriou

Evening was fading late into the night.
Finally the glow of dawn faded.
Mist enveloped the prairie.

---

[13] Again the author wishes to say that the sun was eclipsed.
[14] A deity in the form of a bird that represented foreboding for th
Russians.
[15] A tributary of the river Dnieper.
[16] Surozh and Kherson: Greek cities in the Crimea.
[17] Idol of Tmutorakan: probably a colossal idol that was held i
veneration by the Kumans.

The song of the nightingale had died out.
The daws have begun to caw.
Russian warriors barred the wide prairie
with their crimson shields.
They seek honor for themselves
and glory for their prince.

Early in the morning of Friday
the Russians trampled the infidel Kuman armies,
and, spreading like arrows over the prairie,
they galloped away with beautiful Kuman maidens.
And with them they took:
  golds and brocades,
  and costly velvets.
With cloaks and coats and fur mantles
and with all kinds of Kuman garments
they began to bridge their way over the swamps and marshes.
The crimson banner,
the white gonfalon,
the scarlet panache, and
the silver lance
were taken to brave Igor,
son of Sviatoslav.

Brave Oleg's[18] clan slumbers in the prairie.
They have strayed far, flying.
They were born to be offended
  neither by the falcon,
  nor by the gyrfalcon,
  nor by you, the black ravens,
  the infidel Kumans.
Khan Gza flees like a gray wolf.
Khan Konchak[19] shows him the way to the great river Don.

V. THE SECOND DAY OF BATTLE: THE VICTORY OF THE KUMANS

Very early on the second morn
a bloody dawn announced the day.
Black clouds arise from the sea
and want to envelop the four suns.[20]
Blue lightning shows through the clouds.

[18] Oleg was Igor's grandfather and the prince of Chernigov, main
city of the region in which Igor's domain was located.
[19] Gza and Konchak: Kuman khans.
[20] "Four suns" refers to the four princes who lead the Russian
armies: Igor, Vsevolod, Oleg, and Sviatoslav.

There is to be a mighty thundering.
The rain of arrows will come from the great river Don.
Here, on the river Kaiala,[21]
here, on the great river Don,
lances will be broken
and swords will be dulled on Kuman helmets.
O Russian land! You are already far beyond the hills.

Here the winds, grandsons of god Stribog,
blow the arrows from the sea
against the regiments of brave Igor.
The earth groans.
The rivers become turbid.
Dust covers the prairie.
The pennants announce:
  "The Kumans have come from the river Don
    and from the sea.
    They encircle the Russian regiments from all sides."
The devil's children bar the prairie with their battle cries.
The brave Russians bar it with their crimson shields.

Fierce auroch Vsevolod!
Your defense is firm,
Your arrows rain down upon Kuman warriors.
Your Frankish swords[22] clang on Kuman helmets.
Where you, fierce auroch, gallop gleaming in your golden
    helmet,
there will lie the heads of infidel Kumans.
There Avar helmets[23] are cloven at your hands,
fierce auroch Vsevolod.
What wound can matter, brethren,
to one who has forgotten honors and fortune,
and his father's golden throne in the city of Chernigov,
and the habits and ways of his dearly beloved
and beautiful wife,
the daughter of Prince Gleb?[24]

---

[21] The river at which Igor was defeated. Its location remains unknown but apparently it was a tributary of the Donets, itself a tributary of the river Don.

[22] Frankish swords or lances: weapons made of steel imported from Western Europe.

[23] Apparently helmets made in the Avar style. The Avars were nomads who in the seventh and eighth centuries lived in southern Russia and Hungary.

[24] The daughter of Prince Gleb, the ruler of Pereyaslavl-Seversk.

VI. Censure of the Princes' Feuds

There were the eras of Trojan.
There passed the years of Yaroslav.
And there were the campaigns of Oleg,
Oleg, son of Sviatoslav.[25]
That Oleg fostered feuds with his sword
and sowed the Russian lands with arrows.
In the city of Tmutorakan
he used to put his foot in the golden stirrup
and its clinking could be heard by great Yaroslav,
who lived long ago.
And Prince Vladimir, son of Vsevolod,
would stop his ears in the city of Chernigov.[26]

And the dubious glory of Prince Boris,[27]
son of Vyacheslav,
brought him to his final Judgment,
and he remained in eternal sleep
on a burial shroud of green grass
for offending brave and young Prince Oleg.

On the river Kaiala Sviatopolk ordered
that his father be taken between two ambling Hungarian
    horses
to be buried in the Cathedral of St. Sophia in Kiev.[28]

Then, in the era of Oleg, son of misfortune,
the feuding spread and grew.
The fortune of god Dazhbog's[29] grandson was destroyed.
Human lives became shortened through the princes' discord.
In those days the plowman spoke but rarely,

[25] Prince Oleg was responsible for the fratricidal warring among the Russian princes. Oleg Sviatoslavovich, previously mentioned as Igor's grandfather, whose feudal wars shattered the unity of Russia, was an antagonist of Vladimir Monomakh. He died in 1115.

[26] So that he might not hear the clinking of Oleg's stirrup.

[27] Boris, son of Vyacheslav, was the first Russian prince to fight other Russian princes in alliance with the Kumans. Boris was killed in this campaign, while his brother, Oleg, escaped to the Kumans.

[28] Sviatopolk's father was killed in battle in 1078 and was taken to Kiev for burial. Slain warriors were carried in a carpet between two horses.

[29] Dazhbog: an ancient Russian deity; Dazhbog's grandson refers to the Russians. Veles and Stribog were also pre-Christian deities.

and the ravens often cawed, dividing corpses among them-
    selves.
And the daws talked in their own tongue,
before flying to feed on corpses.

VII. THE RUSSIAN DEFEAT

And so it used to be.
There were battles and campaigns,
but there had never been such battle as this.
From early morning to night,
from evening to dawn
there flew tempered arrows,
swords rained down upon helmets,
Frankish lances resound,
and all this in the unknown prairie,
in the Kuman land.
The black earth under the hooves
was strewn with bones,
was covered with blood.
Grief overwhelmed the Russian land.

What noise do I hear?
What clinking comes to my ears
so early in the morning, before the dawn?
Igor turns about his troops.
He is saddened by the fate of his brother, Vsevolod.
They fought for one day.
They fought for another day.
At noon on the third day Igor's banners fell.
Here, on the shores of the swift river Kaiala,
the brothers parted.
The wine of this bloody banquet was drunk to the last drop.
The Russians gave their guests to drink from the same cup.
They died for the Russian land.
    The grass withered from sorrow,
    and the saddened trees drooped earthward.

VIII. THE AUTHOR'S LAMENTS

And now, brethren, unhappy times have arrived.
The prairie overwhelmed the Russian forces.
Grief reigned over the forces of god Dazhbog's grandsons.
Grief, like a maiden, entered the land of Trojan.
She splashed her swan wings at the river Don,
by the blue sea,

The Kumans attack Prince Igor's army. The Russian horses fall from exhaustion. A miniature from the *Radzivil Chronicle* of the fourteenth century.

and splashing, she put an end to the times of good fortune.
The princes' fight against the infidel came to an end.
And brother said to brother:
> "This is mine,
>   and that also is mine."

And the princes began to argue about trifles,
calling them important matters,
and began to create discord among themselves.
The infidels from all lands began to invade
the Russian land and to win victory.

Oh, too far toward the sea has the falcon flown, slaying bird
And Igor's valiant regiments cannot be resurrected!
He is mourned by Grief and Sorrow,
and they spread across the Russian land.
[Shaking the embers in the flaming horn],[30]
the Russian women begin to lament, saying:
> "No more, our dear husbands,
>   can you be envisioned in our thoughts,
>   nor can you reappear in our dreams,
>   nor can you be seen with our eyes,
>   and never again shall we jingle gold and silver."

And, brethren, the city of Kiev began to groan from grief,
and the city of Chernigov also, from their misfortune.
Anguish spread over the Russian land.
Deep sadness flew through the Russian land.
And the princes created discord among themselves.
The infidels, victoriously invading the Russian land,
levied a tribute of one vair from each household.

All this happened because Igor and Vsevolod,
two valiant sons of Sviatoslav,
once more revived evil forces
which were curbed by their cousin, (another) Prince
    Sviatoslav.[31]
This stern prince of Kiev
held (everyone) in fear and awe,
for, as a tempest, his powerful regiments

[30] A part of the mourning ritual (?)
[31] Sviatoslav III, the great prince of Kiev (1177–1194) and the
retical ruler of all Russia. He was the cousin and godfather of Ig
and Vsevolod. In 1183 he defeated Khan Kobiak on the shores of th
Azov Sea and took him as a prisoner to Kiev.

and his Frankish swords defeated and attacked the Kuman
lands.
They trampled under Kuman hills and ravines,
made turbid Kuman rivers and lakes,
dried out Kuman streams and marshes.
Like a tornado, he seized Khan Kobiak
from amongst his great iron regiments
on the shore of the sea bay.
And Kobiak fell in the city of Kiev,
in the hall of Prince Sviatoslav.

Now the Germans and the Venetians,
the Greeks and the Moravians
sing the glory of Prince Sviatoslav
and reproach Prince Igor,
who has lost his fortune on the bottom of the river Kaiala
and filled the Kuman rivers with Russian gold.
And here Prince Igor exchanged his golden saddle of a prince
for the saddle of a slave.
And the cities became saddened
and joy vanished.

IX. THE DREAM OF PRINCE SVIATOSLAV OF KIEV

Sviatoslav had a troubled dream
in Kiev, on the hills:
    "Early this night I was clothed in a black shroud
    upon a bed of yew.
    They ladled out for me
    a blue wine mixed with sorrow.
    From the empty quivers of the infidel strangers
    there poured large pearls into my lap.[32]
    They comforted me.
    And the beams of my gold-roofed palace
    were already without girding.[33]
    During the entire night, since evening,
    the gray-blue ravens were croaking.
    [And at the foothills of the city of Plesensk[34]

[32] Pearls were the symbols of forthcoming tears for the Russians.
[33] It was the custom among Russians to remove the girding of
porches before removing the dead from a house.
[34] Plesensk was a fortified city in the Galician mountains. Probably
the allusion here is to the funeral of the Galician warriors, country-
en, or Igor's wife, who was the daughter of the prince of Galicia.

appeared a sledge,[35]
and this sledge was racing to the blue sea."]
And the boyars told the prince:
"O Prince, sorrow has seized your mind.
There were two falcons who flew
From their father's golden throne,
either to conquer the city of Tmutorakan
or to drink the water of the river Don with their helmet
But their wings were clipped by the sabers of the infidel
and they themselves were put in irons.
It became dark on the third day.
The two suns[36] were eclipsed.
[Two purple columns[37] faded into the sea
Two young moons—Oleg and Sviatoslav—became e
veloped in darkness,[38]
On the river Kaiala darkness overcame the light,[39]
and the Kumans, like a brood of panthers,
spread across the Russian land.
And great violence came from the nomads.]
Already shame has eclipsed glory.
Already violence has defeated freedom.
Already the Div has descended to earth.
And now beautiful Gothic maidens[40]
have begun their song on the shore of the blue sea.
They jingle Russian gold.
They sing of the foreboding time.
They glorify the revenge of Sharokan.[41]
And we, the army, are without joy."

And then great Sviatoslav let fall his golden words
mixed with tears, saying:
"Oh, my young cousins, Igor and Vsevolod,
too early did you begin to disturb
the Kuman lands with your swords, seeking glory,
but you won it without honor,

---

[35] In ancient Russia sledges were used for funerals.
[36] Igor and Vsevolod.
[37] Apparently symbols of the two armies of Igor and Vsevolod.
[38] Young Prince Sviatoslav, Igor's nephew, and Igor's son, Prin
Oleg.
[39] Darkness symbolizes the infidel Kumans, and light, the Russi
army.
[40] In the twelfth century the Goths still maintained settlements
the Crimea, where they penetrated in the third century.
[41] Sharokan: a Kuman khan defeated several times by the Russian

for you spilled the blood of the infidels
without winning glory for yourselves.
Your valiant hearts are forged of Frankish steel
and are tempered in valiance.
What have you done to my silver-gray hairs?
No longer do I behold my powerful
and wealthy,
and well-girded brother,
Yaroslav of Chernigov,[42]
nor his lords.
With his Moguts and Tatrans,
with his Shelbirs and Topchaks,
with his Revugas and Olbers.[43]
They used to defeat the regiments (of the infidels),
and without shields,
only with their knives and ancestors' war cries.
But you said:
   'Let us be valiant.
   Let us assume the glory of the past.
   Let us divide amongs ourselves
   the glory of tomorrow.'
What is there to wonder, brethren,
when an old man feels like a young one?
When a falcon molts, he chases birds high and away
and does not permit harm to come to his nest.
But there is great misfortune,
and the Russian princes are no help to me."

X. THE BARD APPEALS TO THE RUSSIAN PRINCES

E APPEAL TO VLADIMIR, SON OF GLEB[44]

Gloomy times have arrived.
The Russians cry out at the city of Rim
under the Kuman swords.
Prince Vladimir is covered with wounds.
Grief and sorrow to you Vladimir,
son of Gleb.

---

[42] Prince of Chernigov and borther of Sviatoslav, Prince of Kiev.
[43] Moguts, Tatrans, Shelbirs, Topchaks, Revugas, and Olbers: apently Turkic tribes, but their identification is not certain. They tled in the land of Chernigov; in the principality of Yaroslav.
[44] Vladimir, son of Gleb: In 1185 the Kuman Khans Gza and nchak invaded the Russian land, destroying the city of Rim on the er Sula. During this invasion Vladimir Glebovich was mortally unded.

THE APPEAL TO VSEVOLOD, PRINCE OF SUZDAL[45]

Great Prince Vsevolod!
Do you not intend to come from far away
to watch over your paternal golden throne?
For you, with the oars (of your fleet),
can scatter the river Volga into droplets.
With the helmets (of your army)
you can pour out the river Don.
If you were here, then (Kuman) slave girls
would go for a *nogata*,
and (Kuman) male slaves for only a *rezana*.
And you can shoot over the dry land
with the fiery arrows,
with the courageous sons of Gleb.

THE APPEAL TO PRINCES RURIK AND DAVID[46]

O valiant Rurik and David!
Was it not your warriors who swam through blood
under the gilded helmets?
Was it not your army that roared like aurochs,
wounded by tempered swords in the unknown prairie?
Lords, set your feet in the golden stirrups
to avenge the outrage of the present day,
of the Russian land,
of Igor's wounds,
wounds of the daring son of Sviatoslav.

THE APPEAL TO PRINCE YAROSLAV OF GALICH[47]

O Yaroslav of Galich,
the prince of eight senses!
You sit high on your throne wrought of gold.
Your iron regiments defend the Hungarian mountains.
You bar the way to the (Hungarian) king.

---

[45] Vsevolod was called "the great nest" because of his numerou and powerful family. He was prince of Suzdal, a powerful princip ity in the vicinity of present-day Moscow, the latter being at t time only a small village in the Suzdalian principality.

[46] Rurik and David: Princes of Belgorod and Smolensk who d in 1215 and 1198. They were known for their courage during fratricidal wars.

[47] Yaroslav of Galich, Prince of Galicia (1152–1187). Igor's fath in-law, he was called *Osmomysl* (eight-sensed) apparently beca of his qualities for ruling. His land bordered on the Kingdom Hungary, and he practically controlled the river Danube.

You close the gates of the river Danube.
You hurl stones over the clouds.
Your law reigns up to the river Danube.
Your thunder resounds above the lands,
You keep the gates of Kiev open,
From your father's golden throne you shoot at the sultans
beyond the (Russian) lands.
Lord, shoot at Konchak, the infidel slave,
for the revenge of the Russian land,
for the wounds of Igor,
the wounds of the valiant son of Sviatoslav.

THE APPEAL TO PRINCES ROMAN OF VOLYNIA AND MSTISLAV OF RODNO[48]

And you, daring Roman and Mstislav,
your courageous thoughts direct your minds to action.
In your bravery you soar to valiant deeds,
like a falcon over the winds,
which desires, in its daring, to surpass the bird.
Your iron men are under Latin helmets[49]
and they make the earth tremble,
and (they make) many nations (tremble):
   the Nomads,
   the Lithuanians,
   the Deremelas,
   the Yatvags,[50]
   the Kumans.
(All of them) have dropped their lances
and have bowed their heads under your Frankish swords.

But Prince Igor, the sunlight has already dimmed for you.
And, by misfortune, the tree lost its foliage.
The enemies have already divided amongst themselves
the cities of the rivers Ross and Sula.[51]
The valiant regiments of Igor will not be resurrected.
The river Don appeals to you, Prince,
and summons the princes to victory.
O valiant princes, grandsons of Oleg,
you are ready for the battle.

[48] Roman (died 1205) and Mstislav (died 1226): Princes of
olynia, a region east of Galicia.
[49] Refers to the helmets of Latin or Western origin.
[50] Deremelas and Yatvags: Lithuanian tribes who lived at the
orthwestern Russian border.
[51] Tributaries of the Dnieper.

THE APPEAL TO MSTISLAV'S SONS

Ingvar and Vsevolod and you three sons of Mstislav![52]
You are six-winged falcons[53] of no mean nest.
You have not won your patrimonies by deeds of victory.
To what avail are your golden helmets,
    your Polish lances and shields?
Bar the gates of the prairie with your sharp arrows
    for the Russian lands,
    for the wounds of Igor,
    the wounds of the daring son of Sviatoslav.

EVOCATION OF PRINCE IZIASLAV'S[54] DEATH IN THE BATTLE (
GORODETS (1162)

No more do the silver streams of the River Sula
protect the city of Pereyaslavl.
And the river Dvina, which flows to Polotsk,
that city of stern men,
became turbid under the cries of the infidels.

Only Iziaslav, son of Vasilko,
rained his sharp arrows upon Lithuanian helmets
and tarnished the glory of his grandfather Vseslav.
And, having been worsted by the Lithuanian swords,
he fell upon the bloody grass
[(as if it were) the marriage bed,]
under the crimson shields.

And Boyan said:
    "Prince, the wings of birds cover your warriors
        and the beasts already have begun to lick their blood."

Neither his brother, Briachislav,
nor the other brother, Vsevolod, was there (in battle).
And (you, Iziaslav) remained alone.
And you let drop from your valiant body,
through the golden necklace of a prince,
the pearl of your soul,
and voices became saddened,

[52] Princes of Volynia.
[53] Some of the Russian falcons have wings that have three distin
sections, and are therefore called "six-winged falcons."
[54] Prince Iziaslav was killed at Gorodets in a war between the R
sians and Lithuanians.

and joy ceased to be,
And the trumpets mournfully resound at the city of Gorodets.

THE APPEAL TO PRINCE YAROSLAV OF CHERNIGOV AND VSESLAV'S[55]
HEIRS

O sons of Yaroslav and the grandsons of Vseslav,
lower your banners!
Put your dented swords into their sheaths!
You do not deserve the glory of your ancestors,
since, through your feuding,
you brought the infidels into the Russian land,
into the domain of Vseslav.
Your warring brought Kuman violence (into Russia).

THE EVOCATION OF PRINCE VSESLAV THE SORCERER

During the seventh age of Trojan
Vseslav cast lots for the maiden he desired, and,
cunningly leaning on the lance,
he leaped to the city of Kiev and
touched the golden throne of Kiev
with the staff of his lance.
Like a fierce beast he leaped from Belgorod at midnight,
under the cover of blue mist.
[He managed to cast thrice a lucky lot:]
    he opened the gate of the city of Novgorod,
    he tarnished the glory of Prince Yaroslav, and
    he leaped like a wolf to Nemiga [from Dudutki].

On the river Nemiga they built haystacks of heads.
They are threshed with steel flails
and lives are left behind on the threshing floor.
Souls abandon their bodies.
The bloody shores of the river Nemiga
    were sown with misfortune,
    were strewn with the bones of Russia's sons.

Prince Vseslav used to judge the people.
And, as prince, he ruled over the cities.
But, in the night, he prowled like a werewolf.

[55] Vseslav (d. 1101): Prince of Polotsk who in 1067 attacked and
burned Novgorod, but was defeated at the river Nemiga. In 1068 he
became Prince of Kiev for seven months. The "maiden" he cast lots
for was the city of Kiev. He was considered a sorcerer.

He was able to go from Kiev to Tmutorakan
before the cock could crow.
And, prowling as a werewolf, he crossed
the way of great god Hors.[56]
At the Church of St. Sophia of Polotsk
the bells tolled the matins for him,
and he could hear them in Kiev.
His magician's soul lived in a valiant body,
but he still often suffered miseries.
Of him Boyan the Seer said wisely in his refrains:
    "Neither a crafty man,
        nor a clever man,
        nor a clever bird,
    can escape divine judgment."

O Russian land, you must mourn,
remembering your early age, your early princes.
And Vladimir of yore
could not be retained by the hills of Kiev.[57]
But now Prince Rurik's banners stand in readiness,
and so do Prince David's (his brother's).
Thus, they are blown (by the wind) in different directions.

XI. IGOR'S WIFE, EUPHROSINIA, DAUGHTER OF PRINCE YAROSLA
    OF GALICH, LAMENTS OF THE WALLS OF PUTIVL

At the river Danube lances sing their song,
but it is the voice of Yaroslavna which is heard.
Since morning, she sings like an unknown seagull:[58]
    "Like a seagull I will fly along the river Danube.
    I will dip my beaver-trimmed sleeve into the river Kaiala
    I will cleanse the bloody wounds of my prince,
        on his mighty body."

Since morning Euphrosinia has lamented on the walls
of the city of Putivl, saying:
    "O wind, why do you, my lord wind,
        blow so fiercely?
    Why do you bring on your light wings
    Kuman arrows against the warriors of my beloved?

[56] God of the sun in ancient Russia.
[57] Because he unceasingly campaigned against his enemies.
[58] The seagull was considered to be the bird of mourning.

Isn't it enough for you to blow under the clouds,
to loll the ships on the blue sea?
Why, my lord, did you scatter my joy .
over the feathergrass of the prairie?"

Since morning Euphrosinia has lamented on the walls
of the city of Putivl, saying:
"O river Dnieper, son of Slovuta,
it is you who have broken through
the stone mountains[59] of the Kuman land.
You lolled the boats of Sviatoslav
(when he went to meet Khan Kobiak's army.
O my lord wind, loll my beloved
and (bring) him to me that I might not
send him my tears to the sea so early in the morning,
at dawn."

Since morning Euphrosinia has lamented on the walls
of the city of Putivl, saying:
"O my bright and thrice bright sun!
For everyone you are warm and beautiful.
Why did you spread, my lord, your burning rays
upon the warriors of my beloved?
In the waterless prairie you parched their bows
and closed their quivers with misfortune."

XII. PRINCE IGOR FLEES FROM KUMAN CAPTIVITY

The seas splashed at midnight
and the tornado rushes through the mist.
God shows the way to Igor,
the way from the Kuman land,
to the Russian land,
to his father's golden throne.

The glow of the sunset had faded.
Igor sleeps.
Igor keeps his vigil.
Igor's thoughts cross the prairie,
from the great river Don
to the small river Donets.

[59] Stone mountains: apparently a reference to the cataracts in the
river Dnieper, and the surrounding rocky shores.

Beyond the river, Ovlur whistles,[60]
having caught a horse.
He warns the prince.
Prince Igor will not remain a prisoner.
The earth rumbled,
the grass rustled,
and the Kuman tents began to stir.
Prince Igor raced to reeds like an ermine,
like a white duck (he races) on the water.
He leaps to his swift steed.
He (later) springs from it, like a gray wolf.
He rushed toward the curve of the river Donets.
He flew under the clouds like a falcon
which kills geese and swans
    for lunch,
    for dinner,
    and for supper.

If Prince Igor flies like a falcon,
then Ovlur races like a wolf,
shaking off the chilling dew.
And both of them exhausted their swift steeds.

XIII. Igor Speaks with the River Donets

The river Donets speaks:
    "Oh, Prince Igor,
        there will be no small glory for you,
        but dislike for Konchak,
        and joy for the Russian land."

And Igor spoke:
    "Oh, my river Donets!
        There will be no small glory for you,
        for you have lolled the prince on your waves,
        for you have spread for him green grass
        on your silver shores,
        for you have enveloped him in your warm mists
        in the shadow of green trees,
        for your drakes watched over him on the water,
        and your seagulls on the streams,
        and your black ducks in the winds."

[60] Ovlur was Igor's faithful servant.

But different words came to him from the river Stugna.
Its stream is weak.
It has swallowed up other brooks and rivulets,
[and, therefore, has grown wide at its delta.
It hid young Prince Rostislav.[61]
It concealed him on its bottom near its dark bank.]
And Rostislav's mother mourned the young prince.
Flowers withered from sorrow,
and the saddened trees dropped earthward.

XIV. THE KUMAN KHANS PURSUE IGOR

It is not the magpies which have begun croaking,
it is Khans Gza and Konchak
who search for Igor's path.
At that time the crows did not caw.
The daws became silent and
the jackdaws did not chatter.
Only the snakes were crawling,
and the woodpeckers show the way to the river with their
    sounds.
The nightingale announces the dawn with its gay song.

And Khan Gza told Khan Konchak:
    "If the falcon fly to his nest,
    we will shoot at the falconet[62]
    with our gilded arrows."

And Khan Konchak replied to Khan Gza:
    "If the falcon flies to his nest,
    we will enmesh the falconet
    with the charms of a beautiful maiden."

And Khan Gza said to Khan Konchak:
    "If we enmesh him with the charms of
    a beautiful maiden,
    we will have neither the falconet
    nor the beautiful maiden,
    and (their) birds will start fighting us
    in the Kuman prairie."

[61] Prince Rostislav was drowned at the age of twenty-two in 1093, during a fording of the river Stugna, a tributary of the Dnieper.
[62] The term "falconet" refers to Igor's son, Vladimir, who remained a prisoner of the Kumans.

XV. Apodosis

And Boyan, [the bard of olden times,
said of the time of Sviatoslav,
  of Yaroslav,
    and of Kagan Oleg:]
      "It is difficult for a head
        to be without shoulders.
        But it is also a misfortune
        for the body to be without the head."
And so it is difficult for the Russian land
to be without Prince Igor.
The sun gleams in the sky.
Prince Igor is in the Russian land.
Maidens sing on the Danube.
Their voices reach across the sea to Kiev.
Igor rides along the Borichev[63]
to the Church of the Holy Virgin of Pirogoshch.
The lands are jubilant.
The cities rejoice.
Once the glory of the princes of yore was sung,
now glory will be sung for the young.
Glory to Igor, son of Sviatoslav,
to fierce auroch Vsevolod,
and to Vladimir, son of Igor.
Hail to the princes and the armies
who fight for Christendom against the infidel hosts.
Glory to the princes and to the army. Amen.

20. *Prince Roman, Khan Otrok, and the Wormwood*

THE *Galician and Volynian Chronicle*, from which this tale is taken, gives a rather detailed account of the fate of southern Russia in the thirteenth century. The authors of the first part demonstrate an unmistakable talent for narration and some

---

[63] Borichev: a location of the Dnieper shore in the vicinity of Kiev where a church was built in honor of the Holy Virgin of Pirogoshch. This name comes from the name of an icon in a tower (*pyrios* is Greek for "tower") in Constantinople.

poetic inclination. The present excerpt gives a short but poetic account of the circumstances under which Khan Otrok returned to his native land.

The text upon which this translation is based is to be found in N. K. Gudzy's *Khrestomatiia po drevnei russkoi literature,* Moscow, 1955.

◆ ◆ ◆

Great Prince Roman, the unforgettable ruler of all Russia, died. He was the one who conquered all the heathen nations and with wisdom fulfilled all the divine commandments. He would strike against the infidels (Kumans) like a lion. He could be as full of wrath with them as is a lynx. He annihilated them like a crocodile. Many were the times he crossed their lands like an eagle. He was as courageous as an aurochs. He continued the deeds of his grandfather, Prince Vladimir Monomakh, who destroyed the infidel sons of Ishmael, who are usually called Kumans. He drove Khan Otrok from the steppes to beyond the Iron Gates (of the Caucasian Mountains) into Abkhasia.[1] Only the horde of Khan Syrchan remained on the river Don, and he had only fish for food. It was that time when Prince Vladimir Monomakh drank water from the river Don with his golden helmet. He conquered the entire Kuman land and drove away these accursed sons of Hagar.[2]

After the death of Prince Vladimir Monomakh, Khan Syrchan sent his bard, Oria, to his brother, Khan Otrok, who was still in the land of Abkhasia. And Syrchan told Oria to tell his brother: "Vladimir is dead. Come back, brother; return to your native land." And he added to Oria: "Tell these words I have spoken to my brother and sing him our Kuman songs. But, if he does not want to return, let him smell the fragrance of our prairie grass that is called wormwood."

When Khan Otrok wanted neither to return nor to listen to the songs of his brother's bard, the bard presented him a bouquet of wormwood from the prairie.

And when Khan Otrok inhaled the fragrance of the prairie wormwood, he began to weep, and said: "It is still better to die in one's native land then to win glory in a foreign one." And thus Khan Otrok decided to return to his native land.

---

[1] A small nation on the eastern shores of the Black Sea.

[2] Following the Byzantine tradition, the Russians considered all nomads to be the descendants of Ishmael, the son of Hagar.

21. *Tales from the Novgorodian Chronicle*

IN southern and central Russia the princes eventually established their undisputed rule over the Russian cities and principalities, and the ancient people's assembly, the *Veche*, which had played an important role in Russia before the eleventh and twelfth centuries, gradually declined in importance. But in the cities of Novgorod and Pskov, in northwestern Russia, the power of the princes was curbed and the *Veche* became the principal ruling institution. The princes, who served as commanders of the army, the *posadniks*, who headed the civil administration, other administrators, and the bishops were all elected by the *Veche*, and often removed by it if its members became dissatisfied with them. Like such European merchant cities as Venice, Genoa, Hamburg and Lubeck, both Pskov and Novgorod had a powerful merchant class. Novgorod became a member of the Hanseatic League and maintained lively trade relations with Germany and other nations of northern Europe.

The style of the *Novgorodian Chronicle* strongly reflects the commercial atmosphere that prevailed in these two cities. The entries tell little about political events, but furnish details concerning matters of commerce, such as the state of the harvest, the prices of merchandise, trade activities, and climatic conditions that might have a bearing on the economic situation. Most of the longer stories in these northern annals are of southern origin, and were taken from the Kievan or central Russian chronicles.

The translation of the *Novgorodian Chronicle* presented here is based on *Novgorodskaia pervaia letopis*, Second Version, published by the Academy of Science of the U.S.S.R., Moscow and Leningrad, 1950.

❖ ❖ ❖

LIFE IN THE CITY OF NOVGOROD

1128 (6636)   Kiriak, the Abbot of St. George, died. In the same year John, son of Vsevolod, grandson of Mstislav, died on the 16th of April. In the same year Zavid Dmitrevich was made *posadnik* in Novgorod. This was a cruel year: an *osminka* of rye cost a *grivna*; the people ate lime leaves, birchbark; they ground wood pulp and mixed it with husks and straw; and some ate buttercups, moss, and horseflesh. And the corpses of those who had fallen from starvation were in the streets, the marketplace, the road, and everywhere. And they hired men to carry the dead out of town, for the serfs could not go out. Sorrow and misery befell all. Fathers and mothers would give their children as gifts to merchants or put them to death. And many people went to other lands. Thus a blight was brought upon our land for our sins. And this year the water of the river Volkhov was very high, and it carried away many houses. And Prince Boris Vsevolodovich of Polotsk died, and Zavid Dmitrevich, *posadnik* of Novgorod, died.

1143 (6651)   All this autumn was rainy; from Our Lady's Day of Nativity until the winter solstice it was warm and wet. The water was very high in the river Volkhov, and it carried away hay and wood. The lake froze, and there was great coldness in the night. And the wind broke up the ice and carried it into the river Volkhov, where it broke the bridge and carried away four of the bridge piles. In the same year Sviatopolk married in Novgorod. He brought his bride from Moravia between Christmas and Epiphany. And in the same year the Korelians campaigned against the Yamians, but were forced to retreat.

1156 (6664)   The Novgorodians expelled Sudila, the *posadnik* of the city, and he died five days later. And they gave the position of *posadnik* to Yakun Miroslavovich. In the same spring, on April 29th, Archbishop Nifont passed away. Before he died he went to Kiev to oppose the metropolitan bishop, but many people say that he went to Constantinople after having plundered the Cathedral (St. Sophia in Kiev). They say many things about him, but it is their sin for doing so. We should remember that he was the one who embellished the Cathedral (St. Sophia of Novgorod), who decorated the porches, who made the icon case, and who adorned the church on the outside. He also built the Church of the Holy Savior in Pskov and the Church of St. Clement in Ladoga. I believe that God, because of our sins, did not desire that we should have his grave for our consolation and so he sent him to Kiev, where he died. And he was buried in the Crypt Monastery.

In the same year the whole populace of the city gathered and decided to elect as bishop a holy man, Arkady, who was chosen by God. And all the people went to the Monastery of the Holy Mother of God and took him, Prince Mstislav, the entire clergy of the Cathedral of St. Sophia, and all the priests, abbots, and monks of the city and brought them to the court of St. Sophia. And they entrusted the bishopric to Arkady until the Metropolitan of Russia should arrive and consecrate him.

And in the same year the merchants from over the seas erected the Church of Good Friday on the market square.

1157 (6665)   There was malice among the people, and they rose against Prince Mstislav Yurievich and began to drive him from Novgorod, but the merchants took up arms for him. And brother quarreled with brother. The bridge over the river Volkhov was seized. Guards took their stand on either side of the town gates, and it nearly came to the shedding of blood between them. And then Sviatoslav Rostislavich and David Rostislavich arrived. That very night Mstislav fled from Novgorod. And in three days Rostislav himself arrived. And the brothers came together, and no harm came of it.

In the spring Prince George died at Kiev, and the people of Kiev set Iziaslav Davidovich on the throne. In the same year Andrew, Abbot of the Church of the Holy Mother of God, died. And Alexis was appointed in his place. And in the fall the weather was fearsome with thunder and lightning, and on November 7th, at five in the night, there was hail of the size of apples.

NOVGOROD AT WAR WITH SUZDAL

The chronicle entries for the years 1169 and 1170 which follow below, give a clear picture of the struggle between the princes of Novgorod and those of central Russia. First the princes of Suzdal and later those of Moscow tried to unify all Russia and to bring the prosperous merchant city of Novgorod under their sway. The struggle described in these two entries is against the armies of Suzdal, led by the autocratic Prince Andrey, and their allies, led by Prince Roman and Prince Mstislav. At this time the troops of Novgorod were commanded by young Prince Roman. These entries are written in short, telegraphic style. For a better understanding of the text some explanatory notes have been added in parentheses.

❖   ❖   ❖

1169 (6667)   Danislav Lazutinich went with his troops beyond the Volok[1] to collect tribute, but (Great Prince Andrew) sent his army against them. And it came to a battle. There were only four hundred men of Novgorod against seven thousand soldiers from Suzdal, but God helped the Novgorodians, and the Suzdalians suffered thirteen hundred casualties, while Novgorod lost only fifteen men. Novgorod retreated, but then

---

[1] Volok (Portage) was the name of the region which formed the watershed between the West Dvina and Dnieper.

returned and collected tribute (beyond the Volok), and received tribute also from the peasants of Suzdal. And all returned home in good health.

In this same year in the winter the army of Suzdal, under the command of the son of Prince Andrew, Prince Mstislav, and Prince Roman, and with troops from Smolensk, Toropetz, and Murom; the armies of Riazan led by two princes, the Prince of Polotsk with his armies, and men from the entire Russian land all approached the city of Novgorod. But the people of Novgorod were firmly behind their leader, Prince Roman, and their *posadnik,* Yakun. And so they built fortifications about the city. On Sunday (the emissaries of the princes of Suzdal) came to Novgorod to negotiate, and these negotiations lasted for three days. On the fourth day, Wednesday, February 25th, the Day of St. Tarasy, Patriarch of Constantinople, the Suzdalians attacked the city and fought the entire day. Only toward evening did Prince Roman, who was still very young, and the troops of Novgorod manage to defeat the army of Suzdal with the help of the holy cross, the Holy Virgin, and the prayers of the Right Reverend Bishop Elias. Many Suzdalians were massacred, many were taken prisoner, while the remainder escaped only with great difficulty. And the price of Suzdalian prisoners fell to two *nogatas.*

1170 (6678) There were high prices in Novgorod. A barrel of rye cost four *grivnas,* bread cost two *nogatas,* and honey ten *kunas* a pood. After deliberations, the Novgorodians decided to renounce Prince Roman. And they sent their emissaries to Great Prince Andrew Bogoliubsky (of Suzdal), suing for peace. They asked Prince Andrew to give them another prince who would preserve their liberties. In the same year on the 4th day of October, St. Erofey's Day, Prince Rurik Rostislavich (the prince sent to Novgorod by Prince Andrew) arrived in Novgorod. This same year the God-loving archbishop, Elias, and his brother, Gabriel, founded a monastery and erected the Church of the Annunciation of the Holy Mother of God. And this year Prince Mstislav Iziaslavich, the grandson of Vladimir, died. In the same year Prince Gleb Giorgivich died at Kiev, and (the Kievans) put in Vladimir Mstislavovich.

THE ELECTION OF ARCHBISHOP MANTURY, AND NOVGOROD WARS AGAINST THE UGRIANS

THE entry for the year 1193 gives an interesting account of the election and consecration of a new archbishop. The second part

of the entry is concerned with the description of a Novgorodian
campaign against the people of Ugra (kinsmen of the present
day Hungarians) who occupied the area both east and west of
the northern Urals. The Novgorodians began building their
colonial empire in what is now northern Russia. By the fifteenth
century, when this empire was nearing its end, it extended into
Siberia and covered an area the size of present-day France,
Germany, and Italy combined.

❖ ❖ ❖

1193 (6701) The archbishop of Novgorod, Gabriel, passed
away on May 24th, the Day of Our Holy Father St. Simon. And
he was solemnly buried in the porch of the Cathedral of St.
Sophia next to his brother whose name was George after he
took the holy vows. And then the people of Novgorod, the
abbots, the Chapter of St. Sophia, and the clergy began their
deliberations as to who should be the new archbishop. Some
wanted to elect Mitrofan, while others wanted to elect Mantury,
and still others wanted Grichina in this office. There was a great
feud among them, and they decided to cast lots after High
Mass in the Cathedral of St. Sophia. And they prepared the
lots, and after the service they sent for a blind man and he was
given to them by God. And with the help of divine Grace the
blind man cast, and Mantury was chosen. And they sent for
Mantury and they brought him to the Court of the Archbishop.

And they announced his election to the Metropolitan of Kiev,
and he sent for Mantury with great honors. And Mantury went
to Kiev with the patricians of Novgorod. And he was received
there with love by Prince Sviatoslav and the metropolitan. He
was consecrated on the 10th day of December, the day celebrated for the deaths of the holy martyrs Mina, Hermogen, and
Eugraph. And Mantury returned to Novgorod on January 16th,
the Day of the Falling Off of the Fetters of the Holy Apostle
Peter.

In the same year the Novgorodian troops under Voevoda
Yadreik reached the land of Ugra and took a town. And they
went to another town and besieged it. And they remained there
five weeks, and the people of Ugra sent the Novgorodian force
a deceitful message saying the following: "We are collecting
silver and sables and other valuables for you, so that you should
neither destroy us nor your own tribute." And in the meantime
the Ugrians began collecting their forces, and when their army
had been gathered, the city sent a message to Voevoda Yadreik

ying the following, "Come to the city bringing with you
velve men."

And Voevoda Yadreik went to the city, taking with him the
riest John Legena and other leading men, and they were cut
pieces by the Ugrians on the eve of St. Barbara's Day. And
en they took thirty of the best Novgorodian warriors prisoner
d cut them to pieces. And later fifty more Novgorodian war-
ors were cut down by the Ugrians.

And then Savka (apparently a Novgorodian) came to the
grian prince and said: "Prince, if you don't kill Jacob Prokshe-
ch (presumably the second-in-command of the Novgorodian
rces), but let him live to reach Novgorod, he will bring more
arriors and will devastate your land." And the Ugrian prince
lled Jacob Prokshenich before him and ordered that he be
lled, but Jacob said to Savka: "Brother, God and Holy Sophia
ill judge you if you have in mind the spilling of your brothers'
lood. And you will appear before us and God, and you will be
sponsible for our blood." And after he said this he was killed,
r Savka had secret connections with the Ugrian prince.

And then the army of Novgorod was starving because they
ad remained for six weeks, being induced to do so by Ugrian
eceit. And on the Holy Day of St. Nicholas they broke camp
d were all cut to pieces by the Ugrian army. And there were
rrow and misery among those who remained alive, and there
ere only eighty of them. During the whole winter there was
word in the city of Novgorod as to whether the men of the
my of Voevoda Yadreik were dead or alive. And in Novgorod
e prince, the archbishop, and the entire people of the city
rieved.

In the same year a son, Rostislav, was born to Yaroslav in
ovgorod. And they built a wooden church called Zhivoglozha
the Holy Apostles, and another church to St. Joan the Merci-
l at the Gates of Resurrection.

THE BATTLE ON THE RIVER KALKA

1224 the Mongols, united under Ghenghis Khan, invaded
uthern Russia for the first time. They came there more or less
cidentally, returning to Central Asia after conquests in Persia
d the Caucasus. (The Mongols became known to Russians by
e name Tatar. The Tatars were actually a Mongolian tribe
om which were taken the shock troops for the advancing
ongolian army.) After having defeated the Russian princes

and their allies, the Kumans—who joined with the Russians th
better to resist the invasion—the Mongols disappeared into th
Central Asian steppes and deserts. They returned twelve year
later, and this time they held the Russian land for nearly tw
and a half centuries. The report of this first decisive battle o
the river Kalka is apparently of southern origin, and was in
corporated into the *Novgorodian Chronicle* under the year 1224

◆ ◆ ◆

1224 (6732) In the same year, for our sins, there came un
known tribes. No one knew who they were nor what was the
origin, faith, or tongue, and some people called them Tatar
while others called them Taurmens, and still others called the
Pechenegs. Some say that these are the same people of whom
Methodius of Patras spoke and that they came from the Yetria
Desert, which is between North and East. Methodius said tha
at the end of time there will appear those whom Gideon drov
away, and they will conquer the whole land from the Tigris an
Euphrates rivers to the Pontic Sea, with the exception of Eth
opia. Only God knows who these people are or from whenc
they came. The wise men, who understand the Books, kno
who they are, but we do not. Here we record them in memor
of the misfortunes of the Russian princes that came about
their (the Tatars') hands. We have heard that they have con
quered many lands and have killed many Yassians, Abkhasian
Kossogians,[1] and godless Kumans. And many Kumans wer
driven away and many others were killed, owing to the wrat
of God and his Immaculate Mother. Much evil has befallen th
Russian land at the hands of these Kumans, and therefore mo
merciful God desired that these godless Kumans, son of Ishmae
should die in order to revenge the Christian blood that wa
upon them, these lawless ones.

These Taurmens (Mongols) came across the whole Kuma
land and came close to the Russian border. And the remnan
of these godless Kumans under the leadership of Khotian an
other princes came to the so-called Kuman Wall, where man
were killed together with princes David Koviakovich an
George. This Khotian was the father-in-law of Mstislav Msti
lavich, the Russian Prince of Galich. And he (Khotian) arrive
in Galich with greetings for his son-in-law, Mstislav Mstislavic
and all the other Russian princes. He brought them numero
presents: horses, camels, buffaloes, and girls. And he presente

[1] Yassians, Kossogians, and Abkhazians were Caucasian tribes.

these gifts to them, and said the following: "Today the Tatars took away our land and tomorrow they will come and take away yours." And Khotian begged his son-in-law (for help). And Mstislav Mstislavich began to beg his brothers, the Russian princes, saying, "Brethren, if we do not help them, they will turn to the Tatars, and so later they (the Kumans) will be more powerful."

And hence, having deliberated for some time, they decided to start a campaign, responding to the appeals of the Kuman princes. And the warriors began to gather in their respective regions, and began a march against the Tatars after the whole Russian land was united. Soon the Russian army came to a place called Zarub on the Dnieper.

The Tatars, learning that the Russian princes had begun to march against them, sent their envoys to them, saying: "We hear that you, having followed the advice of the Kumans, do march against us. But we have neither occupied your lands nor your cities and villages, and we are not campaigning against you. We came because God let us conquer the godless Kumans who are our slaves and cattle herders. You should make peace with us. If the Kumans came to you, fight them and take all their belongings. We tell you this because we understand that they have done much harm to you and that is why we fight them."

The Russian princes paid no heed to these speeches, but killed the envoys and marched against the Tatars. They set up camp on the Dnieper in the vicinity of Oleshie. And the Tatars once again sent envoys, and they said the following: "You have listened to the Kumans and have killed our envoys. Come, then, though we have not occupied your lands, and it will be an injustice against God and everyone." And the Russians permitted the envoys to go away.

And Prince Mstislav Mstislavich forded the Dnieper and charged the Tatar outpost and took it with a thousand warriors. The rest of the Tatars of this outpost escaped to the Kuman Hills under the command of Gwemia Beg. Since the Tatars found no assistance, they hid their leader, Gwemia Beg, underground so that he would not be killed. But they were attacked at that place by the Kumans, and Gwemia Beg was killed with the approval of Mstislav Mstislavich.

As soon as the other Russian princes learned of this action, they all crossed the Dnieper, and after nine days they came to the river Kalka. They sent the Kuman vanguard, under the command of Yarun, ahead, while the Russian princes and their armies set up camp. Yarun began fighting with the Tatars, but

his Kuman warriors failed, and retreated in such haste that the
galloped over the Russian camp and trampled it underfoot. An
there was not time for the Russian forces to form ranks. And s
it came to complete confusion, and a terrible slaughter resulted

Mstislav, Prince of Kiev, having witnessed this misfortune
decided not to retreat, but took his position over the rive
Kalka. It was a rocky, rugged place on which he built a stockad
and fought off the Tatars for three days. In this fortificatio
with Prince Mstislav there remained his brothers-in-law, Andrev
and Alexander of Dubrovich. The Tatar troops that besiege
the fortification were led by Chigyz Khan and Teshu Khan
With the Tatars there were also a number of Brodniks[1] (Cos
sacks) under the command of Ploskyn. This accursed com
mander pledged by the holy cross that Prince Mstislav and hi
two brothers-in-law would not be killed, but released for ran
som. But this accursed Ploskyn lied, and he bound the prince
hand and feet and turned them over to the Tatars. The prince
were taken by the Tatars and crushed beneath platforms place
over their bodies on the top of which the Tatars celebrate
their victory banquet. And the fortified camp of Mstislav wa
taken, and all his warriors were slain.

The other princes were pursued to the Dnieper, and six o
them were killed there: Sviatoslav of Yanev, Iziaslav, son o
Ingvar, Sviatoslav of Shumsk, Mstislav of Chernigov and hi
son, and George of Nesvizh. But Prince Mstislav Mstislavich
Prince of Galich, escaped by crossing the Dnieper, and he cu
loose the boats from the shore to ensure his escape. Only on
Russian warrior in ten lived through this battle; in returning t
their homelands, many of these were killed by the Kumans fo
their horses and clothes.

In such a way did God bring confusion upon us, and an end
less number of people perished. This evil event came to pas
on the Day of Jeremiah the Prophet, the 31st day of May. A
for the Tatars, they turned back from the Dnieper, and w
know neither from whence they came nor whither they have
now gone. Only God knows that, because he brought them upo
us for our sins.

---

[1] Russian outlaws and adventurers who lived in the prairie amon
the Kumans.

PART II

the period of feudal divisions

(1240–1478)

Russia Toward 1480 A.D.

MILITARY TALES

22. *Orison on the Downfall of Russia*

THE *Orison on the Downfall of Russia* belongs to a well-known, but still obscure Russian thirteenth-century literary fragment. It is usually found in miscellanies that contain the *Tale of the Life and Heroic Deeds of the Great Prince Alexander Nevsky*, and always precedes it. However, its style differs strikingly from the tale of Alexander Nevsky. It is very probable that it is the beginning of a longer orison or lamentation bewailing the conquest of Russia by the Mongols. It ends abruptly with the indication that a catastrophe befell Russia. Its style is both rhetorical and pathetic, and reflects a strong nationalistic spirit embittered by the catastrophe. One can presume that a longer description of the Mongol invasion originally followed this introductory part.

Although this orison was not written in verse, it can easily be divided into short rhythmic units, many of which rhyme, as for instance, lines three to eleven. The rhythm and diction of this work have many features in common with those of the *Lay of Igor's Campaign*. Since the author mentions the ruler at the time of the orison's writing as being Yaroslav (Great Prince of Vladimir, 1238–1246), it can be concluded that this work was composed no earlier than 1237, the year the Tatars invaded Russia, and no later than 1246, the year of Yaroslav's death.

This translation is based on the Russian text edited by Kh. Loparev to be found in *Pamiatniki drevnei pismenosti i iskusstva*, Volume LXXXIV, St. Petersburg, 1892.

◆ ◆ ◆

O Russian land, brightest of the bright,
most beautifully adorned,
thou art marvelous to us, with thy many beauties.
Marvelous are thy numerous lakes,
thy rivers and venerated springs,
steep mountains, high hills,
oak forests, beautiful fields,
many beasts and countless birds,

great cities, wonderful villages, and monastery gardens,
honorable boyars and countless lords,
Christian churches and stern princes.
Thou, Russian land, art rich in wealth
and the Orthodox Christian faith.
Thou spreadest from Hungary to Poland and Bohemia,
from Bohemia to the land of the Yatvags,
from the land of the Yatvags to the Lithuanians and
          Germans,
from the land of the Germans to Karelia,
from Karelia to Ustiug
where live the pagan Toymians,
and beyond The Breathing Sea,[1]
and from the sea to the Bulgars,
from the Bulgars to the Burtasians,
from the Burtasians to the Cheremiss, and
from the Cheremiss to the Mordvians.
All these vast areas and the people that live on them
were subjugated by God to the Christian people (of Russia)
and to Great Prince Vsevolod
and to his father, Yury, Prince of Kiev,
and to his grandfather, Vladimir Monomakh,
with whose name the Kumans frightened
their children in their cradles,
and in whose reign the Lithuanians
did not dare show themselves from their swamps,
and in whose reign the Hungarians fortified
the stone walls of their cities with their iron gates
so that great Vladimir might not pass through.
And at that time the Germans did rejoice
in being so far (from the Russians) beyond the sea.
And the Burtasians, Cheremiss, Votiaks, and Mordvians
worked hard to pay tribute to Vladimir the Great.
And even the Emperor of Byzantium, Manuel,
fearing lest Vladimir the Great take Constantinople,
was sending rich presents to him.

And so it used to be.
But now a great misfortune has befallen the Russian land,
the land that was once ruled by the great Yaroslav and
          Vladimir,
and is now ruled by Prince Yaroslav
and his brother, Yury, Prince of Vladimir. . . .

[1] The White Sea and the Arctic Ocean, because of frequent fogs,
were called "The Breathing Sea" by Old Russians.

23. *Tale of the Destruction of Riazan*

THE *Tale of the Destruction of Riazan* is one of the most inter-esting and best written accounts of the invasion of Russia by the Mongols under the leadership of Batu. Though the writer of this tale called Batu "tsar," meaning emperor, Batu was actually only a commander of the Mongolian armies that operated in Europe. The Mongolian emperor resided either in Mongolia or in northern China.

This story is contained in many manuscripts of the sixteenth and seventeenth centuries. Apparently it once formed a part of a miscellany that was composed and revised many times by the clergy of the Church of St. Nicholas of Zaraisk, which, according to legend, is located on the very spot where Princess Eupraxy killed herself. The composition of this account, which in our translation is divided into distinct parts, shows its heterogeneous origins. The first contains typical chronicle entries slightly em-bellished by the usual phraseology of old Russian military tales. The story of the knight, Eupaty Kolovrat, is one of the oldest examples of the Russian heroic tale and has several stylistic fea-tures to be found also in Russian *bylinas*, or heroic epic songs. Many features of this knightly epic resemble those of the deeds of medieval knights in western Europe. The joust between Eupaty and the Tatar knight, Hostovrul, and Batu's respect for the body of Eupaty Kolovrat and the survivors of his army, would fit perfectly well into the knightly tradition of western Europe. Other details seem to be patterned after the *Lay of Igor's Campaign*, such as the appeal by Great Prince Yury Ingvarevich to the princes of Riazan. In the last part, with its description of the mourning over and burial of the princes who fell on the field of battle, and in the remarkable lamentation of Prince Ingvar Ingvarevich, folkloric and biblical styles are skill-fully blended.

It is evident that this is a fictionalized account of the destruc-tion of Riazan and that it was actually written many years after the events occurred. The author apparently used for his source material a short account of the events and a list giving the names of the princes of Riazan but not the dates of their deaths. Therefore, the writer oversimplified the family relationships among the Riazan princes and also mentioned several princes who had actually died either before the battle or some time after: *i.e.*, Prince Vsevolod and Prince Oleg the Handsome are mentioned as heroic defenders of the Riazan land. Actually, Prince Vsevolod died in 1208 and Prince Oleg in 1258. Still, most of the facts and details given in this tale do not correspond to information provided in other documents and chronicles.

This translation is based on the Russian text published by V. P. Adrianova—Peretts in *Voinskie povesti drevnei Rusi*, Moscow and Leningrad, 1949, pages 9–17, 18, and 19.

❖ ❖ ❖

I. Batu Invades Russia

Within twelve years after bringing the miraculous icon of St. Nicholas from Kherson, the godless Emperor Batu invaded the Russian land with a great multitude of his Tatar warriors and set up camp on the river Voronezh in the vicinity of the principality of Riazan. And he sent his faithless envoys to the city of Riazan, to Great Prince Yury Ingvarevich, demanding tithes from everyone—from the princes and from all kinds of people. And they also demanded one-tenth of all the horses in the city. As soon as Great Prince Yury Ingvarevich learned of the invasion by godless Batu, he sent his people to the city of Vladimir, to the faithful and Great Prince George Vsevolodovich, asking that he either send succor against the godless emperor or come personally with his army. However, the great prince neither came personally nor sent help, since he had decided to fight Batu himself. And the Great Prince Yury Ingvarevich, having learned that he would receive no help from the Grand Prince of Vladimir, immediately sent to his kin for help, to Prince David Ingvarevich of Murom, to Prince Gleb Ingvarevich of Kolomna, to Prince Oleg ⁓the Handsome, and to Prince Vsevolod of Pronsk, and to other princes. And they started to deliberate as to how to satisfy the godless emperor with tribute. And the Great Prince Yury Ingvarevich decided to send his son, Fedor Yurevich, to Batu with many gifts and supplications that he not invade the land of Riazan.

Prince Fedor came to the Emperor Batu whose camp was on the river Voronezh. And he pleaded with the emperor. The godless, false, merciless emperor accepted the gifts and deceitfully promised not to launch a campaign against the principality of Riazan, but he bragged, and threatened to conquer all other Russian lands. And the emperor began to entertain the Riazan princes, and after this entertainment asked that they send their sisters and daughters to be his concubines. And one envious Riazan courtier told Batu that the wife of Prince Fedor belonged to the Byzantine Imperial Family and that she had a most beautiful body. Emperor Batu, who was false and merciless, became excited, and told Prince Fedor, "Prince, give me your wife so that I may enjoy her beauty."

But Prince Fedor laughed at Batu's suggestion, and said: "It is not our Christian custom to bring to you, the godless emperor, our wives so that your lust may be satisfied. If you conquer us, then you will be the ruler of our wives."

The godless Emperor Batu felt offended, and became angry. He ordered the immediate death of Prince Fedor, and commanded that his body be thrown in a field where it would be devoured by beasts and birds. And the retinue and the warriors of Prince Fedor were also put to death.

One of the servants of Prince Fedor, by name Aponitsa, managed to escape, and wept bitterly, seeing the body of his master. Having noticed that no one guarded the corpse, he took his beloved master's body and buried it secretly. Then he hurried to Princess Eupraxy and told her that Emperor Batu had killed her husband. At that moment the princess happened to be on the upper floor of the palace with her infant son, Prince Ivan. When she heard from Aponitsa that her husband had been slain, she was seized with grief, and threw herself from the window with the child in her arms. And so both were killed.

When Great Prince Yury Ingvarevich learned of his son's death and of the deaths of his son's retinue and warriors, he fell to mourning with Princess Agrippina. And for a long time there were lamentation and sorrow throughout the city. As soon as the great prince recovered from his bereavement, he began to gather an army and to groom his regiments. When Great Prince Yury Ingvarevich saw his kin, his boyars, and his voevodas fearlessly and bravely astride their horses, he raised his hands to the heavens and said with tears in his eyes: "Save us, God, from our enemies and those that march against us. And preserve us from the faithless and make their way dark and difficult."

And then he said to his men: "O my lords and brethren! Since we have received from God his blessing, we must also accept his punishment. It is better, through death, to win eternal glory than to be under the power of the heathen. And I, your brother, am ready to sacrifice my life for the holy divine Church, for the Christian faith, and for the country of our father, Great Prince Ingvar Sviatoslavovich."

And then he went to the Church of the Assumption of the Blessed Virgin, and prayed there. And he cried before the icon of the Blessed Virgin and prayed to the great worker of miracles, St. Nicholas, and to his holy kin, Sts. Boris and Gleb. And for the last time he kissed Great Princess Agrippina. And he received the blessings of the bishop and the priests.

II. Batu Defeats Prince Yury

And they marched against the infidel Batu, and meeting him on the border of the principality of Riazan, attacked and began to fight both fiercely and bravely. And it was a terrible and awesome battle, and many of Batu's regiments were defeated. And Emperor Batu, seeing how fiercely and bravely did the warriors of Riazan fight, became frightened. But who can resist the wrath of God? Batu's forces were innumerable and invincible. Each Riazan warrior had to fight with a thousand of the enemy. And every two Riazan warriors had to fight with ten thousand of the enemy. And Prince Yury Ingvarevich saw the slaying of his brother, David, and exclaimed in anguish: "O my kind brothers and dear warriors, the flower of Riazan's troops, be brave and resist mightily. Our dear brother, Prince David, was the first to drink the bitter cup to the dregs, and we shall do the same."

And the princes and the warriors changed horses and once again began to fight fiercely. And they cut through the many strong lines of the Tatar regiments, fighting bravely and fiercely. And all the Tatar regiments were struck with awe upon seeing the bravery and power of the Riazan armies. And they fought with such intensity that even the earth began to moan, and confusion reigned in the ranks of Batu's armies. The strong Tatar regiments were hardly able to overcome the Riazan offensive. In this battle were killed Great Prince Yury Ingvarevich, Prince David Ingvarevich of Murom, Prince Gleb Ingvarevich of Kolomna, Prince Vsevolod Ingvarevich of Pronsk, and many other brave Riazan princes, powerful voevodas, and warriors. Heroes and brave warriors, the flower of Riazan's army, all drank the same bitter cup to the dregs, and fell on the field of battle.[*] And Prince Oleg was taken prisoner half alive. All of this happened according to the will of God and because of our sins.

And the Emperor Batu, seeing that numerous regiments of his army had been defeated, was seized by awe and grief. He began conquering the Riazan lands, ordering that everyone and everything be cut down and burned without mercy. And he lay

[*] None of the men of Riazan deserted the battlefield; all were slain.

low the cities of Pronsk, Belgorod, and Izheslavets, killing everyone in these cities without mercy. And Christian blood flowed
like a great river. And all this because of our sins.

When Emperor Batu saw Prince Oleg Ingvarevich, the most
handsome and bravest of the Riazan princes, dying from his
grievous wounds, he wanted to heal his wounds and win him
over to his faith. But Prince Oleg began to reprimand Batu, and
called him godless and the enemy of all Christendom. And fire
came from the evil heart of Batu, and he ordered that Prince
Oleg be cut to pieces. And so he became the second Stephen
the Martyr, having received the crown of suffering from the
all-merciful God. And he drank his bitter cup to the dregs with
all his brethren.

III. THE TAKING OF RIAZAN

The accursed Batu began the conquest of the land of Riazan,
and soon approached the city of Riazan itself. They encircled
the city and fought without surcease for five days. Batu changed
his regiments frequently, replacing them with fresh troops,
while the citizens of Riazan fought without relief. And many
citizens were killed and others wounded. Still others were exhausted by their great efforts and their wounds. On the dawn
of the sixth day the pagan warriors began to storm the city,
some with firebrands, some with battering rams, and others with
countless scaling ladders for ascending the walls of the city.
And they took the city of Riazan on the 21st day of December.
And the Tatars came to the Cathedral of the Assumption of the
Blessed Virgin, and they cut to pieces the Great Princess Agrippina, her daughters-in-law, and other princesses. They burned
to death the bishops and the priests and put the torch to the
holy church. And the Tatars cut down many people, including
women and children. Still others were drowned in the river.
And they killed without exception all monks and priests. And
they burned this holy city with all its beauty and wealth, and
they captured the relatives of the Riazan princes, the princes of
Kiev and Chernigov. And churches of God were destroyed, and
much blood was spilled on the holy altars. And not one man remained alive in the city. All were dead. All had drunk the same
bitter cup to the dregs. And there was not even anyone to mourn
the dead. Neither father nor mother could mourn their dead
children, nor the children their fathers or mothers. Nor could a
brother mourn the death of his brother, nor relatives their relatives. All were dead. And this happened for our sins.

IV. Eupaty the Fearless

Seeing this terrible letting of Christian blood, the heart of godless Batu became even more hardened, and he marched against the cities of Suzdal and Vladimir, intending to conquer all Russian lands, to uproot the Christian faith, and to destroy the churches of God. At that time a Riazan lord, Eupaty Kolovrat, who was in Chernigov at the time of the destruction of the city of Riazan, heard of Batu's invasion. He left Chernigov with a small force and hurried to Riazan. When he came to the land of Riazan he saw it devastated and the cities destroyed, the rulers killed, and the people dead. And he rushed to the city of Riazan and found it destroyed, the rulers killed, and the people slaughtered. Some of them were cut down, while others were burned, and still others were drowned. And Eupaty wept with great sorrow and his heart became angry. He gathered a small force of seventeen hundred men who had been preserved by God outside the city. And they hurriedly pursued the godless emperor. And with difficulty they caught up with him in the principality of Suzdal, and suddenly fell upon his camp. And there began a battle without mercy, and confusion reigned. And the Tatars lost their heads from fear as Eupaty fought so fiercely that his sword became dull, and, taking a sword from a fallen Tatar, he would cut them down with their own swords. The Tatars thought that the Russians had risen from the dead, and Eupaty was riding through the ranks of the Tatar regiments so bravely that Batu himself became frightened.

With great effort the Tatars managed to capture five men from Eupaty's regiments, and then only because they were exhausted from their wounds. They were brought before the Tatar emperor, and he asked them, "Why do you cause me such evil?"

The warriors answered: "We are of the Christian faith, knights of the Great Prince Yury of Riazan, and from the regiment of Eupaty Kolovrat. We were sent by Prince Ingvar Ingvarevich to you, the powerful emperor, to honor you, to chase you away with honors, and to render unto you all honors. Do not wonder, Emperor, that we have not had time to serve up the bitter cup to your entire army." And the emperor admired their witty answers. And he sent his brother-in-law, Hostovrul, against Eupaty, and with Hostovrul went strong regiments. Hostovrul bragged to the emperor, and promised to bring back Eupaty alive.

Eupaty was encircled by Tatar troops because they wished to take him alive. And Hostovrul rode out against Eupaty, but

Eupaty was a giant, and with one blow he cleft Hostovrul to the saddle. And once more he began to cut down the Tatar troops, and he killed many of Batu's best knights. Some were cut down, while others were cleft to their waist, and still others were cleft to their saddles. The Tatars became afraid, seeing what a giant Eupaty was. And then they brought up catapults and began showering rocks upon him. And they finally killed Eupaty Kolovrat, but only with great difficulty.

Eupaty's body was brought before Batu, and the emperor sent for his princes, lords, and commanders, and all marveled at the courage, power, and bravery of the Riazan warriors. And the lords, commanders, and princes told Batu: "We were in many battles with many emperors in many lands, but never have we seen such courageous heroes, and even our fathers never told us of such. They are winged people. They do not think about death, and they fight bravely and courageously on their horses, one against a thousand, and two against ten thousand warriors. None of them would abandon the battlefield alive."

And Batu looked at Eupaty's body, and said: "O Kolovrat Eupaty, you have honored us with your courage, and you, with your small army, have killed many knights of my powerful horde and have defeated many of my regiments. If such a knight would serve with me, I would keep him very close to my heart." And he gave up Eupaty's body to the remainder of the Riazan force that had been captured on the battlefield. And Batu gave orders that the prisoners should be released and that no harm should come to them.

V. Prince Ingvar Buries the Dead

Prince Ingvar Ingvarevich (the brother of Great Prince Yury Ingvarevich of Riazan) returned from Chernigov, having been there with his relative, Prince Michael, at the time of the destruction of Riazan. And so he was preserved by God from the enemy of all Christendom. Prince Ingvar Ingvarevich found his fatherland devastated, and learned that all his brothers had been killed by the impure, lawbreaking Batu. And he came to the city of Riazan and found the city destroyed, and his mother and sisters-in-law, his relatives, and many other people lying dead. And he found the churches burned and all valuables taken from the common treasury of Chernigov and Riazan. When Prince Ingvar saw this great and enduring destruction he shrieked aloud in his sorrow, sounding as a trumpet summoning the army or as an organ resounding. And after these rending shrieks and horri-

fying lamentations, Prince Ingvar fell to the ground as if dead.
With great difficulty and the help of water and a fresh breeze
did he recover. And finally his soul did revive in his body.

Who would not so lament such a catastrophe? Who would not
bewail the deaths of so many Orthodox people? Who would not
mourn the death of so many rulers? Who would not mourn such
a dispersion?

And Prince Ingvar searched through the bodies, and found
the body of his mother, Princess Agrippina, and those of his
brothers' wives. And he called a priest from villages that were
preserved by God, and he buried his mother and the wives of
his deceased brothers with great lamentations in place of the
psalms and chants. And he cried and lamented terribly. And he
buried the bodies of the other dead and he cleaned the city.
And he had the city blessed by a priest and he gathered the few
survivors and comforted them. And he lamented for a long time,
thinking of his mother, his brothers, his relatives, and all the
people of Riazan who had met such untimely deaths.

And all this happened because of our sins. There used to be
the city of Riazan in the land of Riazan, but its wealth disappeared and its glory ceased, and there is nothing to be seen in
the city excepting smoke, ashes, and barren earth. All churches
and the cathedral were burned. And not only this city, but many
others were conquered. There is neither the ringing of the church
bells nor church services. And instead of joy, there are only
uninterrupted lamentations.

And Prince Ingvar went to the place where his brethren were
killed by the impious emperor Batu. Great Prince Yury of Riazan,
Prince David of Murom, Prince Vsevolod of Pronsk, Prince Gleb
of Kolomna, many other princes, boyars, voevodas, and warriors
—indeed, all the best souls of Riazan—were lying on the barren
earth and frozen grass. And they were covered with snow and
ice, and no one cared for them. Beasts devoured their bodies,
and a multitude of birds tore them to pieces. And they were
lying together, even as they had fallen together. They all drank
the same bitter cup to the dregs.

And when Prince Ingvar Ingvarevich saw this great number of
corpses lying on the earth, he shrieked bitterly, like a trumpet
resounding. He fell to the ground, and tears flowed from his
eyes in a stream. And Prince Ingvar spoke in great sadness:

"O my dear brethren and warriors!
 O my treasured lives!
 How could you close your eyes

and leave me alone in such misfortune?
How could you disappear from my sight,
treasures of my life?
O my beautiful flowers!
O my unripened vineyard!
Why won't you speak to me, your brother?
Never again will you make my life sweet.
Why won't you look at me?
Why won't you talk with me?
How could you, fruitful gardens,
born of the same father,
and from the same womb of Great Princess Agrippina,
and fed by the same breast, forget me?
To whom have you forsaken me, your brother?
You did fade too early, my dear eastern stars.
You set so early, my dear suns.
You lie on this deserted land watched over by no one!
No one renders you honor or glory.
Indeed, your days of glory have dimmed.
Where is your power?
You, who used to be rulers of many lands,
now lie on this barren earth,
and your faces darken from decay.
O my dear brothers!
O my dear warriors!
Never again shall we share joys.
O my bright lights,
Why were you extinguished?
I have not had enough joy with you!
If God hears your prayers,
pray that I, your brother, might join you!
After days of joy have come those of tears and sorrow.
After pleasures and happiness,
have come lamenting and mourning.
O, why did I not die before you
so that I would not have had to see your deaths?
This is my bitter fate!
Do you hear my unhappy words that fall so sadly?
O mother earth!
O forest of oak, lament with me!
And how shall I describe these days
in which perished
so many rulers and warriors,
so many brave and dashing heroes of Riazan?

None returned,
but all drank the same bitter cup to the dregs.
My tongue does not obey me,
my lips close,
my sight darkens,
my strength ebbs,
for great is the sorrow of my soul."

And there was great sorrow and sadness, tears and sighs, fe
and trembling, because of the evil ones that attacked our la
Great Prince Ingvar raised his hands to the heavens, and pray
tearfully:

"O Lord, my God,
I place my hope in thee.
Save and preserve me from my persecutors.
O my most holy Mother of Christ, my Savior,
don't forsake me in my hour of grief.
Boris and Gleb, our great martyrs and ancestors,
be of help to me in battle, lowly sinner that I am.
My brethren and warriors,
help me with your prayers in my struggles against the
enemy,
these children of Hagar,
these grandchildren of Ishmael."

And then Prince Ingvar began to search among the bodies
the dead, and he took for burial the bodies of his broth
Great Prince Yury, Prince Gleb of Kolomna, and of other prin
related to him, as well as those of many other boyars
voevodas well known to him. And he transported the bodies
the city of Riazan, and buried them with honor. And the boo
of the others, which were lying on the devastated earth,
buried and had the last rites pronounced over them. Hav
buried all of them, Prince Ingvar then went to the city
Pronsk where he gathered the pieces of his slain brother,
peaceful and Christ-loving Prince Oleg. And he ordered the b
returned to the city of Riazan, and he himself carried the v
erable head of Prince Oleg to the city. And he kissed it v
respect, and placed the body in the same coffin with the b
of Great Prince Yury. In the vicinity of this grave were bur
the remains of Princes David and Gleb in a single coffin. A
then Prince Ingvar went to the river Voronezh where Pri
Fedor Yurevich had been killed at the order of Batu. A

ince Ingvar shed many tears over the body of Prince Fedor
d he brought it to the city of Riazan, and in the vicinity of
e icon of the great maker of miracles, St. Nicholas, he buried
ince Fedor together with his wife, faithful Princess Eupraxy,
d his son, Prince Ivan. And he placed stone crosses over the
aves. . . . [A fragment has been omitted.]

Then faithful Prince Ingvar, whose baptismal name was
osmas, took the throne of his father, Ingvar Sviatoslavovich.
nd he restored the land of Riazan and he erected churches
d monasteries. And he consoled the settlers and gathered his
eople together. And he was a great joy for the Christians who,
ith the help of God's strong hand, had escaped the godless
fidel, Emperor Batu. And he put Prince Michael Vsevolodovich
Pronsk in his father's patrimony.

24. *Sofony of Riazan: Zadonshchina*

N SEPTEMBER 8, 1380, Russian troops, under the command of
e Great Prince of Moscow, Dmitry, defeated the Tatar armies,
00,000 strong, lead by Mamay, Khan of the Golden Horde. It
as the first time, after one and a half centuries of Tatar domi-
ation over the Russian land, that the Russians defeated the
atars. This battle did not bring an immediate end to the Tatar
oke, but it was a great victory for the Russians, both weaken-
g the domination of the Tatars and fostering the unification of
e Russian lands. Thus, it is not surprising that this important
istorical event is recorded in various literary works. Among
em, the most interesting is the *Lay of Great Prince Dmitry*
anovich and his Brother, Prince Vladimir Andreevich, written
 Sofony of Riazan. It is known in Russian as *Zadonshchina*,
eaning "The Tale of Events Beyond the Don," because the
attle took place not far from the Don River, on the Kulikovo
airie. *Zadonshchina* was the title used in one of several extant
anuscripts by Sofony of Riazan.

The purpose of this poetic lay was not to give a detailed his-
rical account of the background and development of this bat-
e, one of the most memorable in Russian history. The author
mitted a considerable number of events that were of impor-
nce to the final outcome of the conflict, while many others
ere consolidated for the sake of poetic unity. Instead, the
thor wished to give an epic account of the Russians' efforts,

and to stress the importance of this, the first decisive victor
over the Tatars.

For the basic patterns of this lay, Sofony of Riazan turned t
the greatest poetic work of Kievan Russia, the *Lay of Igor
Campaign.* In many respects he imitated this work, using i
symbolic parallelisms, metaphors, alliterative patterns, and poet
imagery. Some sentences are taken word for word from the te:
of the earlier *Lay* (*Slovo*). Still, Sofony of Riazan created a la
that is very different from that about Igor, not only in its histor
cal perspectives and political conceptions but also in its stru
ture and in the development of narrative line.

Like the author of the tale of Igor, Sofony of Riazan, i
writing this work, had in mind not only a poetic account of th
battle but also an appeal to Russian unity and Russian nation
feelings. But, whereas the *Lay of Igor's Campaign* is primaril
a lyrical appeal, *Zadonshchina* has a very definite narrativ
scheme that gives a more realistic account of events. Unlike th
Lay, the lyrical elements in this work are minimized, and th
reminiscences of past feuds, so central to the *Lay,* are practicall
absent. *Zadonshchina,* like the *Lay,* was written not in verse b
in rhythmic prose consisting of clearly distinguishable units.

The present translation is based on the text edited by V.]
Adrianova-Peretts, which is itself based on various mediev
manuscripts of the work. This text was published in *Voinsk
povesti drevnei Rusi,* in the series *Literaturnye Pamiatniki,* Mo
cow and Leningrad, 1949, pages 33–41. The division into chap
ters and stanzas, as well as the typographic arrangement, w
made by the translator to facilitate reading.

❖   ❖   ❖

PROEMIUM

Great Prince Dmitry Ivanovich, with his brother,[1] Princ
Vladimir Andreevich, and his voevodas, attended a banquet
the house of Mikula Vasilievich. (And Prince Dmitry Ivanovic
spoke, saying:)

"Do you know, dear brothers, that Emperor Mamai
    invaded the Russian land at the swift river Don
    and is advancing into the midnight land?
    Let us go, brothers, into that midnight land,
    the lot of Japheth, the son of Noah,

[1] Prince Vladimir was actually his cousin, but among close relativ
it was customary to call each other "brother."

from whom has come most glorious Russia.
Let us ascend the mountains of Kiev
and view the glorious river Dnieper.
Let us view the entire Russian land
and beyond the east, the lot of Shem,
the son of Noah, from whom were born
the pagan nomads, the Moslem Tatars."

I. EXHORTATION

They have defeated the race of Japheth on the river Kalka.[2]
And since that time the Russian land has been sad.
And, from the battle on the Kalka to the defeat of Mamai,
the Russian land has been covered with grief and sorrow,
shedding tears and lamenting the loss of her children.
Princes, boyars, and all courageous men!
Let us leave our homes, our wealth, our women and children,
  our cattle,
that we may receive glory and honor in this world.
Let us lay down our lives for the Russian land and the Christian
  faith.
First, the sorrow of the Russian land did I describe,
as it has been done before in the books.
Then, I have described my sorrows and my glorifications
of the Great Prince Dmitry Ivanovich
and his brother, Vladimir Andreevich.
Let us come together, brothers, friends, and sons
of the Russian land.
Let us knit word after word.
Let us bring joy to the Russian land
and cast sorrow on the eastern country, the lot of Shem.
Let us sing of the defeat of Mamai, the infidel.
Let us sing glory to the Great Prince Dmitry Ivanovich
and to his brother, Prince Vladimir Andreevich.

Let us say the following words:
 "It behooves us, brothers, to begin with new words
  the telling of the glorious tale of the army of Prince Dmitry
    Ivanovich
  and his brother, Prince Vladimir Andreevich, great-
    grandsons
  of holy Prince Vladimir of Kiev."

[2] In most of the manuscripts the river is called Kaiala, but Sofony
apparently refers to the river Kalka, the site of the battle with the
Mongols in 1223.

Let us tell the tale in the tradition of yore.
Let us race in thought across the lands.
Let us remember the deeds of former years.
Let us glorify wise Boyan, the great bard of Kiev,
for he, wise Boyan, would put his nimble fingers
on the living strings and would sing the glory of
the princes of Russia, of Igor Rurikovich, the first Great
        Prince of Kiev,
of Great Prince Vladimir Sviatoslavovich and
of Great Prince Yaroslav Vladimirovich.
So let us glorify with our melodies and powerful lyrics
this Great Prince Dmitry Ivanovich
and his brother, Prince Vladimir Andreevich,
great-grandsons of those princes who devoted all their
bravery and efforts to the Russian land and the Christian
        faith.

II. THE RUSSIANS PREPARE FOR THE CAMPAIGN

Great Prince Dmitry Ivanovich and
his brother, Prince Vladimir Andreevich,
strengthened their minds with valor,
quickened their hearts with courage, and
imbued their thoughts with martial spirit.
And they gathered their regiments throughout the Russian
        land.
And they remembered the deeds of their great-grandfather,
Prince Vladimir of Kiev.

Skylark, joy of beautiful days!
Fly high into the beautiful blue sky.
Look on the powerful city of Moscow,
sing the glories of Great Prince Dmitry Ivanovich
and his brother, Prince Vladimir Andreevich.
The storm will bring the gyrfalcon
from the Russian lands into the Kuman prairie.
Steeds neigh in Moscow.
Glory rings out over all Russian lands.
Trumpets blare in Kolomna.
Drums resound in Serpukhov.
Banners are raised at the shore of the great river Don.
Bells resound in the great city of Novgorod,
but men of Novgorod remain in Holy Sophia, saying,
    "O brethren, we shall not have time to help
    Great Prince Dmitry Ivanovich."

It seems that eagles fly from the midnight land,
but they are not eagles.
They are Russian princes who fly together
to help Prince Dmitry Ivanovich and his brother,
Prince Vladimir Andreevich, telling them such words:
  "Lord, Great Prince, the infidel Tatars have begun
         advancing into our lands.
  They take from us our patrimony.
  They camp on the river Mech,
  between the rivers Don and Dnieper.
  Our lord, we will go beyond the swift river Dnieper.
  We will win glory for our land in the tradition of old.
  We will gain memories for our youth.
  We will put our brave warriors to the test
  for the Russian land and the Christian faith."

And then Prince Dmitry Ivanovich said:
  "Brethren and princes of the Russian land,
  we are all descendants of Prince Vladimir of Kiev.
  Since our birth we have never permitted ourselves to be
         offended,
  neither by the falcon nor the gyrfalcon,
  nor by the black raven nor by the infidel Mamai."

If only the nightingale could sing the glories
of the two brothers of the Lithuanian land,
Andrew and Dmitry, the sons of Olgerd,
and of Dmitry of Volynia,
for these courageous sons, gyrfalcons in time of battle,
our brave army captains,
were swaddled under trumpets,
were raised under helmets, and
were fed at lance point in the Lithuanian land.

And Andrew, son of Olgerd, spoke to his brother, Dmitry:
  "We are two brothers, sons of Olgerd,
  grandsons of Adiman, great-grandsons of Skolomend.
  Let us gather together our dear brethren,
  the nobles of brave Lithuania, bold and brave fellows.
  Let us mount on swift steeds.
  Let us view the swift river Don.
  Let us drink the water of the Don from our helmets,
  Let us test our Lithuanian swords on Tatar helmets,
  and our German javelins on the armor of the Muslims."

And Dmitry, son of Olgerd, said to him:

"Brother Andrew, let us not spare ourselves
in defense of the Russian land and the Christian faith,
and in defense of the honor of Prince Dmitry Ivanovich.
Already, brother, thunder resounds and clamor raises in
          the stone city of Moscow.
But it is not thunder, brother.
It is the clamor of the powerful army of Dmitry Ivanovich.
The brave Russian warriors thunder in their gilded armor
and with their crimson shields.
Andrew, saddle your swift steed,
for mine has been long saddled.
Let us go, brother, into the open fields.
Let us go, brother, and view our regiments."

III. The Coming of the Tatars

Already from the sea there have begun blowing strong wind
into the mouth of the rivers Don and Dnieper.
And they have wafted great clouds over the Russian land,
and these clouds made the sunsets as crimson as blood,
and blue lightning flashes through these clouds.
There will be great clamor on the river Nepriadva,
between the rivers Don and Dnieper.
Many men will fall on the field of Kulikovo,
and blood will be shed on the river Nepriadva.

The carts (of the nomads) have begun to creak
between the Don and the Dnieper.
The Tatars march into the Russian land.
Gray wolves follow after them
from the mouths of the Don and the Dnieper.
They howl on the river Mech and
they wish to advance into the Russian land.
But they are not wolves.
They are the infidel Tatars who wish
to march into the Russian land and conquer it.

The geese have begun to cackle on the river Mech.
Swans have begun to flutter their wings.
But it is not geese that cackle
nor swans that flutter their wings.
It is the infidel Mamai who has entered the Russian land,
and he brought his warriors there.
These winged birds have been brought by misfortune.

They fly high under the clouds.
Ravens croak and magpies speak in their own speech.
The eagles screech menacingly, wolves howl,
and foxes bark, waiting for bones.
O, Russian land, you are far away beyond the hills.

IV. The Russian Army Marches to Battle

Already the falcon and the gyrfalcon
and the goshawks of Belozersk[3] race from the stone city
    of Moscow,
fly high under the blue sky,
ring their golden bells,[4]
and prepare to swoop down upon numerous flocks
of geese and swans.
And so the brave knights of Russia prepare
to strike the great armies of the infidel, Mamai.

Great Prince Dmitry Ivanovich sets in the golden stirrup
and takes his sword in his right hand.
The sun shines brightly from the east,
showing him the road (to victory).
What rumbles? What roars so early before the dawn?
It is Prince Vladimir Andreevich
who prepares his regiments for battle
and leads them to the great river Don.
And he speaks to his brother:
  "Prince Dmitry, Great Prince, don't yield to these Tatars,
    for these infidels destroy our fields and
    invade our fatherland."
Prince Dmitry Ivanovich speaks to his brother:
  "My dear brother, Vladimir Andreevich,
    we are two brothers.
    Our voevodas are appointed and our armies are well known
        to us.
    We mount swift steeds and we wear gilt armor.
    We have Circassian helmets and Muscovite shields.
    We have German javelins and Frankish lances,
    and our swords are made of steel.
    The roads are known to us.
    The rivers are prepared for fording.
    The armies are eager to sacrifice their lives

---

[3] Allusion to the princes of Belozersk.
[4] Hunting falcons had small bells attached to their talons.

for the Christian faith.
Our banners flap in the wind,
and Russians seek honor and glory."

V. THE BATTLE BEGINS

Already the falcons, the gyrfalcons, and
the goshawks from Belozersk swiftly cross the river Don.
And they strike against flocks of geese and swans.
They are Russian sons who strike against the great Tatar
army,
And who, with their steel lances, clash against Tatar armors,
whose tempered swords sunder Tatar helmets,
on the field of Kulikovo,
at the small river, Nepriadva.

The earth became black from horse hooves.
The field became strewn with Tatar bones.
Much blood was spilled upon the field.
Strong regiments came together and clashed,
and they trampled the hills and the meadows.
The calm waters of rivers and lakes became stirred up.
The Div[5] called out in the Russian land,
calling all lands to listen.
And the glory of the Russian princes resounded,
from the roar of battle to the Iron Gates,
to Rome and to Kafa-on-the-Sea,
to Tyrnovo and to Constantinople.[6]
O great land of Russia.
you have defeated Mamai on the field of Kulikovo.

The storm clouds began to gather
and from them shone lightning,
and thunder roared mightily.
It was the clash of the sons of Russia
with the Tatar infidels, for they seek revenge for Tatar
offenses.
The gilt armor of the Russian princes gleamed.
Their steel swords rained upon the Tatar helmets.
It is not aurochs that roar upon the field of Kulikovo.

[5] A god or bird of misfortune that was mentioned in the *Lay of Igor's Campaign.*
[6] Iron Gates: a narrow canyon on the lower Danube; Kafa-on-the-Sea: an Italian city in the Crimea; Tyrnovo: the capital of medieval Bulgaria.

It is the wailing of Russian princes, boyars, and voevodas of
      Prince Dmitry,
and the princes of Belozersk who were defeated at the swift
      river Don.
And there voevodas Fedor Semionovich, Timofey Valuevich,
Andrey Serkizovich, Mikhail Ivanovich,
and a great many warriors were cut to pieces by the Tatars.
And their bodies lie on the shore of the river Don.
And then a boyar of Briansk, Monk Peresvet,
was ordered to the place where he was fated to meet death.
And Monk Peresvet said to Prince Dmitry Ivanovich:
  "It is better that we fall in battle
  than become slaves of these infidels."
And Peresvet, galloping on his horse,
filled the air with his battle cry.
And his armor gleamed as he called
to his younger brother, Osliabia:
  "Well, brother, it is time for those who are old
  to feel young and for the young to win glory
  by trying the arms of brave warriors."
And the brother, Monk Osliabia, answered:
  "Brother Peresvet, I already see that there
  will be heavy wounds on your body and
  that your head will lie on the feathergrass.
  I can see that my son, Jacob, will also lie in the green grass
  on the field of Kulikovo and for the defense
  of the Christian faith and revenge of the offenses
  done to Great Prince Dmitry Ivanovich."

And at that time in the land of Riazan
at the river Don there was heard neither
the voice of the plowman nor of the shepherd.
Only the crows cawed and the cuckoos cuckooed,
circling above the corpses.
And it was awesome and bitter to look about,
for the grass was covered with blood
and the trees bowed down to the earth in their sorrow.

VI. The Lamentation of the Widows

The birds began to sing their songs of sorrow.
And the princesses and wives of the boyars and voevodas
began to lament the deaths of their husbands.
Maria Dmitrievna, the wife of Mikula,
cried early in the dawn on the fortress wall of Moscow:

"O river Don, my swift river,
   mountains crumble before you, and
   you flow to the land of the Kumans.
      Oh, that you might bring me from there my lord, Mikula!"
And Fedosia, the wife of Timofey Valuevich, also lamented:
   "Joy has abandoned the glorious city of Moscow.
      Never again will I see my dear lord, Timofey Valuevich."
And Maria, the wife of Andrey,
and Xenia, the wife of Michael, lamented since dawn:
   "For both of us the sun has set in the glorious city of
         Moscow.
      News of our relatives has come from the swift river Don
      and has brought great sorrow upon us.
      Russian knights have dismounted their swift steeds
      on the fateful field of Kulikovo."

And the Div cries under the Tatar sabers,
and there the wounded Russian knights weep.

And since dawn nightingales sing sadly
from the walls of the city of Kolomna.
But these sad songs are not sung by nightingales,
but by the wives of Kolomna who lamented:
   "O Moscow, Moscow, our swift river,
      why did you take our husbands from us to the Kuman
            land?"
And they addressed their great prince, saying:
   "Oh, our Lord, why wouldn't you close
      the river Dnieper with your oars?
      Why wouldn't you empty the swift river Don
      with the helmets of your warriors?
      Why wouldn't you build a dam
      on the river Mech from Tatar corpses?
      Why wouldn't you close the gates of the river Oka,
      that we might be preserved from the infidels,
      for our husbands have succumbed in battle."

VII. THE DEFEAT OF THE TATARS

Prince Vladimir Andreevich, with the Prince of Volynia,
threw seventy thousand warriors from his right flank against
      the infidels.
And they rapidly struck down the infidel Tatars,
their golden helmets gleaming,
their tempered swords raining on Tatar helmets.

And Prince Dmitry praises his brother:
  "Brother, Prince Vladimir, you are our shield of iron
  in this time of evil.
  Don't let your regiments cease fighting.
  Don't give in to these evil Tatars.
  Don't pardon these traitors,[7]
  for these infidels destroy our fields
  and have killed most of our valorous army.
  Oh, my brother, it is so sad to see
  so much Christian blood spilled!"
And then Prince Dmitry Ivanovich addressed his boyars:
  "Fellow boyars, voevodas, and sons of boyars,
  This is not a banquet for drinking sweet Muscovite mead.
  This is not a court in which to win higher ranks.
  This is the place to win glory for your names.
  This is the place where an old man must act as a young
        man,
  and the young man must win glory."

And it seemed that a falcon flew to the swift river Don,
but it was not a falcon that flew beyond the swift Don.
Prince Dmitry galloped with his regiments beyond this river.
And Prince Dmitry said:
  "Brother, Prince Vladimir,
  now is the time to drink of the cup.
  Let us attack the infidel army, brother,
  with our strong regiments."

And the princes advanced onto the field of battle.
Once more tempered swords rained upon Tatar helmets.
Now the infidels can protect their heads only with their arms.
The infidels begin to retreat swiftly from the princes.
Banners flap in the wind.
The infidels flee while Russian cries of victory cover the field.
Their gilt armor gleams.
The aurochs have taken the stronger position.

Indeed, the tide turned, and the Russian
regiments began to cut the Tatars to pieces.
And despair seized the infidels.
Princes fell from their mounts,

[7] Apparently some of the Russian leaders hesitated in attacking the Tatars.

and Tatar corpses began to cover the field.
And blood flowed in a stream.
The infidels began fleeing on all sides.
They fled by impassable routes to the sea,
and they gnashed their teeth
and they clawed their faces in despair, saying:
   "Alas, brothers, we shall never escape to our land.
   We shall never again see our children.
   We shall never again caress our wives,
   but we must kiss the damp earth.
   We shall never again campaign against Russia.
   We shall never again receive tribute from the Russian
      princes."

And the Tatar lands began to mourn,
and sorrow and sadness covered the land.
And they lost their courage for campaigning against the
      Russian land.
Their joy disappeared.
The sons of Russia pillaged the Tatars of
cloths and silks, weapons and horses,
oxen and camels, wines and sugars,
jewelry and velvets, and they carried
the wealth of the Tatars to their wives.
Tatar gold jingled in the hands of Russian women.
Joy and happiness spread over the Russian land.
Russian glory was exalted,
while shame was brought upon the Tatars.
And the Div was enthroned, and the fear
of Russian princes spread over the earth.

Oh, great princes of Russia,
fight the enemy with your valorous army.
Fight for the Russian land and the Christian faith,
fight against the infidel emperor, Mamai.

And the infidels threw down their weapons,
and they bowed their heads to the Russian sword.
Their trumpets stopped sounding, and their voices became
      saddened.

VIII. The Escape of Mamai

Like a gray wolf, the infidel emperor, Mamai,
ran away with his guards.

And he came to the city of Kafa-on-the-Sea.
And the Italians asked him:
"Infidel Mamai, how did you dare to attack the Russian
　　lands?
Once Tatar power spread over the Russian land of forest,
but the time of Emperor Batu has long passed.
Emperor Batu had four hundred thousand, and he
　　　　conquered the whole Russian land,
the whole earth, from the east to the west.
And God punished the Russian land for its sins.
But this time you, Emperor Mamai,
came to the Russian land with a large army,
with nine hordes and seventy princes,
and yet you run away to the sea, and with only eight
　　soldiers.
And there is no one to pass the winter with you in the
　　prairie.
Did the Russian princes treat you so badly
that there are no longer princes or commanders with you?
Did they really become drunk with your own blood
on the field of Kulikovo, on the feathergrass?
Go away from us, infidel Mamai!
Go from us, as you went from the Russian forest!"

IX. APODOSIS

We love the Russian land as a mother loves her dear child.
The mother caresses her child and praises it for good deeds,
but she also punishes it for bad deeds.
In the same way, our Lord God
was merciful unto the Russian princes
who fought between the Don and the Dnieper,
unto the Great Prince Dmitry Ivanovich,
unto his brother, Vladimir Andreevich.

And so Princes Dmitry Ivanovich and Vladimir Andreevich
remained victorious on the bone-strewn field of Kulikovo,
on the river Nepriadva.
And Prince Dmitry Ivanovich said:
"It is horrible, brethren, to see the earth
　covered with the corpses of Christians,
　even as the field is covered with haystacks.
　And it is horrible to see that the river Don
　has flowed blood-red for three days."

And then Prince Dmitry Ivanovich commanded:
"Count how many voevodas perished,
    count how many young men were killed."
And Mikhail, a boyar of Moscow replied:
"Our lord, Great Prince Dmitry Ivanovich,
    we are missing forty boyars from Moscow,
    twelve princes from Belozersk,
    thirty *posadniks* from Novgorod,
    twenty boyars from Kolomna,
    forty boyars from Serpukhov,
    thirty magnates from Lithuania,
    twenty boyars from Pereslavl,
    twenty-five boyars from Kostroma,
    thirty-five boyars from Vladimir,
    eight boyars from Suzdal,
    forty boyars from Murom,
    seventy boyars from Riazan,
    thirty-four boyars from Rostov,
    twenty-three boyars from Dmitrov,
    sixty boyars from Mozhaisk,
    thirty boyars from Zvenigorod,
    and fifteen boyars from Uglich.
    And altogether 253,000 Russian men were
    cut down by the infidel Emperor Mamai.[8]
    But God was merciful to the Russian land,
    and still more Tatars fell on the battlefield."
And then Prince Dmitry Ivanovich addressed the dead:
"Fellow princes, boyars, and sons of boyars,
    you have found peace everlasting here, between
    the Don and the Dnieper, on the field of Kulikovo.
    Here you gave your lives for the holy Church,
    for the Russian land and for the Christian faith.
    Forgive me, brethren, and give me your blessing
    for this life and for the life everlasting."

And then Prince Dmitry Ivanovich addressed his brother:
"Let us go, my brother, Vladimir Andreevich,
    back to the Russian land,
    back to the glorious city of Moscow.
    And let us rule there on our throne,
    for we have won glory and veneration.
    Glory be to God!"

[8] Actually, the Russian casualties were barely higher than 100,000

25. Serapion of Vladimir

ʀᴀᴘɪᴏɴ of Vladimir is one of the outstanding Russian writers
the first century under the Tatar yoke. Probably of southern
gin, Serapion was abbot of the Kievan Crypt Monastery at
ᴇ time of the Tatar invasion, and later became Bishop of
adimir, the capital city of the Vladimir-Suzdal principality.
ter the invasion, Vladimir became a new nucleus for Russian
tional life and culture. Bishop Serapion died in 1275.

The eloquent homilies of Serapion are distinguished by their
ᴣhly rhetorical style, and are composed principally of short,
ʏthmic sentences. Very often these sentences are rhymed and
ᴐw repetition of an initial word or syllable through several
es. These characteristics tend to convey a sense of poetic
ᴉty.

The first sermon is entitled *Sermon on the Merciless Heathens.*
the term "merciless heathens" Serapion refers to those Chris-
ᴉs who do not follow the commandments of God and are not
ᴂritable to their fellowmen. In the second sermon, *Sermon on
ᴉens,* Serapion speaks of God's wrath, which has manifested
ᴇlf in earthquakes, conflagrations, and the Tatars' invasion of
 Russian land.

The old Russian texts used as the basis for this translation can
 found in *Serapion Vladimirskii, russkii propovednik XII veka*
 E. V. Petukhov, St. Petersburg, 1888.

◆ ◆ ◆

SERMON ON THE MERCILESS HEATHENS

ᴇet us contemplate, brethren, our Lord's love for men.
ᴉow does he try to bring us to himself?
ᴡhat commandments does he place upon us?
ᴡhat words does he chastise us with?
ᴇt, in spite of this, we do not turn to him.

ᴉe has seen our trespasses multiply.
ᴉe has seen us forsake his commandments.
ᴍany admonitions have we heard from him.
ᴍany fears has he inspired in us.

Many of his servants has he enlightened,
Yet what man has become the better for all this?

Then he released upon us the merciless heathens,
violent heathens, people having mercy neither
for the young,
for the weak and aged,
nor for infants.
The wrath of the Lord has descended upon us
even as David said: "He cast upon them the fierceness of
    anger."

The sacred churches were destroyed.
The sacred vessels were defiled.
The saints were trodden upon.
The prelates were victims of the sword.
The bodies of holy monks became food for birds.
The blood of our priests and brothers,
as if it were water, soaked into the earth.
The strength of our princes and voevodas has disappeared.
Our valiant warriors, seized with great fear, have fled.
Many of our brothers and our children
have been led into captivity.
Weeds overgrow our villages.
Our pride has been humbled.
Our serenity has vanished.
Our wealth was taken from us by the heathens,
inheriting the fruits of our labors.
Our land has become the property of foreigners.
Our land taken from us,
we became the objects of the jibes
of those who live beyond our lands.

Then we realized that
God's wrath is like a torrent from heaven.
Yet we brought his anger upon ourselves.
His favor abandoned us,
and we became deprived of his merciful vigilance.
And now there is no misfortune which will pass us by.
And now we are punished without surcease.
Yet we do not turn to God.
We do not rue our trespasses.
We do not forsake our malevolent ways.
We do not cleanse ourselves of sin,

forgetting the awesome castigation meted out upon our land.
Being reduced to paucity, we act grandiosely.
And therefore evil forces will not cease to torment us.
Envy has increased and wickedness has overcome us.
Pride has turned our heads.
Hatred for friends has taken root in our hearts.
Avarice for possessions has enslaved us
and does not permit us to have mercy upon orphans,
nor does it permit us to be human beings.
We are predatory beasts desiring flesh to appease their
    hunger.
Nothing would prevent us from seizing the possessions of
    others,
even if it came to killing.
But even the beasts are satiated, after having eaten,
but we cannot appease our hunger,
for, when we have gained one thing,
we desire only another.

For wealth rightly come by, God will not be angered,
but as the prophet said:
  "The Lord looked down from heaven
    to see if they were any that did
    understand and seek God."
And he saw that they had all gone astray.
  "Have they no knowledge,
    these evildoers who eat up my people
    as if they eat bread?"

And Apostle Paul unendingly admonished:
  "Brothers, refrain from evil and dark deeds,
    for usurer-robbers will be judged with the idolaters."
And what did God say to Moses?
  "You shall not afflict any widow or orphan.
    If you do afflict them, and they cry out to me,
    I will surely hear their cry;
    and my wrath will burn,
    and I will kill you with the sword."

And now that prophecy has been fulfilled,
for didn't we perish by the sword
and not once, but twice?
What can we do to end the evils which oppress us?
Remember the words of the Holy Scriptures:

to love each other,
to be charitable to all men,
to love thy neighbor as thyself,
to keep the body pure
so that it will not be defiled by lechery;
to cleanse the body with penitence,
if it has been defiled,
to be free of haughtiness,
to render good for evil.

No one does the Lord hate more than the rancorous,
for they will say: "Our Father, forgive us our trespasses,"
yet they themselves will not forgive others.
It is clearly written: "And with what measure you mete,
so shall it be measured to you again."

SERMON ON OMENS

The blessing of the Lord be with you!
Brethren, you have heard what the
Lord himself said in the Gospel:
  "And there shall be signs in the sun,
    and in the moon, and in the stars,
    and there will be earthquakes in many places,
    and famines."

This prophecy of our Lord
has now been fulfilled in our days.
Many times have we seen the sun extinguished,
the moon darkened,
and the stars disquieted.
And recently with our own eyes
have we seen the quaking of the earth.[1]
Now the earth, firm and immovable from time immemorial
by the will of God,
is today moved, quaking because of our sins,
unable to withstand our evil ways.

We have obeyed neither the Gospel
nor the Apostles,
nor the prophets,
nor those enlightened in God's ways:

[1] According to the chronicles, an earthquake occurred in 1230
just six years before the Tatar invasion of Russia.

Basil and Gregory the Theologians,
John Chrysostom,
and the other blessed fathers
by whom the Faith was upheld,
the heretics were driven out,
and God made known to all the lands.
They have taught us without surcease,
but we are living in evil ways.

For this does God punish us,
bringing upon us calamities and earthquakes.
He no longer chastizes us with words,
but punishes us with afflictions.
God has castigated us in all ways,
yet he has not dispelled our evil ways.
Now he shakes the earth and makes it quake,
wishing to shake, like leaves from a tree,
our evil ways from the earth.
If any should declare that there have been earthquakes
    before,
I should not deny it.
But what has happened to us after the earthquakes?
Were there not famines, plagues, and numerous wars?
But we did not repent.
Thus, by the will of God,
there fell upon us a merciless people
who devastated our land,
took entire cities off to captivity,
destroyed our holy churches,
put our fathers and brothers to death,
and defiled our mothers and sisters.
Now, brethren, that we have experienced such calamities,
let us pray to the Lord, and repent,
lest we incur the wrath of God even more,
and thus bring upon us an even greater castigation.

Much is still wanting in our repentance and contrition.
If we turn from dissolute and merciless judgments,
if we turn from bloody usury,
and from greed, thieving, blasphemy, lies,
slander, malediction, denunciations, and other diabolical ways;
if we turn away from all these,
I know full well that good times will come to us,
both in this life and the next.

For the Lord himself has said:
 "Turn unto me, and I will turn to you.
  Refrain from all evil things,
  and I will keep all afflictions from you."
When will we turn from sins?
Let us spare ourselves and our children.
When have we seen so many deaths?
Many were taken away before they could care for their
  houses.
Many lay down to sleep in the evening,
never to rise again.
Be fearful of such a sudden death, brethren.
If we follow the ways of God,
He will comfort us with his solace,
He will cherish us as his own children,
He will remove the burden of our earthly grief,
He will give us peace in the next life,
where we shall know elation and unending joy
with those who do the will of God.

I have told you many things, brethren and children,
but I perceive that our afflictions will neither lessen
nor change, for many take no heed,
acting as if they deemed themselves immortal.
I am afraid that the prophecy of the Lord
will come to pass for such people.
If I had not told them of God's ways,
they would not have sinned in their ignorance,
but I have told them, and now
there can be no pardoning of their sins.
And so I repeat again to you
that if we do not change our ways,
we shall have no pardoning before God.

I, your sinful pastor,
have followed the command of the Lord
in giving his word to you.

LIVES OF SAINTS AND
BIOGRAPHICAL TALES

26. *Epiphanius the Wise*

THE names of Epiphanius the Wise, St. Stephen of Perm, St.
Sergius of Radonezh, and the great painter Andrey Rublev
signify the Russian spiritual and cultural revival of the late
fourteenth and early fifteenth centuries. St. Sergius, and to
some extent St. Stephen, gave a new impetus to Russian monasticism. St. Sergius became the holy patron of Muscovite Russia.
His spirit of humility, his contemplation and unending prayers
inspired and comforted the Russian people of the late Middle
Ages. The wonderful icons and frescoes of Andrey Rublev
offered a harmonius and colorful expression of the spirit of
complete serenity and humility. For the Russian people these
icons became the finest achievement of religious art and the
highest expression of Russian spirituality. A contemporary of
Andrey Rublev, Epiphanius the Wise, described the lives of St.
Sergius and St. Stephen. In these works he made wide use of new
literary devices, and perfected a completely new style of writing.
Thus a new page in Russian literary history appeared.

Epiphanius gives a consistent, detailed, and well-organized
account of the lives of these two saints. His main purpose in
writing these biographical works was not to give an account of
the life and deeds of each saint, but to portray an ideal type of
sanctity. He endowed the heroes of his *vitae* with a number of
general traits that he describes in lengthy panegyrics, containing
a great number of epithets. The literary style that Epiphanius
the Wise perfected was termed "weaving of words" (*pletenie
sloves*, in Russian). In this style sentences are nearly deprived
of verbs, consisting almost entirely of the adjectives and nouns
that characterize the deeds and humility of the saints. Another
feature of Epiphanius' "word-weaving" is the abundance of
neologisms formed by nouns or combinations of nouns and adjectives, such as "songbeautifier," rather than "beautifier of
songs."

Particularly representative of this style is the *Panegyric to St.
Stephen of Perm*. Stephen of Perm was a well-known fourteenth-
century missionary who converted the Finnic tribe of Permians

to Christianity. He also created a Permian alphabet, thus be
coming the founder of the Permian written tradition. The tex
of the present translation is based on the Russian text of th
Life of St. Stephen of Perm published by V. G. Druzhinin ir
*Zhitie sv. Stefana episkopa Permskago, napisannoe Epifaniem
Premudrym*, St. Petersburg, 1897.

The life of St. Sergius, which likewise abounds in epithet
and lengthy panegyrics, was reworked in the fifteenth century
by Pachomius the Serb. The present translation is taken fron
the work *St. Sergius, Builder of Russia* by Nicholas Zernov, anc
is based upon the simplified Russian text of G. P. Fedotov, wh
removed the panegyrics and especially cumbersome passages
Even though there have been some stylistic deletions, the over
all meaning and continuity of the work remain.

✦ ✦ ✦

PANEGYRIC TO ST. STEPHEN OF PERM

My father, lord, and bishop, although you have passed away
I should like to sing your praises with my heart, with m
tongue, and with my mind. When you were alive, I often wa
your annoyance, but now I am your panegyrist; and sometime
I would argue with you about happenings and works, abou
some verses or some lines, but now, remembering your endurin
patience, your great reasoning, and your blessed humility,
humble myself; I cry, shedding tears.

And now, how shall I call you, my bishop?
How shall I name you?
How shall I appeal to you?
How shall I announce you?
How shall I regard you?
How shall I proclaim you?
How shall I praise you?
How shall I esteem you?
How shall I gratify you?
How shall I present you?
How shall I weave lauds to you?

Shall I call you a prophet,
since you prophesied prophetic prophecies,
and, like a prophet, explained the hopes of the prophets
and among the people, faithless and unlearned,
you were a prophet?

Shall I call you an Apostle,
since you performed apostolic deeds
and, acting like an Apostle, following the examples of
  Apostles,
acted, following in the steps of the Apostles?

Shall I call you a lawgiver or a lawmaker,
since you gave the law to the lawless,
brought faith to the lawless,
and established the law among them?

Shall I call you the Baptist,
since you baptized many
who came to you to be baptized?

Shall I call you a preacher, since,
like a herald who announces in the town square,
you loudly preached the word of God to the heathens?

Shall I call you an evangelist,
since you proclaimed grace to them
and the Holy Evangel of Christ,
and performed many deeds of the annunciator of grace?

Shall I call you bishop,
since you were the great archbishop and the eldest
  bishop,
since you consecrated priests in your land,
and since you were above all other priests?

Shall I call you a teacher,
since you taught the heathens who had gone astray,
since you brought the faith to the heathens
and taught men who were unlearned?

Shall I call you a sufferer or a martyr,
since, like a martyr, you surrendered yourself
into the hands of men who were cruel in torturing,
since you were as a sheep among wolves,
since you accepted martyrdom, suffering, and torment?

And I, a great and unlearned sinner,
following the words that eulogize you,
do knit words and create words,

attempting to glorify you with words.
Gathering the words of praise,
and adding and weaving words,
I ask: How shall I eulogize you?
Shall I call you
    the pastor of those who have gone astray,
    the redeemer of those who have perished,
    the teacher of those who were enticed,
    the leader of those whose sight has been darkened,
    the cleanser of those who have been defiled,
    the guardian of the soldiers,
    the consoler of those who are afflicted,
    the nourisher of those who hunger,
    the provider for those in need,
    the punisher of those who are simpleminded,
    the sustainer of the offended,
    the one who prays for others fervently,
    the intercessor for the faithful,
    the savior of the heathen,
    the curser of demons,
    the breaker of idols,
    the destroyer of graven images,
    the servant of God,
    the upholder of wisdom,
    the lover of philosophy,
    the protector of chastity,
    the defender of the truth,
    the writer of books,
    the creator of Permian letters?

Many epithets have you received, O Bishop!
Many titles have you won!
Many gifts have you deserved!
Many blessings have enriched you!

THE LIFE, ACTS, AND MIRACLES OF OUR REVERED AND HOLY FATHER ABBOT SERGIUS

I. CHILDHOOD

Our holy Father Sergius was born of noble, Orthodox, devout parents. His father was named Cyril and his mother Mary. They found favor with God; they were honorable in the sight of God and man, and abounded in those virtues which are well-pleasing unto God.

Cyril had three sons, Stephen, Bartholomew, and Peter, whom he brought up in strict piety and purity. Stephen and Peter quickly learned to read and write, but the second boy did not so easily learn to write, and worked slowly and inattentively; his master taught him with care, but the boy could not put his mind to his studies, nor understand, nor do the same as his companions who were studying with him. As a result he suffered from the many reproaches of his parents, and still more from the punishments of his teacher and the ridicule of his companions. The boy often prayed to God in secret and with many tears: "O Lord, give me understanding of this learning. Teach me, Lord, enlighten and instruct me." His reverence for God prompted him to pray that he might receive knowledge from God and not from men.

One day his father sent him to seek for a lost foal. On his way he met a monk, a venerable elder, a stranger, a priest, with the appearance of an angel. This stranger was standing beneath an oak tree, praying devoutly and with much shedding of tears. The boy, seeing him, humbly made a low obeisance, and awaited the end of his prayers.

The venerable monk, when he had ended his orisons, glanced at the boy and, conscious that he beheld the chosen vessel of the Holy Spirit, he called him to his side, blessed him, bestowed on him a kiss in the name of Christ, and asked: "What art thou seeking, or what dost thou want, child?"

The boy answered, "My soul desires above all things to understand the Holy Scriptures. I have to study reading and writing, and I am sorely vexed that I cannot learn these things. Will you, holy Father, pray to God for me, that he will give me understanding of book-learning?"

The monk raised his hands and his eyes toward heaven, sighed, prayed to God, then said, "Amen."

Taking out from his satchel, as it were some treasure, with three fingers, he handed to the boy what appeared to be a little bit of white wheaten bread of the Holy Sacrament, saying to him: "Take this in thy mouth, child, and eat; this is given thee as a sign of God's grace and for the understanding of Holy Scriptures. Though the gift appears but small, the taste thereof is very sweet."

The boy opened his mouth and ate, tasting a sweetness as of honey, wherefore he said, "Is it not written, How sweet are thy words to my palate, more than honey to my lips, and my soul doth cherish them exceedingly?"

The monk answered and said, "If thou believest, child, more

than this will be revealed to thee; and do not vex thyself
about reading and writing; thou wilt find that from this day
forth the Lord will give thee learning above that of thy brothers
and others of thine own age."

Having thus informed him of divine favor, the monk prepared
to proceed on his way. But the boy flung himself, with his
face to the ground, at the feet of the monk, and besought him
to come and visit his parents, saying, "My parents dearly love
persons such as you are, Father."

The monk, astonished at his faith, accompanied him to his
parents' house. At the sight of the stranger, Cyril and Mary
came out to meet him, and bowed low before him. The monk
blessed them, and they offered him food, but before accepting
any food, the monk went into the chapel, taking with him the
boy whose consecration had been signified even before birth,[1]
and began a recitation of the Canonical Hours, telling the boy
to read the Psalms.

The boy said, "I do not know them, Father."

The monk replied, "I told thee that from today the Lord
would give thee knowledge in reading and writing; read the
Word of God, nothing doubting."

Whereupon, to the astonishment of all present, the boy,
receiving the monk's blessing, began to recite in excellent rhythm; and from that hour he could read. His parents and brothers
praised God, and after accompanying the monk to the house,
placed food before him. Having eaten, and bestowed a blessing
on the parents, the monk was anxious to proceed on his way.
But the parents pleaded, "Reverend Father, hurry not away,
but stay and comfort us and calm our fears. Our humble son,
whom you bless and praise, is to us an object of marvel. While
he was yet in his mother's womb three times he uttered a cry in
church during holy Mass. Wherefore we fear and doubt of what
is to be, and what he is to do."

The holy monk, after considering and becoming aware of
that which was to be, exclaimed, "O blessed pair, O worthy
couple, giving birth to such a child! Why do you fear where
there is no place for fear? Rather rejoice and be glad, for the
boy will be great before God and man, thanks to his life of
godliness."

Having thus spoken the monk left, pronouncing a dark saying that their son would serve the Holy Trinity and would lead

---

[1] According to an introductory passage here omitted, the future
spiritual life of St. Sergius was revealed to his mother shortly before
his birth.

many to an understanding of the divine precepts. They accompanied him to the doorway of their house, when he became of a sudden invisible. Perplexed, they wondered if he had been an angel, sent to give the boy knowledge of reading. After the departure of the monk, it became evident that the boy could read any book, and was altogether changed; he was submissive in all things to his parents, striving to fulfill their wishes, and never disobedient. Applying himself solely to glorifying God, and rejoicing therein, he attended assiduously in God's church, being present daily at Matins, at the Mass, at Vespers. He studied holy scripts, and at all times, in every way, he disciplined his body and preserved himself in purity of body and soul.

Cyril, devout servant of God, led the life of a wealthy and renowned boyar, in the province of Rostov, but in later years he was reduced to poverty. He, like others, suffered from the invasions of Tatar hordes into Russia, from the skirmishes of troops, the frequent demands for tribute, and from repeated bad harvests, in conjunction with the period of violence and disorder which followed the great Tatar war. When the principality of Rostov fell into the hands of the Grand Duke Ivan Danilovich of Moscow, distress prevailed in the town of Rostov, and not least among the princes and boyars.[2] They were deprived of power, of their properties, of honors and rank, of all of which Moscow became the possessor. By order of the Grand Duke they left Rostov, and a certain noble, Vassili Kotchev, with another called Mina, were sent from Moscow to Rostov as pevodas. On arrival in the town of Rostov these two governors imposed a levy on the town and on the inhabitants. A severe persecution followed, and many of the remaining inhabitants of Rostov were constrained to surrender their estates to the Muscovites, in exchange for which they received wounds and humiliations, and went forth emptyhanded and as veriest beggars. In brief, Rostov was subjected to every possible humiliation, even to the hanging, head downward, of their governor, Averky, one of the chief boyars of Rostov. Seeing and hearing of all this, terror spread among the people, not only in the town of Rostov but in all the surrounding country. Cyril, God's devout servant, avoided further misfortune by escaping from his native town. He assembled his entire household and family and with them

---

[2] Grand Duke Ivan Danilovich of Moscow (1301–1341), called Kalita ("Moneybag"), was the actual founder of the Muscovite state. He spread his reign over a considerable part of the land between the Oka and Volga rivers. Rostov was an important city of the Volga.

removed from Rostov to Radonezh,[3] where he settled near th
church dedicated to the Birth of Christ, which is still standin
to this day.

II. The Hermitage

Cyril's two sons, Stephen and Peter, married, but his secon
son, Bartholomew, would not contemplate marriage, being de
sirous of becoming a monk. He often expressed this wish to hi
father, but his parents said to him, "My son, wait a little an
bear with us; we are old, poor and sick, and we have no one t
look after us, for both your brothers are married." The won
drous youth gladly promised to care for them to the end of thei
days, and from henceforth strove for his parents' well-being
until they entered the monastic life and went one to a mon
astery, and the other to a convent. They lived but a few years
and passed away to God. Blessed Bartholomew laid his parent
in their graves, mourned for them forty days, then returned t
his house. Calling his younger brother Peter, he bestowed hi
share of his father's inheritance on him, retaining nothing fo
himself. The wife of his elder brother, Stephen, died also, leav
ing two sons, Clement and Ivan. Stephen soon renounced th
world and became a monk in the Holy Mother of God Mon
astery at Khotkov.

Blessed Bartholomew now came to him, and begged him t
accompany him in the search for some desert place. Stephe
assented, and he and the saint together explored many parts o
the forest, till finally they came to a waste space in the middl
of the forest, near a stream. After inspecting the place the
obeyed the voice of God and were satisfied. Having prayed, the
set about chopping wood and carrying it. First they built a hu
and then constructed a small chapel. When the chapel wa
finished and the time had come to dedicate it, Blessed Bartholo
mew said to Stephen, "Now, my lord and eldest brother by birt
and by blood, tell me, in honor of whose feast shall this chape
be, and to which saint shall we dedicate it?"

Stephen answered: "Why do you ask me, and why put me t
the test? You were chosen of God while you were yet in you
mother's womb, and he gave a sign concerning you before eve
you were born, that the child would be a disciple of the Blesse
Trinity, and not he alone would have devout faith, for he woul

---

[3] Radonezh was a village that belonged to St. Sergius' family an
after which his family was named. This village, some nine miles fro
the Monastery of St. Sergius, is the present-day industrial city o
Zagorsk.

ad many others and teach them to believe in the Holy Trinity.
t behooves you, therefore, to dedicate a chapel above all others
to the Blessed Trinity."

The favored youth gave a deep sigh and said, "To tell the
ruth, my lord and brother, I asked you because I felt I must,
although I wanted and thought likewise as you do, and desired
with my whole soul to erect and dedicate this chapel to the
Blessed Trinity, but out of humility I inquired of you." And
he went forthwith to obtain the blessing of the ruling prelate
or its consecration. From the town came the priest sent by
Theognost, Metropolitan of Kiev and all Russia, and the chapel
was consecrated and dedicated to the Holy Trinity in the reign
of the Grand Duke Simon Ivanovich,[4] we believe in the beginning of his reign. The chapel being now built and dedicated,
Stephen did not long remain in the wilderness with his brother.
He realized soon all the labors in this desert place, the hardships, the all-pervading need and want, and that there were no
means of satisfying hunger and thirst, nor any other necessity.
As yet no one came to the saint, nor brought him anything, for
at this time, nowhere around was there any village, nor house,
nor people; neither was there road or pathway, but everywhere
n all sides were forest and wasteland. Stephen, seeing this, was
roubled, and he decided to leave the wilderness, and with it
his own brother the saintly desert-lover and desert-dweller. He
went from thence to Moscow, and when he reached this city
e settled in the Monastery of the Epiphany, found a cell, and
dwelt in it, exercising himself in virtue. Hard labor was to him
joy, and he passed his time in ascetic practices in his cell,
disciplining himself by fasting and praying, refraining from all
indulgence, even from drinking beer. Alexis, the future metropolitan, who at this time had not been raised to the rank of
bishop, was living in the monastery, leading a quiet monastic
fe. Stephen and he spent much time together in spiritual
exercises, and they sang in the choir side by side. The Grand
Duke Simon came to hear of Stephen and the godly life he led,
nd commanded the Metropolitan Theognost to ordain him
priest and, later, to appoint him abbot of the monastery. Aware
of his great virtues, the Grand Duke also appointed him as his
confessor.

Our saint, Sergius, had not taken monastic vows at this time

---

[4] Grand Duke Simon Ivanovich the Proud (1323–1353) was the
on of Ivan Kalita. Metropolitan Theognost, the former Metropolitan
of Kiev, lived in Moscow and was one of the upholders of the rise of
Muscovy.

for, as yet, he had not enough experience of monasteries, an
of all that is required of a monk. After a while, however, h
invited a spiritual elder, who held the dignity of priest an
abbot, named Mitrofan, to come and visit him in his sol
tude. In great humility he entreated him, "Father, may th
love of God be with us, and give me the tonsure of a monl
From childhood have I loved God and set my heart on him
these many years, but my parents' needs withheld me. Now, m
lord and father, I am free from all bonds, and I thirst, as th
hart thirsteth for the springs of living water."

The abbot forthwith went into the chapel with him, an
gave him the tonsure on the 7th day of October on the fea
day of the blessed martyrs Sergius and Bacchus. And Sergiu
was the name he received as monk. In those days it was th
custom to give to the newly tonsured monk the name of th
saint whose feast day it happened to be. Our saint was twenty
three years old when he joined the order of monks. Blesse
Sergius, the newly tonsured monk, partook of the Holy Sacra
ment and received grace and the gift of the Holy Spirit. Fron
one whose witness is true and sure, we are told that whe
Sergius partook of the Holy Sacrament the chapel was filled wit
a sweet odor; and not only in the chapel, but all around was th
same fragrant smell. The saint remained in the chapel seve
days, touching no food other than one consecrated loaf give
him by the abbot, refusing all else and giving himself up to fast
ing and prayer, having on his lips the Psalms of David.

When Mitrofan bade farewell, St. Sergius in all humilit
said to him: "Give me your blessing, and pray regarding m
solitude; and instruct one living alone in the wilderness how t
pray to the Lord God; how to remain unharmed; how to wrestl
with the evil and with his own temptations to pride, for I am
but a novice and a newly tonsured monk."

The abbot was astonished and almost afraid. He replied
"You ask of me concerning that which you know no less we
than we do, O Reverend Father." After discoursing with him fo
a while on spiritual matters, and commending him to God
Mitrofan went away, leaving St. Sergius alone to silence an
the wilderness.

Who can recount his labors? Who can number the trials h
endured living alone in the wildnerness?

Under different forms and from time to time the devi
wrestled with the saint, but the demons beset St. Sergius i
vain; no matter what visions they evoked, they failed to over
come the firm and fearless spirit of the ascetic. At one momen

it was Satan who laid his snares; at another, incursions of wild beasts took place, for many were the wild animals inhabiting this wilderness. Some of these remained at a distance; others came near the saint, surrounded him and even sniffed him. In particular a bear used to come to the holy man. Seeing the animal did not come to harm him, but in order to get some food, the saint brought a small slice of bread from his hut, and placed it on a log or stump, so the bear learned to come for the meal thus prepared for him, and having eaten it went away again. If there was no bread, and the bear did not find his usual slice, he would wait about for a long while and look around on all sides, rather like some moneylender waiting to receive payment of his debt. At this time Sergius had no variety of foods in the wildnerness, only bread and water from the spring, and a great scarcity of these. Often, bread was not to be found; then both he and the bear went hungry. Sometimes, although there was but one slice of bread, the saint gave it to the bear, being unwilling to disappoint him of his food.

He diligently read the Holy Scriptures to obtain a knowledge of all virtue, in his secret meditations training his mind in a longing for eternal bliss. Most wonderful of all, none knew the measure of his ascetic and godly life spent in solitude. God, the beholder of all hidden things, alone saw it.

Whether he lived two years or more in the wilderness alone we do not know; God knows only. The Lord, seeing his very great faith and patience, took compassion on him and, desirous of relieving his solitary labors, put into the hearts of certain god-fearing monks to visit him.

The saint inquired of them, "Are you able to endure the hardships of this place, hunger and thirst, and every kind of want?"

They replied, "Yes, Reverend Father, we are willing with God's help and with your prayers."

Holy Sergius, seeing their faith and zeal, marveled, and said: "My brethren, I desired to dwell alone in the wildnerness and, furthermore, to die in this place. If it be God's will that there shall be a monastery in this place, and that many brethren will be gathered here, then may God's holy will be done. I welcome you with joy, but let each one of you build himself a cell. Furthermore, let it be known unto you, if you come to dwell in the wilderness, the beginning of righteousness is the fear of the Lord."

To increase his own fear of the Lord he spent day and night in the study of God's word. Moreover, young in years, strong and healthy in body, he could do the work of two men or more.

The devil now strove to wound him with the darts of con-
cupiscence. The saint, aware of these enemy attacks, disciplined
his body and exercised his soul, mastering it with fasting, and
thus was he protected by the grace of God. Although not yet
raised to the office of priesthood, dwelling in company with the
brethren, he was present daily with them in church for the reciting of the offices, Nocturnes, Matins, the Hours, and Vespers.
For the Mass a priest, who was an abbot, came from one of
the villages. At first Sergius did not wish to be raised to the
priesthood and especially he did not want to become an abbot;
this was by reason of his extreme humility. He constantly remarked that the beginning and root of all evil lay in pride of
rank, and ambition to be an abbot. The monks were but few in
number, about a dozen. They constructed themselves cells, not
very large ones, within the enclosure, and put up gates at the
entrance. Sergius built four cells with his own hands, and performed other monastic duties at the request of the brethren; he
carried logs from the forest on his shoulders, chopped them up,
and carried them into the cells. The monastery, indeed, came to
be a wonderful place to look upon. The forest was not far distant from it as now it is; the shade and the murmur of trees
hung above the cells; around the church was a space of trunks
and stumps; here many kinds of vegetables were sown.

But to return to the exploits of St. Sergius. He flayed the
grain and ground it in the mill, baked the bread and cooked the
food, cut out shoes and clothing and stitched them; he drew
water from the spring flowing nearby, and carried it in two
pails on his shoulders, and put water in each cell. He spent the
night in prayer, without sleep, feeding only on bread and water,
and that in small quantities; and never spent an idle hour.

III. The Humble Abbot

Within the space of a year the abbot who had given the tonsure to St. Sergius fell ill, and after a short while, he passed out
of this life. Then God put it into the hearts of the brethren to
go to blessed Sergius, and to say to him: "Father, we cannot
continue without an abbot. We desire you to be our abbot, and
the guide of our souls and bodies."

The saint sighed from the bottom of his heart, and replied,
"I have had no thought of becoming abbot, for my soul longs
to finish its course here as an ordinary monk." The brethren
urged him again and again to be their abbot; finally, overcome
by his compassionate love, but groaning inwardly, he said:
"Fathers and brethren, I will say no more against it, and will

(*Above*) St. Sergius. A portrait worked in embroidery of
about 1450. (*Below*) St. Sergius and his monks build a
fence around the monastery. A sixteenth-century miniature
from the *Life of St. Sergius*.

submit to the will of God. He sees into our hearts and souls.
We will go into the town, to the bishop."

Alexis, the Metropolitan of all Russia, was living at this time
in Constantinople, and he had nominated Bishop Athanasius
of Volynia in his stead in the town of Pereiaslavl. Our blessed
Sergius went, therefore, to the bishop, taking with him two
elders; and entering into his presence made a low obeisance.
Athanasius rejoiced exceedingly at seeing him, and kissed him
in the name of Christ. He had heard tell of the saint and of
his beginning of good deeds, and he spoke to him of the work-
ings of the Spirit. Our Blessed Father Sergius begged the bishop
to give them an abbot, and a guide of their souls.

The venerable Athanasius replied, "Thyself, son and brother,
God called in thy mother's womb. It is thou who wilt be father
and abbot of thy brethren." Blessed Sergius refused, insisting
on his unworthiness, but Athanasius said to him, "Beloved,
thou hast acquired all virtue save obedience."

Blessed Sergius, bowing low, replied: "May God's will be
done. Praise be the Lord forever and forever." They all answered, "Amen."

Without delay the holy bishop, Athanasius, led blessed Sergius
to the church, and ordained him subdeacon and then deacon.
The following morning the saint was raised to the dignity of
priesthood, and was told to say the holy liturgy and to offer the
bloodless Sacrifice. Later, taking him apart, the bishop spoke to
him of the teachings of the Apostles and of the holy fathers, for
the edification and guidance of souls. After bestowing on him a
kiss in the name of Christ, he sent him forth, in very deed an
abbot, pastor, and guardian, and physician of his spiritual
brethren. He had not taken upon himself the rank of abbot; he
received the leadership from God; he had not sought it, nor
striven for it; he did not obtain it by payment, as do others who
have pride of rank, chasing hither and thither, plotting and
snatching power from one another. God himself led his chosen
disciple and exalted him to the dignity of abbot.

Our revered father and abbot Sergius returned to his monastery, to the abode dedicated to the Holy Trinity, and the
brethren, coming out to meet him, bowed low to the ground
before him. He blessed them, and said: "Brethren, pray for me.
I am altogether ignorant, and I have received a talent from the
Highest, and I shall have to render an account of it, and of the
flock committed to me."

There were twelve brethren when he first became abbot, and
he was the thirteenth. And this number remained, neither in-

reasing nor diminishing, until Simon, the archimandrite of Smolensk, arrived among them. From that time onward their numbers constantly increased. This wondrous man, Simon, was chief archimandrite, excellent, eminent, abounding in virtue. Having heard of our Reverend Father Sergius' way of life, he laid aside honors, left the goodly city of Smolensk, and arrived at the monastery where, greeting our Reverend Father Sergius with the greatest humility, he entreated him to allow him to live under him and his rules in all submission and obedience: and he offered the estate he owned as a gift to the abbot for the benefit of the monastery. Blessed Sergius welcomed him with great joy. Simon lived many years, submissive and obedient, abounding in virtue, and died in advanced old age.

Stephen, the saint's brother, came with his younger son, Ivan, from Moscow and, presenting him to Abbot Sergius, asked him to give him the tonsure. Abbot Sergius did so, and gave him the name of Theodore; from his earliest years the boy had been taught abstinence, piety, and chastity, following his uncle's precepts; according to some accounts he was given the tonsure when he was ten years old, others say twelve. People from many parts, towns and countries, came to live with Abbot Sergius, and their names are written in the book of life. The monastery bit by bit grew in size. It is recorded in the *Paterikon* —that is to say, in the book of the early fathers of the Church— that the holy fathers in assembly prophesied about later generations, saying that the last would be weak. But, of the later generations, God made Sergius as strong as one of the early fathers. God made him a lover of hard work, and to be the head over a great number of monks. From the time he was appointed abbot, the holy Mass was sung every day. He himself baked the holy bread; first he flayed and ground the wheat, sifted the flour, kneaded and fermented the dough; he entrusted the making of the holy bread to no one. He also cooked the grains for the "kutia," and he also made the candles. Although occupying the chief place as abbot, he did not alter in any way his monastic rules. He was lowly and humble with all people, and was an example to all.

He never sent away anyone who came to him for the tonsure, neither old nor young, nor rich nor poor; he received them all with fervent joy; but he did not give them the tonsure at once. He who would be a monk was ordered, first, to put on a long, black cloth garment and to live with the brethren until he got accustomed to all the monastic rules; then, later, he was given full monk's attire of cloak and hood. Finally, when he was

deemed worthy, he was allowed the "schema," the mark of th
ascetic.

After Vespers, and late at night, especially on long dar
nights, the saint used to leave his cell and go the round of th
monk's cells. If he heard anyone saying his prayers, or makin
genuflections, or busy with his own handiwork, he was gratifie
and gave thanks to God. If, on the other hand, he heard two c
three monks chatting together, or laughing, he was displase
rapped on the door or window, and passed on. In the mornin
he would send for them and, indirectly, quietly and gently, b
means of some parable, reprove them. If he was a humble an
submissive brother he would quickly admit his fault and, bov
ing low before St. Sergius, would beg his forgiveness. If, instea
he was not a humble brother, and stood erect thinking he wa
not the person referred to, then the saint, with patience, woul
make it clear to him, and order him to do a public penance. I
this way they all learned to pray to God assiduously; not t
chat with one another after Vespers, and to do their own hand
work with all their might; and to have the Psalms of David a
day on their lips.

In the beginning, when the monastery was first built, mar
were the hardships and privations. A main road lay a long wa
off, and wilderness surrounded the monastery. Here the monk
lived, it is believed, for fifteen years. Then, in the time of th
Grand Duke Ivan Ivanovich,[5] Christians[6] began to arrive fror
all parts and to settle in the vicinity. The forest was cut dowr
there was no one to prevent it; the trees were hewn down, non
were spared, and the forest was converted into an open plain a
we now see it. A village was built, and houses; and visitors cam
to the monastery bringing their countless offerings. But in th
beginning, when they settled in this place, they all suffere
great privations. At times there was no bread or flour, and a
means of subsistence was lacking; at times there was no win
for the Eucharist, nor incense, nor wax candles. The monk
sang Matins at dawn with no lights save that of a single birc
or pine torch.

One day there was a great scarcity of bread and salt in th

[5] Grand Duke Ivan Ivanovich, son of Ivan Kalita and brother c
Simon the Proud, reigned from 1353–1359. His son, Dmitry, was th
hero of the Battle of Kulikovo.

[6] The word "Christians" here refers to the Russians themselves; su
rounded by Moslem, pagans, and unorthodox Christians, the Russian
called themselves Christians. This is reflected in the Russian word fo
peasant—krest'ianin.

whole monastery. The saintly abbot gave orders to all the brethren that they were not to go out, nor beg from the laity, but to remain patiently in the monastery and await God's compassion. He himself spent three or four days without any food. On the fourth day, at dawn, taking an ax, he went to one of the elders, by name Danila, and said to him: "I have heard say that you want to build an entrance in front of your cell. See, I have come to build it for you, so that my hands shall not remain idle."

Danila replied, "Yes, I have been waiting it for a long while, and am awaiting the carpenter from the village; but I am afraid to employ you, for you will require a large payment from me."

Sergius said to him: "I do not require a large sum of money. Have you any mildewed loaves? I very much want to eat some such loaves. I do not ask from you anything else. Where will you find another such carpenter as I?"

Danila brought him a few mildewed loaves, saying, "This is all I have."

Sergius said: "That will be enough, and to spare. But hide it until evening. I take no pay before work is done."

Saying which, and tightening his belt, he chopped and worked all day, cut planks and put up the entrance. At the close of day, Danila brought him the sieveful of the promised loaves. Sergius, offering a prayer and grace, ate the bread and drank some water. He had neither soup nor salt; the bread was both dinner and supper.

Several of the brethren noticed something in the nature of a faint breath of smoke issuing from his lips, and turning to one another they said, "Oh, brother, what patience and self-control has this man!"

But one of the monks, not having had anything to eat for two days, murmured against Sergius, and went up to him and said: "Why this moldy bread? Why should we not go outside and beg for some bread? If we obey you we shall perish of hunger. Tomorrow morning we will leave this place and go hence and not return; we cannot any longer endure such want and scarcity."

Not all of them complained, only one brother, but because of this one, Sergius, seeing they were enfeebled and in distress, convoked the whole brotherhood and gave them instruction from Holy Scriptures: "God's Grace cannot be given without trials; after tribulations comes joy. It is written, at evening there shall be weeping but in the morning gladness. You, at present, have no bread or food, and tomorrow you will enjoy an abundance."

And as he was yet speaking there came a rapping at the gates.

The porter, peeping through an aperture, saw that a store of provisions had been brought; he was so overjoyed that he did not open the gates but ran first to St. Sergius to tell him. The saint gave the order at once, "Open the gates quickly, let them come in, and let those persons who have brought the provisions be invited to share the meal"; while he himself, before all else, directed that the *bilo* should be sounded,[7] and with the brethren he went into the church to sing the *Te Deum*. Returning from church, they went into the refectory, and the newly arrived, fresh bread was placed before them. The bread was still warm and soft, and the taste of it was of an unimaginable strange sweetness, as it were honey mingled with juice of barley and spices.

When they had eaten, the saint remarked: "And where is our brother who was murmuring about moldy bread? May he notice that it is sweet and fresh. Let us remember the prophet who said, 'Ashes have I eaten for bread and mixed my drink with tears.'" Then he inquired whose bread it was, and who had sent it. The messengers announced, "A pious layman, very wealthy, living a great distance away, sent it to Sergius and his brotherhood." Again the monks, on Sergius' orders, invited the men to sup with them, but they refused, having to hasten elsewhere.

The monks came to the abbot in astonishment, saying, "Father, how has this wheaten bread, warm and tasting of butter and spices, been brought from far?" The following day more food and drink were brought to the monastery in the same manner. And again on the third day, from a distant country. Abbot Sergius, seeing and hearing this, gave glory to God before all the brethren, saying, "You see, brethren, God provides for everything, and neither does he abandon this place." From this time forth the monks grew accustomed to being patient under trials and privations, enduring all things, trusting in the Lord God with fervent faith, and being strengthened therein by their holy Father Sergius.

According to an account by one of the elders of the monastery, Blessed Sergius never wore new clothing, nor any made of fine material, nor colored, nor white, nor smooth and soft; he wore plain cloth or caftan; his clothing was old and worn, dirty, patched. Once they had in the monastery an ugly, stained, bad bit of cloth, which all the brethren threw aside; one brother had it, kept it for a while and discarded it, so did another, and a third and so on to the seventh. But the saint did not despise it,

[7] Bilo: a wooden or iron rod used to beat a gong, gongs being used in Russia instead of bells.

e gratefully took it, cut it out and made himself a habit, which
e wore, not with disdain but with gratitude, for a whole year,
ll it was worn out and full of holes.

So shabby were his clothes, worse than that of any of the
onks, that several people were misled and did not recognize
im. One day a Christian from a nearby village, who had never
en the saint, came to visit him. The abbot was digging in
e garden. The visitor looked about and asked, "Where is
ergius? Where is the wonderful and famous man?"

A brother replied, "In the garden, digging; wait a while,
ntil he comes in."

The visitor, growing impatient, peeped through an aperture,
nd perceived the saint wearing shabby attire, patched, in holes,
nd face covered with sweat; and he could not believe that this
as he of whom he had heard. When the saint came from the
arden, the monks informed him, "This is he whom you wish
 see."

The visitor turned from the saint and mocked at him: "I
ame to see a prophet and you point out to me a needy-looking
eggar. I see no glory, no majesty and honor about him. He
ears no fine and rich apparel; he has no attendants, no trained
rvants; he is but a needy, indigent beggar."

The brethren, reporting to the abbot, said, "We hardly dare
ll you, Reverend Father, and we would send away your guest
 a good-for-nothing rude fellow; he has been discourteous and
srespectful about you, reproaches us, and will not listen to us."

The holy man, fixing his eyes on the brethren and seeing their
onfusion, said to them: "Do not do so, brethren, for he did not
ome to see you. He came to visit me." And, since he expected
 obeisance from his visitor, he went toward him, humbly
owing low to the ground before him, and blessed and praised
m for his right judgment. Then, taking him by the hand, the
int sat him down at his right hand, and bade him partake of
od and drink. The visitor expressed his regret at not seeing
ergius, whom he had taken the trouble to come and visit; and
s wish had not been fulfilled. The saint remarked, "Be not
d about it, for such is God's Grace that no one ever leaves
is place with a heavy heart."

As he spoke a neighboring prince arrived at the monastery,
ith great pomp, accompanied by retinue of boyars, servants,
d attendants. The armed attendants, who preceded the prince,
ok the visitor by the shoulders and removed him out of sight
 the prince and of Sergius. The prince then advanced and,
om a distance, made a low obeisance to Sergius. The saint

gave him his blessing and, after bestowing a kiss on him, th
both sat down while everyone else remained standing. The vi
tor thrust his way through, and going up to one of those stan
ing by, asked, "Who is the monk sitting on the prince's rig
hand? Tell me."

The man turned to him and said, "Are you then a strang
here? Have you indeed not heard of Blessed Father Sergius?
is he speaking with the prince."

Upon hearing this, the visitor was overcome with remors
and after the prince's departure, taking several of the brethr
to intercede for him, and making a low obeisance before tl
abbot, he said: "Father, I am but a sinner and a great offende
Forgive me and help my unbelief."

The saint readily forgave, and with his blessing and son
words of comfort, he took leave of him. From henceforth, ar
to the end of his days, this man held a true, firm faith in tl
Holy Trinity and in St. Sergius. He left his village a few yea
later, and came to the saint's monastery, where he became
monk, and there spent several years in repentance and amen
ment of life before he passed away to God.

IV. THE MIRACLES

We shall now turn to the miracles God performs through l
elect. Owing to lack of water near the monastery, the brothe
hood suffered great discomfort, which increased with the
numbers and having to carry water from a distance. Some of tl
monks even complained to the abbot, "When you set out
build a monastery on this spot, why did you not observe that
was not near water?" They repeated this query with vexatio
often.

The saint told them: "I intended to worship and pray in tl
place alone. But God willed that a monastery such as th
dedicated to the Holy Trinity, should arise."

Going out of the monastery, accompanied by one of tl
brethren, he made his way through a ravine below the mona
tery, and finding a small pool of rainwater, he knelt down ai
prayed. No sooner had he made the sign of the cross over tl
spot, than a bubbling spring arose, which is still to be seen
this day, and from whence water is drawn to supply every ne
of the monastery.

Many cures have been granted to the faithful from the wate
and people have come from long distances to fetch the wat
and carry it away and to give it to their sick to drink. From tl
time it appeared, and for a number of years, the spring w

led after Sergius. The wise man, not seeking renown, was pleased, and remarked: "Never let me hear that a well is led by my name. I did not give this water; God gave it to us worthy men."

A certain devout Christian living close by the monastery, who believed in St. Sergius, had an only son, a child, who fell ill. The father brought the boy to the monastery, and entreated the saint to pray for him: but while the father was yet speaking the boy died. The man, with his last hope gone, wept and bemoaned, "It would have been better had my son died in my own house." While he went to prepare a grave, the dead child was laid in the saint's cell. The saint felt compassion for this man, and falling on his knees prayed over the dead child. Suddenly the boy came to life, and moved. His father, returning with preparations for the burial, found his son alive, whereupon, flinging himself at the feet of God's servant, he gave him thanks. The saint said to him, "You deceive yourself, man, and do not know what you say. While on your journey hither your son became frozen with cold, and you thought he had died. He has now thawed in the warm cell, and you think he has come to life. No one can rise again from the dead before the Day of Resurrection."

The man however insisted, saying, "Your prayers brought him to life again."

The saint forbade him to say this; "If you noise this abroad you will lose your son altogether." The man promised to tell no one and, taking his son, now restored to health, he went back to his own home. This miracle was made known through the saint's disciples.

Living on the banks of the Volga, a long distance away from the Lavra,[8] was a man who owned great possessions, but who was afflicted incessantly, day and night, by a cruel and evil spirit. Not only did he break iron chains, but ten or more strong men could not hold him. His relatives, hearing tell of the saint, journeyed with him to the monastery, where dwelt the servant of the Lord. When they came to the monastery the madman broke loose from his bonds, and flung himself about, crying, "I will not go, I will not. I will go back from whence I came." They informed the saint, who gave the order to sound the *bilo*, and when the brethren were assembled they sang the *Te Deum*

---

[8] Lavra was the name given a monastery which was independent of local bishops, being under the direct authority of the head of the Russian Church. There were four such monasteries in Russia.

for the sick. The madman grew calmer little by little, and wh
he was led into the monastery, the saint came out of chur
carrying a cross, whereupon the sufferer, with a loud cry, f
from the spot, and flung himself into a pool of rainwater star
ing nearby, exclaiming, "O horrible, O terrible flame." By t
grace of God and the saint's prayers he recovered, and was
stored to his right mind. When they inquired what he mea
by his exclamation, he told them, "When the saint wanted
bless me with the cross, I saw a great flame proceeding fr
him, and it seized hold of me. So I threw myself into the wat
fearing that I should be consumed in the flame."

One day the saint, in accordance with his usual rule, w
keeping vigil and praying for the brotherhood late at night wh
he heard a voice calling, "Sergius!" He was astonished, a
opening the window of the cell he beheld a wondrous visic
A great radiance shone in the heavens; the night sky was ill
mined by its brilliance, exceeding the light of day. A secor
time the voice called: "Sergius! Thou prayest for thy childre
God has heard thy prayer. See and behold great numbers
monks gathered together in the name of the Everlasting Trini
in thy fold, and under thy guidance."

The saint looked and beheld a multitude of beautiful bir
flying, not only on to the monastery, but all around; and
heard a voice saying, "As many birds as thou seest by so ma
will thy flock of disciples increase; and after thy time they w
not grow less if they will follow in thy footsteps." Anxious
have a witness of this vision the saint called aloud for Simc
he being the nearest. Simon ran to him with all haste, but
was not found worthy to behold this vision; he saw no mc
than a ray of its light, but even so was greatly astonished. Fill
with awe and wonder at this glorious vision, they rejoic
together.

V. The Patriarchal Charter

One day some Greeks arrived from Constantinople, sent
the patriarch to visit the saint. Making a deep obeisance th
said to him, "The all-powerful Patriarch of Constantinop
Philotheus, sends you his blessing," and they presented him wi
gifts from the patriarch, a cross and a "paramand," and al
handed him a letter from him.

The saint asked: "Are you sure you have not been sent
someone else? How can I, a sinner, be worthy of such gifts fro
the most illustrious patriarch?"

They replied, "We have indeed been sent to you, ho

Sergius." The elder went then to see the metropolitan, Alexis,[9] and took with him the missive brought from the patriarch. The metropolitan ordered the epistle to be read to him. It ran: "By the Grace of God, the Archbishop of Constantinople, the Ecumenical Patriarch Philotheus, by the Holy Spirit, to our son and fellow servant Sergius. Divine grace and peace, and our blessing be with you. We have heard tell of your godly life dedicated to God, wherefore we greatly praise and glorify God. One thing, however, has not been established: you have not formed a community. Take note, Blessed One, that even the great prophet and our father in God, David, embracing all things with his mind, could not bestow higher praise than when he said, 'But now, however good and however perfect, yet, above all, is abiding together in brotherly love.' Wherefore I counsel you to establish a community. That God's blessing and his grace be always upon you." The elder inquired of the metropolitan, "Revered teacher, what would you have us do?" The metropolitan replied, "With all our heart we approve, and return thanks."

From henceforth life on the basis of community was established in the monastery. The saint, wise pastor, appointed to each brother his duties, one to be cellarer, others to be cooks and bakers, another to care for the sick, and for church duties, an ecclesiarch, and a subecclesiarch, and sacristans, and so forth. He further announced that the ordinances of the holy fathers were to be strictly observed; all things were to be possessed in common, no monk was to hold property of his own.

His community having been established with much wisdom, the numbers of his followers soon increased. Also, the larger the supply of offerings to the monastery, the more hospitality was extended. No person in need ever left the monastery empty-handed; and the saint gave orders that the poor and all strangers were to be allowed to rest in the monastery, and no suppliant to be refused, adding, "If you will follow my precepts and continue in them faithfully, God will reward you, and when I leave this life our monastery will prosper and continue to stand with the Lord's blessing for many years." And to the present day it has remained standing.

[9] Metropolitan Alexis (1353–1378), the son of a boyar from Chernigov in southern Russia, was an outstanding Russian Church leader. He became adviser to Prince Ivan II and Prince Dmitry. Following the policy set by Metropolitan Peter and Theognost, he supported Moscow as the main center of Russian political and spiritual life, and fostered the unification of all Russian lands around Moscow.

VI. The Dissensions

Before long dissension arose; the devil, hating goodness, put about the idea of disputing the authority of Sergius.[10] One Saturday, while Vespers were being sung, and the Abbot Sergius, wearing his vestments, was at the altar, his brother, Stephen, who was standing by the choir, on the left, asked the canonarch, "Who gave you that book?" The canonarch replied, "The abbot gave it to me." The other said, "What has the abbot to do with it? Did not I sit in that place before?" and adding other silly remarks.

Although the saint was standing by the altar, he heard what was said, but he kept silence. When they all came out of church he did not go to his cell; he walked away from the monastery, unknown to all. When he arrived at the monastery of Makrisch,[11] he asked the abbot, Stephen, if one of his monks could lead him to some desert place. Together they searched and finally discovered a beautiful spot close to a river called the Kerzhach. The brotherhood, hearing about the saint, took to visiting him, in twos and threes, and more. Our Father Sergius sent two of his followers to the Metropolitan Alexis, with the request for his blessing and permission to erect a church. Aided by divine favor, a church was erected in a short while, and many brethren gathered there.

Soon several monks from the Holy Trinity, unable any longer to bear the separation from their spiritual father, went to the metropolitan and said: "Holy Lord, we are living like sheep without a shepherd. Command our abbot to return to his monastery, that he may save us from perishing and dying of grief without him."

The metropolitan dispatched two archimandrites, Gerasim and Paul, to the abbot with the message: "Your father, Alexis the Metropolitan, sends you his blessing. He has rejoiced exceedingly to hear that you are living in a distant wilderness. But, return now to the monastery of the Holy Trinity; those persons who were dissatisfied with you shall be removed from the monastery."

Whereupon, hearing this, the saint sent reply, "Tell my lord

[10] These dissensions were apparently caused by St. Sergius' desire to introduce a more disciplined and strictly enforced communal life in the monastery, which was in disagreement with earlier Russian monastic tradition.

[11] Makrisch was another monastery situated about twenty miles from the Monastery of St. Sergius.

the metropolitan, all from his lips, as from those of Christ, I
receive with joy and do disobey in nothing."

The metropolitan, glad at his prompt obedience, instantly
dispatched a priest to consecrate the church to the Annunciation
of the Immaculate and Blessed Virgin, Mother of God. Sergius
selected one of his followers, called Romanus, to be the abbot
of the new monastery, and sent him to the metropolitan to be
raised to the priesthood. The saint then returned to the monastery of the Holy Trinity.

When the news reached the monastery that the saint was
returning, the brethren went out to meet him. On beholding
him it appeared as if a second sun were shining; and they were
so filled with joy that some of the brethren kissed the father's
hands, others his feet, while others seized his clothing and kissed
that. There were loud rejoicing and glorifying God for the return of their father. And what of the father? He rejoiced with
his whole heart at seeing this gathering of his flock.

VII.   ST. STEPHEN OF PERM

Now Bishop Stephen,[12] a god-fearing and devout man, had
for St. Sergius a deep spiritual affection. One day he was traveling from his episcopacy of Perm to the capital, Moscow. The
road along which the bishop journeyed lay about seven miles
from St. Sergius' monastery. When the godly bishop came opposite the saint's monastery, he stopped and said, bowing low
toward the direction of the saint, "Peace be with thee, brother
in God!" The saint, at this hour, was seated at table with his
brethren. Perceiving in spirit what Bishop Stephen was doing,
he rose from the supper table, stood for an instant in prayer,
then bowing said aloud, "Be joyful, thou shepherd of Christ's
flock; the peace of God be always with thee." At the end of
supper his disciples inquired of him what he meant. He openly
told them, "At that hour Bishop Stephen, going on his way to
Moscow, did reverence to the Holy Trinity, and blessed us
humble folk." He pointed out to them, also, where this had
taken place.

One time, when Theodore,[13] son of Stephen, was with Blessed
Sergius in the monastery, he was taking part in the divine liturgy
which was being sung by the saint, and with aforenamed

[12] Bishop Stephen: refers to St. Stephen of Perm (see introductory
commentary).

[13] Theodore was the son of Sergius' brother, Stephen. He later became the bishop of Rostov.

Stephen, the saint's brother. Of a sudden Isaac, who had taker
the vow of silence, saw a fourth person serving at the altar witl
them, of a bright, shining appearance, and in dazzling apparel
Isaac inquired of Father Macarius, who was standing by his
side, "What miraculous apparition is this?" Macarius replied
"I do not know, brother; I see a fearful and ineffable vision. Bu
I think, brother, that someone came with the prince." (Prince
Vladimir was at this time in the monastery.) One of the prince's
attendants was asked whether a priest had come with him; but
no, they knew of no one.

When the divine Mass was at an end, seizing a favorable
moment, one of the brethren approached St. Sergius and ques
tioned him. But he, anxious not to disclose the secret, asked
"What wonder did you see, brother? My brother, Stephen, was
saying the Mass; also his son, Theodore and I, unworthy as I
am. No other priest whatever was serving with us." His disciples
insisted, entreating the saint to reveal the mystery to them
whereupon he said, "Beloved brethren, what the Lord God ha
revealed can I keep secret? He whom you beheld was an ange
of the Lord, and not only this time but every time I, unworthy
as I am, serve with this messenger of the Lord. That which you
have seen tell no one, so long as I am on this earth." And his
disciples were astonished beyond measure.

VIII. St. Sergius and Russia

A rumor spread that Khan Mamai was raising a large army
as a punishment for our sins and that with all his heathen Tata
hordes he would invade Russian soil. Very great fear prevailed
among the people at this report. The puissant and reigning
prince, who held the scepter of all Russia, great Dmitry,[14] hav
ing a great faith in the saint, came to ask him if he counseled
him to go against the heathen. The saint, bestowing on him his
blessing, and strengthened by prayer, said to him: "It behoveth
you, Lord, to have a care for the lives of the flock committed
to you by God. Go forth against the heathen; and upheld by
the strong arm of God, conquer; and return to your country
sound in health, and glorify God with loud praise."

The grand duke replied, "If indeed God assist me, Father, I
will build a monastery to the Immaculate Mother of God." And
with the saint's blessing he hurriedly went on his way. As

---

[14] Grand Duke Dmitry, reigned 1363–1385, was the hero o
Zadonshchina, and the first Russian prince to defeat the Tatars in
major battle.

sembling all his armies, he marched against the heathen Tatars; but, seeing the multitudes of them, he began to doubt; and many of his followers, not knowing what to do, were overwhelmed with fear. Of a sudden, a courier from the saint arrived, in all haste, with the message. "Be in no doubt, Lord; go forward with faith and confront the enemy's ferocity; and fear not, for God will be on your side." Forthwith, the Grand Duke Dmitry and all his armies, were filled with a spirit of temerity; and went into battle against the pagans. They fought; many fell; but God was with them, and helped the great and invincible Dmitry, who vanquished the ungodly Tatars. In that same hour the saint was engaged with his brethren before God in prayer for victory over the pagans. Within an hour of the final defeat of the ungodly, the saint, who was a seer, announced to the brotherhood what had happened, the victory, the courage of the Grand Duke Dmitry, and the names, too, of those who had died at the hands of the pagans; and he made intercession for them to all-merciful God.

The Grand Duke Dmitry returned to his country with great joy in his heart, and hastened to visit holy, venerable Sergius. Rendering thanks for the prayers of the saint and of the brotherhood, he gave a rich offering to the monastery and, in fulfillment of his vow, expressed his wish to build at once the monastery of the Immaculate Mother of God. After searching for a favorable place, venerable Sergius fixed upon one by the banks of the river Dubenka, and with the consent of the grand duke a church to the Assumption of our Blessed Virgin Mother of God was consecrated by St. Sergius. As abbot, the saint appointed one of his followers, Sabbas by name, a man of exceeding great virtue. A community was formed, and many brethren joined it.

Once again the Grand Duke Dmitry entreated St. Sergius to come to Kolomna, to consecrate a site for the building of a monastery to be dedicated to the Holy Epiphany. It was the saint's custom to go everywhere on foot. Obedient to the grand duke, he went to Kolomna, consecrated the site, and a church was erected and, at the grand duke's request, he sent him one of his disciples for the founding of the monastery, a priest-monk, Gregory, a devout man and of great virtue. In time a stone church was built, which is standing to this day.

Another time the illustrious Prince Vladimir begged St. Sergius, likewise, to come to his part of the country, to the town of Serpukhov, and consecrate a place by the river Nar, and dedicate a church to the Conception of the Immaculate Mother of God. Once again the saint obeyed the request. This god-fearing prince also begged him to send one of his disciples, Athanasius by name. Although the saint found it hard to grant this request, love prevailed, and he consented. Athanasius being a man of rare virtue, exceedingly learned in Holy Scriptures—many valuable writings by his hand bear witness to him to the present day—the saint loved him dearly. To him the saint entrusted the founding of the monastery, and the forming of the community. Aided by the prayers of the saint, the monastery was built, wonderful and beautiful, and named "On the Height."

But why pursue further the saint's planting of ecclesiastical fruit? It is well known how many monasteries were founded by God's own chosen servant. And, offspring of his offspring, burning bright as stars, they are everywhere radiating a serene and wondrous life, and a blessing to all.

The Metropolitan Alexis, being old, and seeing his weakness increasing, sent for St. Sergius. While they conversed, the metropolitan asked to have the cross with the "paramand" adorned with gold and precious stones brought to him, to give it to the saint; but he, bowing low in great humility, refused it, saying, "Forgive me, Lord, I have worn no gold ornaments since childhood, wherefore all the more do I wish in old age to continue in poverty." The bishop insisted, and said, "I know, beloved, that thou art fulfilling a vow, but be obedient, and take this which we offer thee with a benediction." Further, he said to the saint: "Dost know why I sent for thee? I desire, while I yet live, to find a man able to feed Christ's flock. I have doubted of them all; thee alone have I chosen as worthy. I know with all certainty that, from the puissant prince to the lowliest of his people, thou art the one they want."

On hearing this the saint was deeply grieved, regarding honor for himself as a thing of naught, and he pleaded with the bishop: "Forgive me, Lord, but this of which you speak is beyond my powers, and you never will find it in me. What am I but a sinner, and the least of men?" The bishop quoted many sayings from Holy Scriptures, but the saint, unyielding in his humility, said, "Gracious Lord, if you do not wish to drive away my poverty from your Holiness, speak no more about my poor self, nor permit anyone else, for no one can make me otherwise."

The bishop, understanding that the saint would not yield, allowed him to return to his monastery. Before long the Metropolitan Alexis left this life, in the year 1378 (6885); and once more the princes implored the saint to accept the rank of bishop; but, firm as adamant, he would in no way consent. Then a certain archimandrite, Michael, was raised to the bishopric; but this man, with great presumption, not only invested himself with the episcopal robes but also proceeded to plot against the saint, in the belief that the venerable Sergius would put a check on his audacity, wishing to occupy the episcopal throne himself. Blessed Sergius, hearing of Michael's threats against him, remarked to his disciples that Michael, vaunting himself of his sacred appointment, would not obtain his wish, for, overcome by pride, he would not reach the imperial city. The saint's prophecy was fulfilled. On his way by boat to Constantinople,[15] Michael fell ill and died. Thereupon everyone regarded St. Sergius as one of the prophets.

IX. The Last Miracles and the Passing Away of St. Sergius

One day the blessed father was praying, as was his wont, before the image of the Mother of our Lord Jesus Christ. Having sung the "Magnificat" of the Blessed Virgin, he sat down to rest a while, saying to his disciple, Micah, "Son, be calm and be bold, for a wonderful and fearful event is about to happen." Instantly a voice was heard, "The Blessed Virgin is coming." Hearing this the saint hurried from his cell into the corridor. A dazzling radiance shone upon the saint, brighter than the sun, and he beheld the Blessed Virgin, with the two Apostles Peter and John, in ineffable glory. Unable to bear so resplendent a vision, the saint fell to the ground. The Blessed Virgin, touching the saint with her hand, said: "Be not afraid, mine own elect, I have come to visit thee. Thy prayers for thy disciples for whom thou prayest, and for thy monastery, have been heard. Be not troubled; from henceforth it will flourish, not only during thy lifetime but when thou goest to the Lord, I will be with thy monastery, supplying its needs lavishly, providing for it, protecting it."

Having thus spoken, she vanished. The saint, in ecstasy, stood in trembling awe and wonder. Returning slowly to his senses, he saw his disciple, terror-struck, lying on the ground, whereupon he raised him up; but the other flung himself down at the feet of the elder, saying, "Tell me, Father, for God's sake what miraculous vision was this? For my spirit almost loosed its bonds with the flesh from so resplendent a vision."

[15] From the beginnings of the Russian Church until 1448, the head of the Russian Church, who was first the Metropolitan of Kiev and later the Metropolitan of Moscow, was consecrated by the Patriarch of Constantinople. After 1448, the year the Byzantine Church concluded its union of short duration with the Church of Rome, the Russian Church broke away and became independent.

The saint, so filled with ecstasy that his face glowed therewith, was unable to answer other than a few words, "Wait a while, son, for I, too, am trembling with awe and wonder at this miraculous vision." They continued in silent adoration until, finally, the saint said to his disciple, "Son, call hither Isaac and Simon." When these two came, he recounted to them all that had happened, how he had beheld the Blessed Virgin with the Apostles, and what a wonderful promise she had given him. Hearing this their hearts were filled with indescribable joy, and they all sang the "Magnificat," and glorified God. All night long the saint remained in meditation on this ineffable vision.

After a while, a Greek bishop came from Constantinople to Moscow, but, although he had heard a great deal about the saint, his doubt about him prevailed, for, he reasoned, "How can such a light have appeared in this savage land, more especially in these latter days?" He therefore resolved to go to the monastery and see the saint. When he drew near to the monastery, fear entered his soul, and as soon as he entered the monastery and beheld the saint, blindness fell upon him. The venerable Sergius took him by the hand and led him to his cell. The bishop, with tears, confessed his doubts to the saint, and prayed for the recovery of his sight. The gentle lover of humility touched his blinded pupils, and, as it were, scales fell from his eyes, and instantly he recovered his sight. The bishop proclaimed to all that the saint was indeed a man of God and that in God's mercy he himself had been deemed worthy to behold a celestial man and an earthly angel.

A moneylender, living near the saint's monastery, and who, like the strong in all ages, oppressed the poor, ill-treated a certain poor orphan, and, moreover, carried off his pig which was being fattened, and without paying for it had it killed. The ill-used orphan went to the saint in great distress and, weeping, begged for help. The saint, moved by compassion, sent for the offender, convicted him of wrongdoing, and said, "My son, do you believe that God is a judge of the righteous and of sinners; a father to widows and orphans; that he is quick to avenge and that it is a fearful thing to come under the wrath of God?" Having reproached him and told him he must pay what he owed to the orphan, he added, "Above all, do not oppress the poor." The man, overcome by fear, promised to amend and to pay the orphan, then returned to his own house. Little by little the effect of the saint's rebuke grew faint, and he decided not to pay his debt to the orphan. And, thinking it over in his mind, he went as usual into his larder, where he found the pig half devoured

d swarming with maggots, although it was midwinter. He
as stricken with fear, and without delay paid the debt; and
dered the pig to be thrown to the dogs and birds to eat, but
ey would not touch it and clear the usurer of his offense.

Now, again, one day, the saint was reciting the divine liturgy
ith one of his disciples, venerable Simon, the ecclesiarch, of
hom we have already spoken, when a wonderful vision was
uchsafed to Simon. While the saint was saying the liturgy,
mon saw a flame pass along the altar, illuminating it and sur-
unding the holy table; as the saint was about to partake of the
lessed Sacrament the glorious flame coiled itself and entered
e sacred chalice; and the saint thus received Communion.
mon, who saw this, trembled with fear. The saint, when he
oved away from the altar, understood that Simon had been
eemed worthy of this miraculous vision, and telling him to
pproach, asked, "Son, why are you fearful?" The other replied,
Master, I beheld a miraculous vision; the grace of the Holy
irit operating with you." The saint forbade him to speak of
: "Tell no one of this which you have seen, until the Lord calls
e away from this life."

The saint lived a number of years, continually chastening
mself with fasting, and working unceasingly. He performed
any unfathomable miracles, and reached an advanced age,
ver failing from his place at divine service; the older his body
ew, the stronger grew his fervor, in no way weakened by age.
e became aware of his approaching end six months before,
d assembling the brotherhood he appointed his dearest dis-
ple to take his place, one perfect in all virtue, following his
aster in all things, small of stature, but in mind a continual
ossoming, whose name was Nikon. The saint exhorted him to
ide Christ's flock with patient care and justice. The great
cetic soon began to lose strength and in September was taken
riously ill. Seeing his end, he again assembled his flock and
elivered a final exhortation. He made them promise to be
eadfast in orthodoxy and to preserve amity among men; to
ep pure in body and soul; to love truth; to avoid all evil and
rnal lusts; to be moderate in food and drink; above all, to be
othed with humility; not to forget love of their neighbor; to
oid controversy, and on no account to set value on honor and
aise in this life, but rather to await reward from God for the
ys of heaven and eternal blessings. Having instructed them
many things, he concluded, "I am, by God's will, about to
ave you, and I commit you to Almighty God and the Immac-
ate Virgin, Mother of God, that they may be to you a refuge

and rock of defense against the snares of your enemies." A
his soul was about to leave his body, he partook of the sacre
Body and Blood, supported in the arms of his disciples and
raising his hands to heaven, with a prayer on his lips, he su
rendered his pure, holy soul to the Lord, in the year 139
(6900), September 25th, probably at the age of seventy-eigh
After his death an ineffable sweet odor flowed from the saint
body.

The entire brotherhood gathered around him and, weepin
and sobbing, laid on its bier the body of him who in life ha
been so noble and unresting, and accompanied him with psaln
and funeral orisons. The saint's face, unlike that of other dea
glowed with the life of the living, or as one of God's angels, wi
nessing to the purity of his soul, and God's reward for all h
labors. His body was laid to rest within the monastery of his ow
creation. Many were the miracles that took place at his deat
and after, and still are taking place, giving strength to th
weaker members of the community, deliverance from the craf
and wiles of evil spirits, and sight to the blind. The saint had r
wish during his life for renown, neither in death, but by God
Almighty Power he was glorified. Angels were present at h
passing into the heavens, opening for him the gates of paradis
and leading him toward the longed-for blessings, into the peac
of the righteous, the ever-looked-for glory of the Blessed Trinit

27. *Peter and Fevronia of Murom*

IN RUSSIAN medieval literature the tale of *Peter and Fevronia c
Murom* is a unique instance of a work in which some romant
elements are presented. The love between Peter and Fevronia
considerably spiritualized, however, emphasizing their faithfu
ness to each other both in this life and in life after death. In th
respect, the story of Peter and Fevronia resembles that of Trista
and Iseult, although deprived of any amorous background. Th
tale can be divided into composite segments, as has been dor
in this translation. The first, and the most fantastic, part, "Th
Story of the Evil Serpent," echoes the widely spread motif co
cerning the effect of the blood of an evil serpent, a motif whic
can be found in the *Nibelungenlied*. The second section trea
the miraculous healing of Prince Peter by a wise and fa
maiden, a theme also to be found in both Eastern and Europea

legends and fairy tales. The third part, "The Intrigues of the Boyars," unlike the preceding sections, contains a political polemic attempting to prove that the autocratic rule of a prince is superior to the rule of an aristocracy that leads to its own self-destruction through dissension. The conclusion of this work has hagiographic colorations. Peter and Fevronia appear here as devout and just rulers who care for their subjects, helping the poor and supporting the Church.

Unusual for a work describing the lives of saints—Peter and Fevronia actually were venerated as the saintly patrons of the city of Murom—is their last testament: to remain together in the same casket after death. Here, the elements of the purity and sanctity of the family supersede the usual ascetic tradition of hagiographic works.

Peter and Fevronia, in its language, symbolism, and its use of riddles (as in the speech of Fevronia), clearly reflects a folklore origin. The name Agrica itself plainly shows this influence, for Agrica was an invincible mythological warrior of Russian folk epics who possessed a magic sword with which he slew evil serpents and monsters.

The exact background of this story is not well known. Peter and Fevronia had been venerated in Murom since the middle of the fifteenth century, and they were both canonized in 1547 by an All-Russian Church Council in Moscow. However, this narrative has never been included in the official collection of *vitae* nor was it read in the Church. There are some indications that the life of Prince David of Murom, who ruled there from 1203 to 1228, was the historical source for this work.

This translation is based upon the Old Russian text prepared by Professor M. O. Skripil and published in the collection *Russkie povesti XV–XVI vekov*, Moscow, 1958, pages 108–115.

◆ ◆ ◆

I. THE EVIL SERPENT

There is in the Russian land a city called Murom. I was told that this city was once ruled by a good prince named Paul. The devil, hating everything good among men, sent a serpent to the palace of Prince Paul's wife to seduce and debase her. And when the princess was with the serpent, she saw him as he really was, while it seemed to others who visited the princess's palace that not a serpent, but Prince Paul himself was with the princess. Time passed, and the wife of Prince Paul decided that she could no longer hide her secret. She revealed what had happened to her husband, for the serpent had already debased her.

Prince Paul tried to think of what to do with the serpent, and finally he told his wife: "I cannot discern how I am to deal with this evil spirit. I don't know any means of killing it. But we shall do the following. When you talk with him, ask him cleverly whether he knows how he is destined to die. And when you learn this, tell me, and you will not only be rid of this evil spirit and its debauchery, of which it is disgusting even to speak, but also in the next life you will gain the mercy of our righteous Judge, Jesus Christ."

The princess became gladdened by her husband's words, and thought, It would be good if it would only happen so. And when the serpent came, she began to converse slyly and cleverly with it about various things, keeping in mind her intentions. When it began to brag, she asked humbly and with respect, "You certainly know everything, and so you must certainly know to what kind of death you are destined."

And the great deceiver was himself deceived by the deception of the faithful wife and unknowingly betrayed his secret, saying, "My death will come from Peter's hand and Agrica's sword." The princess, hearing this, concealed it firmly in her heart. After the departure of this evil being, she told her husband, the prince, what the serpent had said. The prince, hearing this, was unable to understand what was meant by the words, "My death will come from Peter's hand and Agrica's sword." But, since he had a brother named Peter, he summoned him and told him what his wife had learned from the evil serpent. Prince Peter, learning from his brother that the serpent gave his namesake as the cause of his death, began to think bravely of how to kill this serpent. Yet he was confused by the fact that he did not know what was the sword of Agrica.

Prince Peter had the custom of going alone to church to pray. Once he came to the Church of the Elevation of the Holy Cross, which belonged to a convent beyond the city wall. There he was approached by a youth who asked the prince if he wished to see the sword of Agrica. The prince, desirous of fulfilling his desire to kill the serpent, answered, "Certainly! Where is it?" And the youth asked Prince Peter to follow him, and he showed him a niche in the bricks of the altar in which a sword was lying. Faithful Prince Peter took the sword and went to his brother, Prince Paul, and told him everything. And from that moment Prince Peter began to wait for the opportunity to kill this evil serpent.

Each day he visited his brother and his sister-in-law. One day, ter he had visited his brother, he went to the room of his ter-in-law, and there he once again found his brother, sitting ith the princess. Leaving her room, he met a man from Prince ul's retinue, and he asked him: "I was just in my brother's om and found him there. Then I went directly to my sister- -law's room and once again I found him there. How is this ssible?"

And the man answered: "It is not possible, my lord. Prince ul has not left his room since you left him." He went to his der brother's room and asked him: "When did you return to ur room? When I left you, I went to the chambers of the incess without losing any time. And yet, when I came there, found you next to her. I can't understand how you could get ere before me. Therefore, I left there, came back here, and w once more I see that you were faster than I in getting re. I don't understand it."

Then Prince Paul explained to Peter that he had not left his om nor had he been with the princess during this time. Then ince Peter understood what had happened. "All this is the tchcraft of this evil serpent. In my presence he assumes your age for his own so that he would not be killed by me. Brother, not leave this room, for I am now going to your wife's cham- rs to fight the evil serpent. I hope that I will be able to slay with the help of God."

Prince Peter then took Agrica's sword and went to the prin- ss's chambers, where he again found the serpent in the form his brother. He struck it with the sword, and the evil spirit urned to its true form and died in convulsions. Before it died, wever, its blood spilled on Prince Peter. The body of Prince ter became covered with sores and ulcers from this blood, and prince became gravely ill. He was attended by many physi- ns, but none were able to cure him.

II. The Healing of Prince Peter

Having heard that there were many physicians in the region Riazan, Prince Peter told his servants to convey him there. eakened by his illness, Prince Peter was no longer able to unt his horse. When he arrived in the land of Riazan, he t all the men of his retinue to look for physicians.

One of the young men of his retinue came accidentally to a lage called Charity. In this village he approached the gate of iouse in which apparently no one was at home. He entered house and found no one. Finally, he entered a room in which

he found a beautiful maiden who was weaving. Before he
hare was jumping and playing about. The maiden said to
young soldier, "It is indeed unfortunate when the yard is wi
out ears and the house without eyes."

The young man didn't understand the meaning of these wor
but asked where the master of the house was. The maiden
swered, "My father and mother have gone alone to weep so
to pay their debt in advance, and my brother has gone to vi
death between his feet."

Once more the young soldier did not understand the maide
words, and things appeared to be strange to him. He again sp
to the maiden: "I came to your place and I saw you weav
and a hare jumping about before you. Now I hear strange wo
from your lips which I cannot understand. First you told
that it is unfortunate when a yard is without ears and a ho
without eyes. Then you told me that your mother and fat
have gone to weep alone so as to pay their debt in advance a
that your brother has gone to view death between his fee
have not understood a word that you have told me."

The maiden smiled, and said: "Well, it is not too difficult
understand. You came into the house and found me sitting h
weaving and dressed in house clothes. If we had a dog, it mi
have heard you and started barking. In such a case the y
would have had ears. If my brother were at home, he mi
have seen you coming here and warned me. In this case
house would have eyes. I told you that my parents went to we
alone so as to pay their debt in advance. Actually, they wen
a burial and wept there. Once death has come to them, oth
will weep after them, and therefore they weep now to pay th
debt in advance. As for my brother, I told you that he had g
to view death between his feet. Actually, he and my fat
climb trees and collect pitch. He went just now to climb tr
and when he does so, he must watch his feet so that he will
fall. If he should fall, it would be his death. Therefore I s
that my brother had gone to view death between his feet."

The young soldier then said to the maiden: "I see that
are very wise. Please tell me your name." Upon learning t
the maiden's name was Fevronia, the young soldier explai
why he had come there: "I have come here on behalf of
lord, Prince Peter of Murom. My prince is sick and covered v
sores and ulcers. He received these afflictions from the blood
an evil serpent which he killed with his own hands. Since t
time many doctors have treated him, but none have been a

ure him. Therefore, he ordered us to bring him to this land,
he heard that there are many physicians here. But we know
her where they live nor what are their names."

evronia answered, saying, "The only one who can cure the
ce is the one who would order that your prince be brought
his place."

Who would that be? What do you mean by these words?"
young man inquired. "The prince will lavishly reward the
sician who will cure him. Tell me the name of such a physi-
—who he is and where he lives."

he maiden then told him: "Bring your prince to this place.
e is kind of heart and not proud in answering my questions,
vill be cured." The young soldier listened to these words and
returned to Prince Peter and told him in detail all that he
seen and heard.

rince Peter then enjoined his retinue to take him immediately
his wise maiden. And they took him to the house wherein
d the maiden. The prince sent a page to the maiden asking:
ll me, maiden, who is the man who can cure me? Let him
me, and he will receive a large part of my wealth!"

Vithout hesitation the maiden answered the page: "I am the
sician who is able to cure your prince, but I do not desire
part of his wealth. However, if I do not become his wife, I
have no reason to cure him."

he page returned to the prince and repeated to him the
ds of Fevronia. Prince Peter did not take her words seriously,
king that it would be impossible for a prince to marry the
ghter of a man whose station in life was as low as that of
who collects pitch. And he instructed his page to tell the
den that she must cure him, and that if she did, she would
ome his wife. The page repeated these words to the maiden.
then took a small pitcher and scooped up some leaven from
arrel and told the page: "Prepare a steambath for your
ce, and, after the bath, spread this leaven over the sores and
rs on his body. But you must take care not to cover all of
scabs, but leave one uncovered. And then your prince will
rn to good health." The young man brought the ointment
e from leaven to the prince, and the servants immediately
ared the steambath.

Vhile the servants were preparing the steambath, the prince
ded to learn how wise this maiden really was, for he had
the word of his servant in this matter. To this end he sent
a small bundle of linen, asking that she make him a shirt,

towel, and pants from this linen while he was in the steamb
and if she were successful, she would thereby prove her wisd

A servant brought the bundle of linen to Fevronia and
peated the command of Prince Peter. Fevronia, without
hesitation, ordered the man to climb up on the stove and fe
down a piece of dry wood. When the servant gave her the pi
of wood, she marked off a piece one foot in length and orde
the man to cut off this piece. When the servant had done
she told him to take the block to his master and ask him
make from it a spinning wheel and a loom, while she
combing the linen in preparation for making the shirt, pa
and towel.

The servant took the block of wood to Prince Peter and
peated Fevronia's request. The prince laughed, and said: "G
Fevronia and tell her that it is not possible to prepare so m
things from so small a block in so short a time."

Fevronia had anticipated this answer, and told the serv
"Well, if your prince is unable to make a spinning wheel an
loom from such a small piece of wood in so short a time, h
can I, in return, weave a shirt, pants, and a towel for him fr
such a small bundle of linen, while he takes a steambat
When the page returned to the prince, he was astounded
the wisdom of her answer.

Then Prince Peter went into the steambath, and his serv
applied the ointment over the sores and ulcers, leaving only
scab uncovered, as was ordered by Fevronia. When Pri
Peter left the steambath, his pains left him, and the next mo
ing all his body was clear and healed excepting the one s
that had been left uncovered. He marveled at the curing pow
of Fevronia. However, since Fevronia was the daughter of
of lowly birth, Prince Peter did not wish to marry her. He
however, send her luxurious gifts, but Fevronia would not
cept them.

Peter returned to his native city of Murom with his b
completely healed excepting the single scab. Soon afterwa
however, more sores and ulcers began to spread from the sin
scab which had not been covered by the ointment. And then
whole body was once again covered with sores and ulcers. S
ing that his affliction had returned, Prince Peter decided
return to Fevronia once again to undergo the proven treatme

He returned to Riazan and to Fevronia's house, and desp
the fact that he was ashamed for not having kept his promise
marry her, he asked her to treat him once more. Fevronia
not the least bit angry, but said that she would treat him o

f he decided to be her husband. This time the prince firmly promised that he would take her as his wife.

The maiden then prescribed the same treatment as before. And when he was healed again, Prince Peter took Fevronia for his wife. And in this way did Fevronia become a princess. And both of them went to Peter's native city of Murom, and there they lived extremely piously, closely obeying the commandments of God. Soon after their arrival in Murom, Prince Paul died, and Prince Peter became the sole ruler of the city.

III. THE INTRIGUES OF THE BOYARS

The boyars of the city of Murom did not find Princess Fevronia to their liking. They, under the influences of their spouses, resented the princess because of her common origin. However, because of her charitable deeds, she was extremely popular among the simple people, and they prayed to God for her. Once, one of the courtiers, wanting to bring strife between Peter and Fevronia, came to the prince and told him: "The princess usually gets up from the table when she is not supposed to do so. Moreover, before leaving the table, she picks up the crumbs as if she were hungry."

Prince Peter decided to see if these accusations were true. He ordered that Princess Fevronia sit beside him at the table. When dinner was over, Fevronia picked up all the crumbs and kept them in her hand as she was accustomed to doing since her childhood. Seeing this, Prince Peter caught her by the hand and told her to open her fist, but when she did so they found fragrant myrrh and incense in the palm of her hand. And from that day on, Peter never attempted to question his wife's deeds.

Many years later the resentful boyars came once again to Peter and said: "Our lord, we want to serve you honestly and want you as our ruler, but we do not want Princess Fevronia as our princess, nor do we want her to rule over our wives. If you are to remain, our lord, you must take another for princess. Fevronia may take her wealth and go away anywhere she may wish to go."

Blessed Prince Peter was of gentle nature and did not become angry, but promised to talk to Princess Fevronia to learn what she would say of this. The shameless courtesans then decided to organize a banquet. They became drunk at this banquet and began to talk arrogantly like loudly barking dogs. And they began to deny Fevronia's miraculous gift of healing, which she had received from God not only for this life but even for after death.

They began talking: "Our lady, Princess Fevronia, the whole city and all the boyars ask you to give back to us Prince Peter because we want him."

Fevronia answered: "You can have him. Only speak with him."

Then the boyars all spoke at once, saying: "Our lady, all of us want Prince Peter to rule over us, but our wives do not want you to rule over them. Please, take as much wealth as you desire and go wherever you like."

Hearing these words, Princess Fevronia told them that she would do as they desired but that now she must ask them to do one thing that she desired. The boyars, who were not very clever, rejoiced, and thought that they would easily rid themselves of her. So they pledged to do as she asked. And Princess Fevronia said, "I want nothing from you but my husband Prince Peter."

The boyars deliberated for a short while and then said, "If Prince Peter will have it this way, we will not contradict him."

They hoped that they would be able to choose another ruler if Prince Peter did not wish to break the divine commandment for it is written in the Gospel of Apostle Matthew: "But I say unto you, that whosoever shall put away his wife, saving for the cause of unchastity, makes her an adultress." And Prince Peter following the commandment of Jesus, gave up his rule over the city of Murom.

The evil lords prepared boats for Peter and Fevronia, for the city of Murom was situated on the river Oka. And so they went down the river in these vessels. On the princess' boat was a courtier who, despite the fact that he was accompanied by his wife, was tempted by evil spirits and began to stare at Princess Fevronia with shameful thoughts. The princess immediately discerned his evil thoughts and exposed them to the man. Approaching him, she ordered him to scoop up water from the river on one side of the boat and drink it. When the man had done so, she ordered him to go to the other side of the ship and do the same. When the man had drunk the water, Fevronia approached him, and asked, "Tell me, did you find that the water tastes the same on both sides of the ship, or was it perhaps sweeter on one side than on the other?"

The man answered: "No, my lady. The water tasted the same on both sides."

Then she replied: "And so is the nature of all women. Why then do you want to leave your wife and think about another woman?" The courtier then realized that the princess possessed the gift of reading the minds of men. Becoming afraid, he gave up his evil intentions.

In the evening the boats docked, and when the travelers were disembarking, Prince Peter became seized with doubts as to whether he was right in giving up his rule in the city of Murom. His sagacious wife perceived his doubts, and comforted him, saying: "Do not grieve, my Prince, for merciful God, our Creator, who directs our life, will never forsake us to misfortune."

That same evening the servants began to prepare dinner for the prince. They cut down branches of some trees and, making a spit, put the kettle on. Princess Fevronia, who was walking along the shore, came upon these branches that had been cut from the trees. Seeing them, she said, "Bless them, for before morning these branches will grow into great trees with rich foliage." And so it happened, for when the travelers got up in the morning they found that these branches had grown into great trees with rich foliage.

And when the servants began to load the boats, there came a lord from the city of Murom, saying: "My lord, Prince Peter, I come to you in behalf of all the courtiers of the city of Murom. They ask that you do not desert them, your poor orphans, but that you return as ruler to your native land. Many lords of the city have perished by the sword. Each, wanting to become ruler of the city, killed the other. Those lords who have survived and all the rest of the people beg you to come back, my lord, and rule over us. And we will neither anger nor irritate you again. Some of our ladies did not wish to be ruled by Princess Fevronia, but now these ladies have perished in the feud. Those of us who remain alive do love her, and we beg you not to leave us alone, your humble servants."

Thus Prince Peter and Princess Fevronia returned to the city of Murom, and they ruled according to the commandments of God.

IV. The Passing Away of Peter and Fevronia

Peter and Fevronia always helped their people with alms and prayers. They treated all as if they were their own children. They loved everyone equally, and disliked only those who were proud or who exploited the people. Peter and Fevronia lay up their treasures, not on earth, but in heaven. They were real pastors of their city. They always ruled with truth and humility, and never with anger. They gave shelter to pilgrims, fed the hungry, and clothed the naked. And they helped the poor in their misfortune.

When death was nearing, Peter and Fevronia prayed to God that they both might die in the same hour. And they requested that they be buried in the same tomb and in a common coffin in which their bodies would be separated only by a partition. And together they took monastic vows, Prince Peter becoming Brother David, and Princess Fevronia, Sister Euphrosinia.

And it happened that, shortly before her death, Princess Fevronia was embroidering a figure of the saints on a coverlet for the chalice of the cathedral. And a messenger came from Prince Peter, now Brother David, saying, "Sister Euphrosinia, I am ready to die, and wait only for you, so that we may die together."

But Princess Fevronia, now Sister Euphrosinia, answered "You should wait, my lord, until I finish the coverlet for the chalice of the holy cathedral."

Then Brother David sent another messenger, who announced "I can wait for you only a short time." Shortly after, another messenger arrived, saying: "I shall soon depart this world. There is no time left for waiting."

Princess Fevronia was just finishing the embroidering of the coverlet, but, hearing these words, she placed the needle in the coverlet and wound up the thread she had been using. Doing so, she sent a message to Brother David saying that they would now die together. And, having prayed, they offered up their souls to God on Friday, the 20th day of June.

After their deaths, some of the people decided that Prince Peter should be buried in the Cathedral of the Holy Virgin which was within the walls of the city of Murom, and that Princess Fevronia should be buried in the Church of the Elevation of the Holy Cross, which was outside the walls of the city. And they actually did so, saying that it was not becoming for a man and woman who had taken monastic vows to be buried in the same casket. The body of Prince Peter was put in a casket and was placed in the cathedral, where it was left overnight. The body of Princess Fevronia was put in another casket and placed in the church outside the city walls. A tomb, which had been carved from a huge rock as a resting-place for Peter and Fevronia, remained empty in the yard of the Cathedral of the Holy Virgin.

The next morning the people went to the caskets of Peter and Fevronia and found them empty. The bodies of the holy prince and princess were found together in the tomb of stone, which

they had ordered prepared for them. The people, not understanding the meaning of this event, once more placed the bodies
in separate caskets. On the following day the bodies of Prince
Peter and Princess Fevronia were once again found together in
the tomb of stone. Since that time no man has dared to disturb
their holy bodies, but left them in their common tomb in the
yard of the Cathedral of the Holy Virgin, which is located in
the city of Murom. And whoever touched with contrition the
tomb wherein lie the holy relics of Peter and Fevronia always
received comfort and healing.

28. The Life of St. Michael, A Fool in Christ

THE life of Michael of Klopsko was one of the most popular
hagiographic works of northern Russia in the fifteenth and sixteenth centuries. Some seventy ancient manuscripts containing
different versions of this *vita* have been preserved, and they
have been rewritten, re-edited, and expanded upon by various
medieval writers. Michael of Klopsko was an actual historical
person, known not only from his *vita* but also from chronicles
and documents. He lived in the first half of the fifteenth century,
came to the Monastery of the Holy Trinity in Klopsko, near the
city of Novgorod, between 1408 and 1412, and died there between 1453 and 1458. This was a period of intense struggle
within the Muscovite ruling dynasty—specifically, between the
Grand Prince of Moscow, Vasily II (or the "Blind"); his cousin,
Prince Dmitry Shemiaka; and the latter's brother, Vasily the
"One-Eyed." The epithets "the Blind" and "the One-Eyed"
indicate the cruelty of this struggle, as each cousin was responsible for the other's mutilation. Shemiaka's memory has become
notorious because of his cruelty and perfidy; in fact, the name
Shemiaka has become a synonym for injustice. His story will be
found in the tale of *Shemiaka's Judgment*. In addition to the
struggle for power among these cousins, the *Life of St. Michael*
also reflects the desire of the Muscovite princes to unify Russia
under their leadership and to incorporate the Novgorodian Republic into the Russian state.

Michael of Klopsko was one of the first Russian *yurodivy*, or
"fools in Christ," as certain people were called who devoted
themselves entirely to the service of God. They accepted voluntarily the role of a fool in order to be able to teach people the
truth of Christ and also to speak the truth to the powerful
princes and lords. These "fools in Christ" usually wore coarse

linen frocks throughout the whole year, ate the barest minimum of food, and walked barefoot, even in winter. In their prophecies they often spoke truths in the forms of parables, and interesting examples of such can be found in this work.

This *vita* consists of a number of episodes that have been placed under subtitles for easier reading. The style of this work clearly recalls the simple, clipped language of the *Novgorodian Chronicle*. Many sentences are so curt that they often require additional words for comprehension, and any such added words have been placed in parentheses. Similar also to the *Novgorodian Chronicle* is the use of "in this same year" to introduce a new topic or episode. The style of "Michael's Advice to the Novgorodian Republic," however, differs considerably from the anecdotal manner and abrupt, curt style of the rest of the story. One can surmise that this section was a late addition to this work and was of a political nature—that is, it was intended to show the people of Novgorod that God himself, speaking through the mouth of Michael, wished Novgorod to become incorporated into the Muscovite realm.

Some of these episodes are presented in the form of anecdotes, and are among the earliest examples of Russian satirical writing. Their language resembles that of later Muscovite satirical tales of adventure, especially *Shemiaka's Judgment*. Michael's *vita* offers an interesting instance of primitive biography written in simple, naïve language and consisting of disconnected episodes from the life of the saint.

This translation is based upon version B of the earlier text of the *Life of St. Michael of Klopsko* to be found in L. A. Dimitrieva's *Povesti o zhitii Mikhaila Klopskogo*, published by the Academy of Sciences of the U.S.S.R., Moscow and Leningrad, 1958, pages 99–110. The subtitles for the various episodes have been supplied by the translator.

◆ ◆ ◆

I. MICHAEL'S ARRIVAL IN KLOPSKO

St. Michael, a fool in Christ, came to the Church of the Holy Trinity in Klopsko in the time of Abbot Theodosius who later became archbishop of Novgorod.

St. Michael came to the monastery on the eve of St. John's Day. The priest Ignatius, who was officiating in the church, began to cense it during the ninth hymn. Then he went to cense the cells (wherein resided the monks). When the priest entered one cell, the door of which was open, he found there Monk Michael who was sitting in a chair before a burning taper. He was writing *The Acts of the Apostles*. Ignatius became alarmed (at the presence of this unknown monk), and returning to the church, informed Abbot Theodosius and the other monks of this. The abbot then took the cross and the censer and himself went to the same cell and found that the door of the porch of this cell was closed. Therefore the abbot went to the window and, looking in, also saw a monk who was sitting and writing inside the cell. The abbot then began to pray, saying: "O Lord, Jesus Christ, Son of God, be merciful unto us."

After he had said his prayers, the abbot addressed the monk: "Who are you, my son, a man or a devil?"

And Michael answered with the same words, "Are you a man or a devil?"

The alarmed abbot then ordered the tearing down of the porch roof and the door to gain entrance to the cell. When Abbot Theodosius entered the cell, he began to cense the icon and the monk with thyme; and the monk, attempting to protect himself with his hand from the incense, made the sign of the cross. Theodosius once more asked him: "Who are you? Why did you come to us? Where are you from? What kind of man are you?"

But Michael, instead of answering, only repeated the words of the abbot: "Who are you? Why did you come to us? Where are you from? What kind of man are you?" And so the abbot did not learn the name (of the newcomer).

A short time later, before the day of Christ's Transfiguration, Prince Constantine and his wife came to the monastery to take Holy Communion and to present a gift to the monastery on the occasion of the holy day. On that occasion Michael was asked to read from the Book of Job during the dinner given in the refectory. Hearing his voice, Prince Constantine turned toward him and, recognizing him, said, "Oh, is it you Michael, the son of Maxim?"

But Michael countered, "God alone knows who I am."

Then Abbot Theodosius questioned the monk: "Well, my son, why won't you reveal your name to us?"

But Michael simply replied, "God alone knows who I am." But then he revealed his name as being Michael, and so he was called by all from that day on. Prince Constantine, however, asked the abbot and the monks to care for Michael because he was his relative. From that time the abbot and the monks began to care for Monk Michael.

II. Michael Predicts the Everlasting Spring

In this same year and in the three that followed, there was a great drought and the river Veriazh was entirely dried up. Toward the end of these years of drought Abbot Theodosius went to this dried up river and noticed the following words written in the sand of the riverbed: "In this place will be the spring of everlasting water." Seeing this, the abbot asked Michael, who was accompanying him, "Tell me, son, what is that which is written here?"

And Michael answered: "Here will be the spring of water everlasting." And both Abbot Theodosius and Michael addressed their prayers of thanksgiving to God. And then they began to dig, and immediately water gushed forth from the earth. And since that time there has been a well in that place, and it still exists. As soon as the inhabitants of that region learned of it, they began to use it, and do so until this day.

III. Michael Predicts the Tonsuring of Prokhor

A short time later, Michael told Abbot Theodosius, "We shall have guests."

And Theodosius asked Michael, "Son, what kind of guests shall we have?" But Michael did not explain who the guests would be. But when Abbot Theodosius and Michael left the church, they found three men standing in the monastery yard.

Michael told the abbot, "Invite them to the refectory, Father, that they might break bread with us."

And Theodosius told the strangers, "Let us go, my children, into the refectory that we may break bread."

One of the strangers answered, "Father, there are other friends with us."

And Theodosius told the man, "One of you must go and invite your other friends to have the meal with us."

One of the strangers then went for their friends, and he returned with thirty men who were in armor and with weapons and javelins. And they entered the refectory to break bread.

Theodosius and Michael addressed them: "Sit down, children, and break bread." All but two began eating.

Then Michael addressed those who were not eating. "It will not come to pass as you believe it will."

Actually, almost immediately after, both strangers who were not eating became ill. After the meal everyone who had eaten got up from the table, glorifying God and the Holy Trinity. And one of the strangers gave the monastery one hundred squir-

el furs[1] (for the meal). And he said the following: "Father,
care for our ill comrades. We leave you in peace."

And the two strangers remained ill for five days. One of them
wanted very much to become a monk, and since Theodosius
hesitated to tonsure him, Michael said to the abbot, "Tonsure
him, Father, and he will be our brother." And so he took monastic vows and received the name of Prokhor. And the other
stranger recovered, and left the monastery.

IV. The Miracle of the Filled Granary

In this same year there was a famine throughout the land of
Novgorod. And Theodosius and all his brothers became saddened, but Michael said to Abbot Theodosius: "Don't grieve,
Father, but remember that our Lord fed forty thousand men,
besides the women and children, in the wilderness." And he
convinced Abbot Theodosius that the monks should commence
cooking rye in kettles and distribute it to pilgrims and travelers.
But the monks began to grumble about this, being dissatisfied
with Abbot Theodosius and with Michael. But Theodosius and
Michael suggested to the monks, "Let us visit our granary."

And they learned that the granaries were overflowing and
that the amount of grain did not diminish (even though many
were fed from this grain). And they ordered that more rye be
prepared so that they might continue to distribute it to the people without hesitation. And they glorified God, the Holy Trinity,
and the blessed saints.

V. The Building of the Church of the Holy Trinity

On the Saturday of St. Lazarus, Prince Constantine arrived at
the Monastery of the Holy Trinity in Klopsko greatly saddened.
And he told Abbot Theodosius and Monk Michael, "I am very
sad now because my brothers do not wish to give me my share
of the patrimony."

And Michael answered him: "Prince, don't grieve. You will
yet come in possession of your estate. In a short time your
brother will send for you. Pray to the Holy Trinity and build a
stone church in its name, and in return the Lord will reserve
a temple in heaven for you."

And then the prince asked Abbot Theodosius: "Do you have
any craftsmen? I want to build a church of stone in honor of

---

[1] Squirrel furs, or, as they are sometimes called, vairs, were a
monetary unit in ancient Russia.

the Holy Trinity, the source of all life, to commemorate the memory of my parents and myself."

Theodosius sent for craftsmen, and there came craftsmen by the names of John, Clement, and Alexis. And the prince ordered these master craftsmen: "Build a church of stone in the honor of the Holy Trinity, the source of all life, and embellish it in the manner of the Church of St. Nicholas in Latki."

And the craftsmen answered: "We can do so, Lord Prince, And we are ready to serve you if God and the Holy Trinity will aid us." And they laid the foundation of the church on the day of the Commemoration of our holy Father Theodore Sekiot, April 22, 1423 (6931). And they began bringing the stone, but a mighty storm hindered them in their work, and they were able neither to bring the stones by the river nor to work on the walls of the church.

Then Michael said to the masters, "Pray to God for help, because the invisible power of God builds churches." And even as Michael spoke, God sent a helpful wind to fill their sails as they were going for the stone and when they returned with the stone.

For the consecration of the church, Prince Constantine came with his princess and the boyars and brought plenty of food and drink, because he was very glad. And, on the Day of the Holy Martyr Tekla, September 24, 1425 (6932), this Church of the Holy Trinity was completed, thanks to the blessings of Abbot Theodosius and the prayers of St. Michael. And Prince Constantine said to Theodosius and Brother Michael, "Father, thanks to your prayers I received the news from my older brothers that they will give me my patrimony."

And Theodosius and Michael answered: "Go in peace, our child, and they will meet you with friendship. Only, don't forget, our child, this house of God, the Church of the Holy Trinity, the source of all life, as well as ourselves, your poor servants."

And the prince promised: "All my life I shall never forget this House of God, the monastery, the Church of the Holy Trinity, and you, my poor brothers, who have prayed for me."

VI. MICHAEL PREDICTS ABBOT THEODOSIUS' ELECTION
TO THE ARCHBISHOPRIC

This same year Simon, Archbishop of Novgorod, passed away. And Michael predicted to Abbot Theodosius, "You will be elected to the chair of the archbishop and will rule for three years, but you will also be deposed before you have become consecrated."

VII. Michael's Miraculous Appearances

On Tuesday of Holy Week during Matins the brethren found that Michael was missing from the monastery. And at that very time he appeared during Matins in the sacristy of the Cathedral of Holy Sophia of Novgorod, and he was there recognized after Matins by Gregory, the *posadnik*, who addressed him, saying, "Come and break bread with us," and he ordered one of his men to attend him. And suddenly Michael was no longer there. But when in Klopsko the priest went that day to celebrate the liturgy in the monastery, Michael was already in the church. When the brothers left the church for the refectory, there arrived a man who was sent by the *posadnik* to inquire the whereabouts of Michael. And Michael was already there.

VIII. Michael Predicts Alfiry's Misfortunes

This very day there was an argument between Alfiry, son of John, and Ivan Loshinsky, son of Simon, over the possession of land. And Michael predicted to Alfiry, "You will remain without hands and feet and you will become mute." And when Alfiry came to the Church of the Holy Virgin in Kurechka, he met Ivan, and said, "Brother Ivan, this land is mine," and he clapped his hands and his gloves dropped to the floor. When he bowed down to pick them up, a stroke hit him. His hands, feet, and tongue became paralyzed, and he could no longer speak.

IX. Michael and Priest Nicephorius

And there was another prophecy made by Michael concerning a certain priest, Nicephorius, who had secretly stolen the venerable icon of the archbishop. And Michael said to this priest, "You will be dishonored." And from that time the priest lost his mind. And Michael ordered that they look in the stove, and there they found the venerable icon that had been stolen.

X. The Prophecy to the Archbishop

Archbishop Euthemius received the taxes due him from the monastery, but he wanted additional collections. And so he took a horse as black as a raven from the monastery. And Michael told the archbishop, "You will live but a short time, and you will leave everything behind." And soon the archbishop fell ill and passed away.

XI. Michael and Archbishop Euthemius II

In this same year, another Euthemius was elected to the archbishopric. For the three years that followed he was not consecrated. Once, the bishop came to Klopsko to help the monastery. During the meal at the table the archbishop asked Michael, "Dear Michael, pray to God for me that I should be invested by Great Prince Vasily."

The archbishop had a kerchief in his hand, and Michael snatched it suddenly from the bishop and placed it on the bishop's head, and said, "You will go to Smolensk and you will be consecrated to the archbishopric." And actually, the bishop did go to Smolensk and was there consecrated.

The bishop returned to Michael, and said, "God and the metropolitan of Moscow gave me their blessing."

And Michael once again spoke to the archbishop: "You will be summoned to Moscow, and you will go there and you will submit yourself to the Great Prince and to the metropolitan.

XII. THE PUNISHMENT OF POSADNIK GREGORY

And the Monastery of the Holy Trinity at Klopsko was heavily oppressed by *Posadnik* Gregory. Once, on Easter Sunday, this Gregory came to Mass at the Church of the Holy Trinity of this monastery. When the abbot finished celebrating the Mass, he and the *posadnik* left the church. The *posadnik* stopped the abbot and the monks in the monastery, and addressed them: "Abbot, do not let your horses and cows into the meadows in the summer, for that is my land. Also, don't hunt or fish along river Voriazh, or in the marshes, or in the vicinity of my estates. And if your people come there, I shall order that their arms and legs be broken."

And Michael replied to the *posadnik*, "You yourself will lose your arms and legs, and, more than that, you will nearly drown in the river."

Once the abbot and Michael sent their men to the river and to the marshes. As the men of the monastery were pulling in the nets, the *posadnik* went to the river. He went up to the men of the monastery and followed them into the water. Chasing the fishermen, he hit one of them with his fist, and wanted to hit another one, but he missed and fell in the water, and nearly drowned. When his people came, he was nearly drowned, and they carried him home because he was unable to use his arms and legs, as was predicted by Michael.

Early in the morning he was brought to the monastery, but Michael forbade him to enter it and he forbade the monks to pray for him, to light a candle for him, or to mention his name in the liturgy. And Michael added, addressing the *posadnik*, "Don't bring us any food or drink; only leave us in peace."

The abbot and the monks were afraid that they had made a mistake by not praying for the *posadnik* or by not mentioning his name in the liturgy. In the meantime the *posadnik's* men decided to complain, and said: "We are going to complain to the bishop and to the authorities of the city of Novgorod, for you would neither pray for the *posadnik* nor mention his name during Mass." And they went to the bishop and to the authorities of the city of Novgorod—to Jacob Andreianov, Fefilat Zakharin, and John Vasiliev to lodge their complaint. And the bishop sent his archpriest and his archdeacon to Michael and Abbot Theodosius, saying, "Do pray for the *posadnik* during Mass, and celebrate special services for his recovery."

But Michael replied to the archpriest and the archdeacon: "We pray to God for the entire world, and not only for Gregory." (And then he addressed Gregory:) "Go to the other monasteries and ask there God's forgiveness."

And the *posadnik* began his pilgrimages to the monasteries, and he began to make gifts to them, as well as to the churches in the cities. His pilgrimages to monasteries lasted a year and one and one-half months. But nowhere, in any of these monasteries, did he find God's forgiveness.

Thereafter (returning to Novgorod), he sent a man to the bishop, saying, "My lord and my father, nowhere in the monasteries could I find help."

(The bishop answered:) "Go now, my child, to the Monastery of the Holy Trinity, and ask there the mercy of the Holy Trinity and of Monk Michael." And the bishop sent a priest (to Michael), and the *posadnik* went there personally. It was decided to hold a special service to the Holy Trinity and to celebrate the Mass. The *posadnik* was brought into the church in a carpet, but he was not even able to make the sign of the cross. The celebration of the service to the Holy Trinity began. And when they began to sing the hymn, the *posadnik* was able to move his hands, even though he had not been able to move his hands and feet for one year and one and one-half months. When the priest began reading the Gospel, the *posadnik* was already able to make the sign of the cross and to sit down. In the middle of the service he was able to stand, and so he remained standing until the end of the service. After Mass, everyone went to the refectory, and the *posadnik* addressed the monks during the meal, "Holy brothers, I wish you health and appetite."

But Michael countered: "Those who live by the sword shall perish by the sword." In such manner did Michael teach a lesson to Gregory the *posadnik*. And Michael added, "My child, be good to Michael and to the monastery."

XIII. MICHAEL AND DMITRY SHEMIAKA

A short time afterward Prince Dmitry Shemiaka visited Novgorod, and he came to the monastery in Klopsko that he might receive Michael's blessing. (And he said to Michael:) "Dear Mikhailushka, I was chased away from my patrimony, and my enemies have driven me from the throne of the great prince."

And Michael replied, "Every power is given by God."

"My dear Mikhailushka, pray to God to help me get back my patrimony, and to become once more the great prince," Shemiaka once again said to Michael.

But Michael answered only, "Prince, all you will get is a three foot coffin." But Prince Dmitry, paying no heed to Michael's words, decided to begin another campaign to become great prince. But Michael said, "It is in vain, Prince, for you cannot receive that which God does not wish you to have." And God did not help Shemiaka, and he escaped once more to Novgorod.

On Friday of the week of Pentecost, Prince Shemiaka returned to the monastery at Klopsko to bring gifts. He gave the brothers much food and drink. And to Michael he gave his own fur coat. When Prince Dmitry, accompanied by the abbot and the monks, returned to his boat, Michael patted the prince's head, and said, "The damp earth is already awaiting you." And he repeated these words thrice.

And the prince said, "My dear monk, I want to return to the city of Rzhev to my patrimony in Konstantinov."

But Michael added: "Prince, your desire will not be fulfilled." And so it came to pass, for the prince died soon afterward.

XIV. MICHAEL ADDRESSES THE NOVGORODIAN REPUBLIC

Once, *Posadnik* John Nemir came to the monastery, and he asked the *posadnik*, "Why do you travel?"

The *posadnik* answered, "I have been at my wife's grandmother, Euphrasinia, and now I come to you to receive your blessing."

And Michael asked, "Well, my child, what kind of problem do you try to solve with women?"

John Nemir answered: "We expect that that great prince (of Moscow) will start a campaign against us. But we expect help from Prince Michael of Lithuania."

[2] Shemiaka led a revolt against his cousin, the Great Prince of Moscow, and for a short time became the ruler of Muscovy.

But Michael retorted: "Your Lithuanian prince will not be a
elp, but worse than nothing at all. Send your envoy to the
Great Prince of Moscow right now, and sue for peace. If you
on't come to an agreement with the Great Prince of Moscow,
e will come with all his forces to Novgorod, and you will have
o divine help. And the Great Prince of Moscow will camp at
ureguy. He will display his army along the river Shelon, and
e will jail many citizens of Novgorod. Some will be sent to
Moscow, some will be executed, and some will be forced to pay
ribute. And the Lithuanian prince will not fight for you, and
ou will receive no help from him. Better that you send your
rchbishop and *posadniks* to Moscow with a petition for peace
o the Great Prince. Better to pay him tribute; otherwise the
Great Prince of Moscow will return here, will take your city,
nd will deprive you of liberty, and God will help him."

And so it came to pass as Michael said.

XV. MICHAEL'S DEATH

Michael had a simple way of living. He lived alone in his cell
nd had neither a headboard and pillow nor a bed; neither
heets nor covers, but he slept on the earth. He heated his cell
vith dried horse manure and lived in the monastery for forty
nd four years. The entire week he ate only break and water.

Once Abbot Theodosius called Michael for Communion, and
fter it Michael said, "Father, I would receive the Divine Sacra-
nent from you."

And the abbot answered, "Have it, my child, and once more
ake Holy Communion."

And all were astounded by these words. And Michael took
he censer and thyme and went to his cell. When everyone went
o the refectory, the abbot had food sent to Michael's cell. And
vhen the monks came to his cell and entered in, they found the
oly man lying as if asleep. And the fragrance of the thyme from
he censer near Michael was rising from the earth to the heav-
ns. On January 11th, the Day of Our Father, Theodosius of
erusalem, Michael was buried in the Monastery of the Holy
'rinity, the source of all life.

Glory be to God, now and forever more.

29. *The Heroic Deeds of Mercurius of Smolensk*

AFTER having conquered central and northern Russia, the Mon-
olian commander, Batu, began his advance into western Russia

in 1237. However, because of the spring floods he was unab
to take the city of Novgorod, and thus turned southward to t
city of Smolensk. For some reason that remains indiscernib
from historical writings, the Tatar troops were unable to ca
ture Smolensk. From this event developed the charming leger
of St. Mercurius of Smolensk, the heroic defender of his cit
Written in a simple style characterized by redundancy, this
probably the most "medieval" of Russian legends. Contrary
this narrative, however, upon leaving the region of Smolen
Batu marched into southern Russia, where he devastated Kie
and other cities, and in 1241 he invaded Hungary. Defeatir
the Hungarians, he left Hungary so that he might return
Mongolia and participate in the selection of a new khan. Th
killing of Batu by King Stephen of Hungary, as mentioned
this tale, is the product of the writer's imagination.

The subject of *The Heroic Deeds*—the fight of a pious Russi
knight against the nomadic invaders—was a common theme
Russian medieval epics, and various details have been suppli
from early Christian and Byzantine hagiography. Very likely th
legend grew out of the life of Mercurius of Caesarea (no
Kaisaria, Turkey) and from the writings of Dionysius Pseud
Areopagite. It was probably written in the late fourteenth ce
tury, and absorbed a considerable amount of Russian folklo
elements.

This translation is based on the Old Russian text, edited l
Professor M. O. Skripil, found in *Russkie povesti XI–XVI veko*
Moscow, 1958, pages 106–107.

◆   ◆   ◆

There used to live in the city of Smolensk a young man calle
Mercurius who was very pious, who studied God's comman
ments both day and night, who distinguished himself by h
holy life, and who, because of his fasting and prayers, show
like the star which announced the birth of Christ to the enti
world. He had a contrite soul and the gift of tears.[1] Often h
would pray before the cross of our Lord for the whole worl
and he lived in the St. Peter's part of the city.

At that time the evil emperor Batu had conquered the Russia
land, had shed rivers of innocent blood, and had tortured th
Christians. This emperor came with a great army to the pio
city of Smolensk, camped at a distance of twenty miles, burne

---

[1] Eastern Christianity considered the capacity for incessant tea
during prayers to be a divine gift.

many holy churches, killed many Christians, and began to prepare for the assault of the city. The people of the city were deeply grieved, and remained incessantly in the Cathedral of the Holy Mother of God. From all their hearts they prayed and worshiped. And, shedding tears, they asked Almighty God, the Holy Mother of God, and all the saints to preserve their city from evil. And God decided to preserve the city and its people.

In the Crypt Monastery, which was located in the vicinity of the river Dnieper outside the city, the sexton of the church had a vision of the most Holy Mother of God. And she addressed him, saying: "O servant of God! Go at once to the cross where my servant, Mercurius, prays. And tell him, 'The Mother of God beckons you to come.'"

The sexton, going there and finding Mercurius praying to God before the cross, called to him by name, "Mercurius."

Mercurius answered, "What do you wish, my lord?"

And the sexton replied: "Go at once, brother. The Mother of God beckons you to the Crypt Monastery."

And when Mercurius, who was made wise by God, entered the holy church, he saw the Most Holy Mother of God sitting on the golden throne with the Christ Child in her arms and surrounded by the host of angels. Seized by awe, he fell at her feet and genuflected low before her.

And the Holy Mother of God raised him, and said: "Mercurius, my chosen one, I send you to take revenge immediately for the Christian blood which has been spilled. Go and defeat the evildoing emperor Batu and all his armies. Afterward, there will come to you a man with a handsome face. Give him all your arms, and he will decapitate you. Then take your head in your hands and return to your city. And there you will pass away and will be buried in my church."

Mercurius was saddened by these words, and, beginning to weep, he said: "O Most Holy Mother of God. How can I, a poor sinner and undeserving servant, be strong enough for such a deed? Is it possible, my Lady, that the heavenly hosts are not enough to defeat this evildoing emperor?"

Thereafter, Mercurius received her blessing, took up weapons and, bowing to the earth, went from this church. Outside the church he found a spirited steed and, mounting it, he left the city. With the help of God and his Holy Mother, he came to the regiments of the evildoing emperor, defeated the enemy, gathered together the Christian prisoners and, sending them back to his city, he courageously galloped over the regiments of

Batu even as an eagle soars through the air. The evildoing emperor, seeing such a rout of his men, and being seized by great
awe and fright, rapidly fled with a small retinue, not having
achieved the smallest success in battle. From Smolensk, Batu
fled to Hungary, and there this evildoer was killed by King
Stephen.

And the handsome warrior appeared before Mercurius. The
latter gave all his arms to him and bowed deeply before him.
And the warrior severed his head from the body. Then the
Blessed One took his head in one hand and, leading his horse
with the other hand, returned to the city decapitated. The people of the city, seeing this, were astounded by God's design.
And when Mercurius came to the Molokhov Gate, he met there
a certain maiden who was going to fetch water. When she saw
the Blessed One walking without his head, she began to abuse
him vilely. But he lay down at this gate and offered up his most
contrite soul to God. And his steed, at that moment becoming
invisible, disappeared.

The archbishop of the city came with a large number of
people carrying crosses and hoping to take the honorable body
of this saint to the church, but they were unable to lift his body
from the ground. Then there began a great wailing and weeping among the people because it was impossible to raise the
body of the saint. Even the archbishop became greatly bewildered and began to pray to God. And there came a voice to
him that announced: "O servant of God! Do not grieve. He will
be buried by the Same who sent him to victory."

And the body of the saint remained there unburied for three
days. In the meantime, the archbishop remained all these nights
praying to God to explain to him this mystery. And he remained
without sleep. Praying, he looked out through the window that
faced the cathedral, and there he saw a great light as if it were
the rising of the sun. And in this light the Most Holy Mother
of God and the Archangels Michael and Gabriel came from the
church. And, coming to the place where the body of St. Mercurius was lying, the Most Holy Mother of God raised the venerable body of the saint and brought it to her cathedral and
placed it in a casket. And this body can still be seen there,
attesting to the miracle and glory of Christ, our God, and spreading the fragrance of cedar.

The next morning, when the bishop went to Matins in the
cathedral, he saw there the wondrous miracle, the body of the
saint lying in its place. And the people flocked to the cathedral,
and, seeing this miracle, they glorified God.

30. The Story of Great John, Archbishop of Novgorod the Great; How, in One Night, He Was Taken from Novgorod to the City of Jerusalem, and Then Returned to Novgorod the Great That Same Night

THIS is one of the oldest Novgorodian legends. Bishop John was a very popular Church leader in the middle of the twelfth century, and around him there arose a number of stories. When Novgorod was threatened with incorporation into the Muscovite realm in the middle of the fifteenth century, Bishop Euthemius II (1430–1458) began collecting the legends and tales concerning the city's history and the deeds of its most outstanding leaders. Most likely this account of Great John was re-edited by Pachomius the Serb after discovery of Bishop John's relics in 1439. Pachomius, one of the innovators of the literary style known as "weaving of words" (*pletenie sloves*), embellished this text with more biblical words, difficult and complex sentences, and its stylistic redundancy.

The motif of a demon confined in a vessel is found both in tales from the East, as for instance in *Tales of the Arabian Nights*, and in early Russian hagiography.

The story is not presented here in its entirety. It ends with an account of the procession of the people and clergy to the St. George Monastery to ask Bishop John to return. Bishop John forgives the people and returns to his see.

This translation is based on the text published by N. K. Gudzy in *Khrestomatiia po drevnei russkoi literature*, Moscow, 1955, pages 207–209.

◆ ◆ ◆

FATHER, MAY YOUR BLESSING BE WITH US

This story should not lapse into oblivion, for God Almighty, who placed John in the bishopric, permits people to be overcome by temptation. He does this to sanctify and glorify them, testing their mettle as one might test gold. God has said, "I will glorify those who glorify me." Wondrous is God among the host of his saints, and God himself glorifies them.

And Christ said, "I give you power over evil spirits."

Once, in the evening, John, Archbishop of Great Novgorod,

went to recite his evening prayers, as was his custom. At that time there was a vessel filled with water near his cell, and the Reverend Father used it for his oblations. Suddenly he heard someone struggling in the water of this vessel. Coming closer to the vessel, and realizing that this was the design of the devil, he read a prayer so as to confine the demon in the vessel. The devil wished to frighten the holy father, but he was defeated in this purpose by the firm adamant.[1] The devil wanted to get out of the vessel, but could not overcome this power. A short time later, the demon could no longer endure and so began to shriek: "Oh, what a miserable plight! I am burned by fire and cannot resist any longer. Let me go at once, O servant of God."

The bishop answered: "And who are you? How did you get in this vessel?"

This devil answered: "I am an evil demon and came to this place so that I might corrupt you, hoping that you would become frightened and cease your praying. But you confined me so cruelly in this vessel, and here I am burned terribly by the fire. O woe is me, a cursed one! How could I become tempted? How could I get in this vessel? I am bewildered! Release me now, you servant of God. I shall not return to this place again!"

And the evil demon shrieked so, that finally the bishop spoke, saying: "For your daring I order that you this very night take me from Novgorod the Great to the city of Jerusalem. And place me before the church wherein is the Lord's Sepulcher. And this very night you must bring me back to my cell, which you have dared to enter. And only then shall I release you."

The demon promised to comply with the will of the bishop, and said, "Please, only release me from confinement, you servant of God."

Without releasing the demon from the power of the cross, the holy bishop let the devil out of the vessel and said to him: "Ready yourself and appear before me as a horse. Then I will mount you and you will fulfill my request."

The devil, like a cloud of darkness, left the vessel and appeared as a horse before the cell door. The bishop went from his cell and, having armed himself with the cross and grace, mounted the demon and that very night arrived in the city of Jerusalem in which is located the Holy Sepulcher of the Lord and the Tree of Life. Retaining his power over the demon, the bishop forbade it to move from the spot where it stood. And

---

[1] Adamant was often used in Russian medieval literature as a symbol of firm strength, and in this case refers to the power of the cross.

the demon, remaining under the power of the cross, was unable to move away.

In the meantime the Reverend Father went to the Church of the Holy Resurrection and, standing before the door of this church, knelt and prayed. And the doors of the church opened of their own accord, while the tapers and censers of the Lord's Sepulcher began to burn. The bishop, shedding tears, thanked God. And he venerated and kissed the Holy Sepulcher and the Tree of Life and the other shrines. Then he left the church, having fulfilled his longing. And the church doors closed after him of their own accord.

The bishop found the demon standing in the form of a horse and in the same place, as he had been ordered. And mounting the demon, the bishop found himself that very night in his cell, in the city of Novgorod the Great.

Leaving the saint's cell, the devil said: "Oh, John, you forced me to labor, carrying you in one night to Jerusalem and that very same night carrying you back to Novgorod the Great. I was bound to do so, by the power of the cross, as if I were bound by shackles. I had to undergo many calamities. Reveal to no one what has happened this night. If you do, I will lead you into temptation. You will be tried and sentenced for lechery, abused, and put on a raft in the river Volkhov.[2]

To prevent the abuse of the demon, Bishop John made the sign of the cross.

The bishop had the custom of discussing problems of the spirit with the honorable abbots, most learned priests, and God-abiding men, since he considered it a necessity that he share his wisdom with others and open to them the sublimity of the Holy Trinity. He never tired of teaching men, and he often told to them the occurrences of his own life, describing them as those of another man. "I know," he told them once, "a certain man who happened to go from Novgorod to the city of Jerusalem in one night, worshiped there at the Lord's Sepulcher, and returned that very night to Novgorod the Great." The abbots and the others were astounded.

But from that time on, and with the permission of God, the demon began to lead the bishop into temptation. The people had the vision many times of a harlot leaving the cell of the bishop. Many officials of the city, who used to come to the bishop's cell to receive his blessing, would see there a woman's

[2] Novgorod was situated on the river Volkhov, and the placing of convicts on a raft in the middle of the river was a common punishment.

necklace of coins and also a woman's robe and sandals. And they felt sore offended, and wondered what to say of this. But all this was the design of this demon who expected that the people would rise up against the bishop, would speak unjustly of him, and would drive him from their midst.

The people took council with the officials, and declared: "It is unjust for such a bishop, who is a whoremonger, to occupy the apostolic seat. Let us go and drive him from our midst, for about such people King David said: 'And words will pour forth from the mouth of the flatterer and they will speak of righteousness, lowliness, pride, and destruction. This they do for they worship the devil, even before the assembly of Jews.'"

But let us return to the narration. When the people came to the cell of the bishop, the demon walked among the people, and they saw him as a girl, leaving the cell of the saint. And the people began to exclaim that she should be seized, but they could not do so, although they followed her for a long time.

The bishop heard the cries of the people and came out to them and said, "What has happened, my children?" But the citizens paid no heed to these words, and told him what they had seen, condemned him as a whoremonger, abused him, and, after wondering what should be done with him, they decided, "Let us put him on a raft in the middle of the river Volkhov so that he may float down the river and away from our city."

And so they took the ascetic, holy, and great bishop of God, John, to the great bridge which spanned the river Volkhov, led him down to the river, and put him on a raft. And so the dream of the evil demon was fulfilled. However, God's grace shone on the face of the bishop, and his prayers to God overcame the demon's design. The demon had begun to rejoice, but when John, the bishop of God, was put on the raft in the middle of the river Volkhov, the raft immediately began to move upstream, although it was not driven by anyone. The raft on which the bishop was sitting was pushed upstream from the great bridge to the Monastery of St. George, and against a strong current. The bishop was praying for the people on the raft, saying, "O Lord, forgive them this sin, for they know not what they do."

And seeing this, the demon was abashed, and began to weep.

The people of Novgorod, seeing this miracle, rent their garments, returned, and said: "We have sinned; we have committed an injustice to this father, and we have condemned our pastor. We now know that this has happened through the designs of a demon."

IDEOLOGICAL WRITINGS

31. The Tale of the White Cowl

THE *Tale of the White Cowl*, which was to become the corner-stone of Russian national ideology, was written toward the end of the fifteenth century in Novgorod, apparently by Archbishop Genady and his co-worker and interpreter, Dmitry Gerasimov. The tale was conceived with the purpose of defending the sovereignty of the Novgorodian Church, in particular, and the Russian Church, in general, from encroachment by the Grand Duke of Muscovy, but the tale grew into an ideological work that glorified the prestige of Russian Orthodox Christianity. Later, in the sixteenth century, after the fall of Constantinople to the Turks, there developed from this work the theory of Moscow being the Third Rome, which theory was clearly and concisely formulated by Monk Philotheus (*circa* 1510–1540) when he wrote: "All Christian realms will come to an end and will unite into the one single realm of our sovereign, that is, into the Russian realm, according to the prophetic books. Both Romes fell, the third endures, and a fourth there will never be."[1] This theory defined Moscow as the sole staunch defender of the Eastern Orthodox Faith, which, in the minds of Greeks, Russians, Southern Slavs, and other Eastern Europeans, was the only true Christian doctrine.

The background of this concept is a rather eclectic one, and can be traced to the Book of Daniel (VII, 27), in which the prophet announced that the final kingdom of the one true faith will come about and will never be destroyed. This concept of Daniel's was taken up by the Chiliasts (from the Greek, *chiliad,* meaning "a thousand"), who proclaimed the forthcoming King-dom of Christ which would last a thousand years.

In the Middle Ages the Irish philosopher John Scotus Erigena (ninth century) and the Italian theologian Joachim de Fiore (twelfth century) modified Daniel's original concept into the theory of the "three kingdoms," that is, the Kingdom of the Father who gave the Law (Old Testament), the Kingdom of

---

[1] The best discussion of the works of Monk Philotheus can be found in V. Malinin's *Starets Eleazarova Monastyria Filofey i ego Poslaniia,* Kiev, 1901. This quotation is to be found on page 45 in the appendix of Malinin's work.

the Son who brought Grace, and the final Kingdom of the Holy
Spirit, of which the Apostles said: "Where there is the spirit of
God, there is freedom." The theory of the final Kingdom of the
Holy Spirit became known in Russia, and later formed the basis
for both the *Tale of the White Cowl* and the Third Rome theory.

In the eyes of Archbishop Genady and Dmitry Gerasimov,
Russia was predestined by God to be revealed as this last kingdom, the Kingdom of the Holy Spirit, which will endure until
the Last Judgment. The authors of the *Tale of the White Cowl*
combined this theocratic, utopian tenet with the Roman Catholic legend of the gift of the city of Rome to Pope Sylvester by
Emperor Constantine (Emperor of Rome, 306–337). This
legend lay the foundation for the secular power of the Pope
of Rome and also for the independence of the pope from the
emperor.

The *Tale of the White Cowl* underwent many revisions and
is extant in several versions; however, its central theme remains
the same in all: the White Cowl, the symbol of the radiant
Resurrection and Orthodox Christianity, remained in Rome as
long as the popes preserved the original teachings of Christ. But
when the popes broke with the Eastern Church and developed
their "Latin heresies,"[2] divine power gave the White Cowl to
the patriarch of Constantinople, which the Greeks of that time
called the "Second Rome." When the Greeks began to "multiply
their sins" and even began negotiating with the Pope of Rome,
God punished them by letting their land be overrun by Turks.[3]
The tale states that a century before the fall of Constantinople,
God, who had predestined the last Orthodox nation, after the
fall of Byzantium, to be Russia, commanded that the White
Cowl be taken to the Archbishop of Novgorod, Vasily.

The present translation is based on the Russian text published
by G. Kushelov-Bezborodko in *Pamiatniki starinnoi russkoi
literatury*, Volume I, St. Petersburg, 1860, pages 287–303.

Since the translation given here is not the complete tale, it is
essential to present a synopsis of the narrative up to the point
where the translation begins.

---

[2] The Byzantines, and later the Russians, called the teachings of
the Western Church "Latin Heresies," since Rome proclaimed the
primacy of the pope and used the Latin tongue exclusively for liturgi-
cal purposes.

[3] The actual conquest of Constantinople by the Turks took place in
1453, some thirty or forty years before the *Tale of the White Cowl*
was written in Novgorod.

SYNOPSIS

The *Tale of the White Cowl* opens with the story of Emperor Constantine's illness, which could be cured neither by physicians nor by magicians. One such magician, who was violently opposed to Christianity, advised the emperor that in order to be cured he must bathe in the blood of three thousand infants killed expressly for that purpose. However, at the last minute Emperor Constantine, moved by the tears and wailings of the mothers of the children who were to be slain, canceled his plan, preferring to die rather than to kill children in order to restore his health. That very night the emperor had a vision of the Apostles Peter and Paul, who told him that Pope Sylvester, who was in hiding from his persecutors at that time, could show him a font of salvation, bathing wherein would cure him of this affliction. In recompense, the emperor was to grant new rights to the Christian Church and to support it as the national religion.

The tale continues that the emperor was cured, ended the persecutions of Christians, and even wished to grant the imperial crown to the pope. The pope most humbly refused to accept it. So the emperor gave him a white cowl, the symbol of the primacy of spiritual power over secular power and of the Resurrection, the color white representing the radiance of the Resurrection of Christ. Having given the supreme power in the city of Rome to the pope, Emperor Constantine then left the Eternal City and went to the ancient city of Byzantium, which was later renamed the "city of Constantine," or Constantinople. Thus did the Eastern, or Byzantine, Roman Empire come into being.

After the death of Pope Sylvester, the tale goes on to say, the White Cowl was highly revered by the popes of Rome. However, in the ninth century, when the West was ruled by Emperor Charlemagne and the papal see was ruled by Pope Formosus,[4] a schism arose between the Eastern and Western Churches. The Western Church, under the leadership of the pope, developed new teachings and doctrines that the Eastern Church considered to be "Latin heresies," particularly the doctrine of the primacy of the Pope of Rome over the entire Church. From that time on the popes ceased to revere the White Cowl, and finally decided to profane and destroy it. However, a miraculous power saved the White Cowl, and the pope was

[4] Pope Formosus reigned from 891 to 896. During his reign there began the first conflicts between Rome and Constantinople over the jurisdiction of the two branches of the Church.

forced to send it to the patriarch of Constantinople, the capita of the still-extant Eastern Roman Empire, or, as it is more ofte called, Byzantium.

The translation begins at this point in the tale—that is, wit the arrival of the White Cowl in Constantinople.

◆ ◆ ◆

At that time the Patriarch of Constantinople was Philotheus, who was distinguished by his strict fasting and his virtuou ways. Once, he had a vision in the night of a youth from whor emanated light and who told him:

"Blessed teacher, in the olden times the Roman Emperoi Constantine, who, through the vision of the Holy Apostles Pete and Paul, was enlightened by God, decided to give Blesse Pope Sylvester the White Cowl to glorify the Holy Apostoli Church. Later, the unfaithful popes of the Latin heresies wante to profane and destroy this cowl, but I appeared to the ev pope, and now this pope has sent this cowl to you. When th messengers arrive with it, you must accept it with all honor Then send the White Cowl to the Russian land, to the city c Novgorod the Great with your written blessing. And there th cowl will be worn on the head of Vasily, Archbishop c Novgorod,[6] so that he may glorify the Holy Apostolic Cathedra of Holy Sophia and laud the Orthodox. There, in that land, th faith of Christ is verily glorified. And the popes, because c their shamelessness, will receive the vengeance of God." An having spoken these words, the youth became invisible.

The patriarch awoke filled with awe and joy, and was unab to sleep throughout the remainder of the night. And he cor templated this vision. In the morning he ordered that the bel should sound the Matins, and when day came he summoned th Church council and revealed his vision. And all praised Goc perceiving that a holy angel had appeared to the patriarch. Yc they did not fully understand the meaning of the messag When they were still in council and were filled with awe du to their great joy, there arrived a servant of the patriarch, an he announced to them that messengers had arrived from th Pope of Rome. The patriarch ordered that they be brougl

---

[5] Philotheus was patriarch of Constantinople from 1353 to 135 and from 1364–1376.

[6] Vasily was archbishop of Novgorod from 1330 to 1342. In 194 his grave was discovered and opened. In it were found both th White Cowl and the vestments embroidered with crosses which a mentioned in this tale.

before him. The messengers came, bowed lowly to the patriarch, and gave him the message. The patriarch read the message and pondered it, praising God. He announced its contents to Emperor John who was reigning at that time and whose name was Kantakuzen.[7] And then he went with the entire council to meet the bringers of the divine treasure which lay in an ark. He accepted it with all honors, broke the seal, and took from the ark the Holy White Cowl. He kissed it with reverence, and looked upon it with wonderment both for its creation and for the wonderful fragrance that emanated from it.

At that time the patriarch had diseased eyes and constant headaches, but when he placed the White Cowl upon his head, these afflictions immediately ceased to be. And he rejoiced with great joy and rendered glory to Christ, our Lord, to Constantine's blessed memory for his creating this wonderful cowl for Blessed Pope Sylvester. And he put the Holy Cowl on the golden salver that was also sent by the pope. He placed them in the great church in an honorable place until he could make a decision with the emperor's counseling.

After the White Cowl was sent from Rome, the evil pope, who was counseled by heretics, became angered against the Christian faith and was driven to a frenzy, extremely regretting his allowing the White Cowl to be sent to Constantinople. And he wrote an evil letter to the patriarch, in which he demanded the return of the White Cowl on the golden salver. The patriarch read this letter and, understanding the pope's evil and cunning design, sent him a letter in return that was based on Holy Scripture, and in it he called the pope both evil and godless, the apostate and precursor of the Antichrist. And the patriarch cursed the pope in the name of our Lord, Jesus Christ, the Holy Apostles, and the Church Fathers. And this letter came to the pope.

When the pope had read the letter and learned that the patriarch intended to send the White Cowl with great honor to the Russian land, to the city of Novgorod the Great, he uttered a roar. And his face changed and he fell ill, for he, the infidel, disliked the Russian land and could not even bear to hear of this land where the Christian faith was professed.

Patriarch Philotheus, having seen that the White Cowl was illumined with grace, began to ponder how he might keep it in

[7] John VI Kantakuzen (or Cantacuzene) was Emperor of Byzantium from 1347 to 1354.

Constantinople and wear it on his own head. He consulted with the emperor about the matter several times, and wanted to write to the other patriarchs and metropolitans to summon them to a council. After Matins one Sunday, the patriarch returned to his chambers and, after the usual prayers, lay down to rest. But he slept but lightly, and in this sleep he saw that two men, who were unknown to him, came through the door. And from them there emanated light. One of them was armed as a warrior and had an imperial crown upon his head. The other wore a bishop's vestments and was distinguished by his venerable white hair.

The latter spoke to the patriarch, saying: "Patriarch! Stop pondering your wearing of the White Cowl on your own head. If this were to be, our Lord, Jesus Christ, would have so predestined it from the founding of this city. And for a long time did divine enlightenment come from heaven, and then God's voice came to me and I learned that Rome had to betray God and embrace their Latin heresies. That is the reason I did not wish to wear this cowl upon my head, and thus I instructed other popes not to do so. And this imperial city of Constantinople will be taken by the sons of Hagar[8] because of its sins and all holy shrines will be defiled and destroyed. Thus has it been predestined since the founding of this city.

"The ancient city of Rome will break away from the glory and faith of Christ because of its pride and ambition. In the new Rome, which will be the City of Constantinople, the Christian faith will also perish through the violence of the sons of Hagar. In the third Rome, which will be the land of Russia, the Grace of the Holy Spirit will be revealed. Know then, Philotheus, that all Christians will finally unite into one Russian nation because of its orthodoxy. Since ancient times and by the will of Constantine, Emperor of the Earth, the imperial crown of the imperial city is predestined to be given to the Russian tsar. But the White Cowl, by the will of the King of Heaven, Jesus Christ, will be given to the archbishop of Novgorod the Great. And this White Cowl is more honorable than the crown of the tsar, for it is an imperial crown of the archangelic spiritual order. Thus, you must send this Holy White Cowl to the Russian land

---

[8] Both the Byzantines and the Russians called all nomads, whether they were Turks, Mongols, or Arabs, the sons of Hagar. "Hagar" refers to the handmaid of the biblical patriarch Abraham.

[9] The Russians of that time used only one word, "tsar," for the English words "king," "King of Heaven," "emperor," and even "kahn." Equally, the word "tsarstvo" was used to mean "realm," "empire," "tsardom," and the "Kingdom of God."

the city of Novgorod the Great, as you were told to do in
the vision of the angel. You should believe and trust in what I
say. And when you send it to the Russian land, the Orthodox
faith will be glorified and the cowl will be safe from seizure
by the infidel sons of Hagar and from the intended profanation
by the Latin pope. And the grace, glory, and honor which were
taken from Rome, as well as the Grace of the Holy Spirit, will
be removed from the imperial city of Constantinople after its
capture by the sons of Hagar. And all holy relics will be given
to the Russian land in the predestined moment. And the Russian
tsar will be elevated by God above other nations, and under his
sway will be many heathen kings. And the power of the patriarch of this imperial ruling city will pass to the Russian land
in the predestined hour. And that land will be called Radiant
Russia, which, by the Grace of God, will be glorified with blessings. And its majesty will be strengthened by its orthodoxy,
and it will become more honorable than the two Romes which
preceded it."

And saying this, the man of the vision who was dressed in a
bishop's vestment wished to leave, but the patriarch, seized by
great awe, fell before the bishop and said: "Who are you, my
lord? Your vision has seized me with great awe; my heart has
been frightened by your words, and I tremble to my very
bones."

The man in the bishop's vestments answered: "Don't you
know who I am? I am Pope Sylvester, and I came to you because I was ordered by God to reveal to you the great mystery
which will come to pass in the predestined time." Then, pointing to the other man in the vision, he added: "This is blessed
Emperor Constantine of Rome to whom I gave rebirth in the
holy font and whom I won over to the faith of our Lord, Jesus
Christ. He was the first Christian emperor, my child in Christ,
who created and gave me the White Cowl in place of the
imperial crown." And saying this, he blessed the patriarch, and
became invisible.

Waking up, the patriarch was seized with awe, remembering
the words about the White Cowl and the conquest of Constantinople by the pagan sons of Hagar. And he wept for a long
time. When the hour of the divine Mass arrived, the patriarch
went to the church, fell before the icon of the Holy Mother of
God, and remained lying there for some time. Then he arose,
took the White Cowl with great reverence, kissed it piously,
placed it upon his head, and then put it to his eyes and his
heart. And his adoration for this cowl increased even more. And

doing this, he wept. His clerics, who were around him an
saw that he wept inconsolably, did not dare to inquire as to wh
he was weeping. Finally the patriarch ceased crying and told h
clerics in detail of the vision of Pope Sylvester and Empere
Constantine. Having heard these words, the clerics wept so
rowfully, and exclaimed, "Thy will be done!"

The patriarch, mourning the forthcoming misfortunes of th
city of Constantinople and fearing to trespass the divine wi'
told them that he must fulfill the will of the Lord and do wit
the White Cowl as he was commanded to do. After havin
deliberated with blessed Emperor John, he took the White Cov
and the golden salver, put them in the aforementioned ar
sealed it with his seal, and, as he was commanded by the ho'
angel and Blessed Pope Sylvester, put in his epistle with h
blessings, and in it he commanded Archbishop Vasily and a
other bishops who would follow Vasily to wear the White Cov
upon their heads. He added many other honorable and marve
ous gifts from his clergy for the bishopric of Novgorod th
Great. And he also sent vestments with their embroidere
crosses[10] for the glorification of the Holy Apostolic Church. An
all this was placed in another ark. And he gave these arks to
bishop named Eumeny, and sent him forth with both joy an
sorrow.

In the bishopric of the city of Novgorod the Great was Arc
bishop Vasily who distinguished himself by his fasting an
virtuous ways. Once, in the night, he prayed to God and the
lay down to rest, but he slept but lightly, and had a dream i
which he saw the angel of God. This angel of God, who ha
a handsome appearance and radiant face, appeared befor
him in the garb of a monk and with the White Cowl upon h
head. With his finger he pointed to his head and in a low voic
announced: "Vasily! This White Cowl which you see on m
head is from Rome. In olden times the Christian Emperor Co
stantine created it in honor of Sylvester, Pope of Rome. H
gave it to this pope to wear upon his head. But God Almight
did not permit the White Cowl to remain there because of the
Latin heresies. Tomorrow morning you must go from the ci
with your clergymen and meet the bishop and messengers ser
by the patriarch. And they will bring an ark, and in this ark yo
will find the White Cowl upon a golden salver. Accept it wit
all honors, for this White Cowl symbolizes the radiant Resurrec

[10] See footnote 4.

on which came to pass on the third day. And from now, you
and all other archbishops of this city will wear it on your heads.
And I have come to you to assure you before hand that all is as
God wills it and to assuage any doubts you may have." And saying this, the angel became invisible.

Waking up, Archbishop Vasily was seized with awe and
joy, pondering the meaning of the vision. The next morning
he sent his clerics outside the city, to the crossroads, to see
whether the messengers really would appear. In the vicinity of
the city the servant of Archbishop Vasily met a Greek bishop
who was unknown to him and who traveled to the city of
Novgorod. They made a low obeisance and returned to the
archbishop and told them all they had seen. The bishop then
sent his messenger into the city to summon the clerics and the
entire population. And he ordered the tolling of the bells, and
both he and his clerics donned their vestments.

The procession had not gone far from the Cathedral of Holy
Sophia when they met the aforementioned bishop, sent by the
patriarch and bearing the ark that had been sealed by the patriarch, and which contained the venerable gifts, came to Archbishop Vasily, made a low obeisance before him, and gave
him the epistles of the patriarch. They blessed and greeted each
other in Christ's name. Archbishop Vasily accepted the epistles
of the patriarch and the arks bearing the venerable gifts. And he
went with them to the Cathedral of Holy Sophia, the Wisdom of
God. There he put them in the middle of the church in an honorable place, and ordered that the patriarchal epistles be read
aloud. When the Orthodox people, who were in the cathedral,
heard these writings read aloud, they rendered glory to God and
rejoiced with great joy. Archbishop Vasily opened one of the arks
and removed the cover. And a wonderful fragrance and miraculous radiance spread through the church. Archbishop Vasily and
all present were in wonderment, witnessing these happenings.
And Bishop Eumeny, who was sent by the patriarch, wondered
about these blessed deeds of God that he had witnessed. And
they all rendered glory to God, and celebrated the service of
thanksgiving.

Archbishop Vasily took the White Cowl from the ark and
saw that it appeared exactly like the one he had seen on the
angel's head in his vision. And he kissed it with reverence. At
that same moment there came a sonorous voice from the icon
of the Lord, which was in the cupola of the church, saying,
"Holy, holy." And after a moment of silence there came the

same voice, which thrice announced, "Ispola eti despota."[11] A
when the archbishop and all those present heard these voic
they were seized with awe and joy. And they said, "The Lo
have mercy upon us!" And the archbishop then ordered that
present in the church be silent, and he revealed to them
vision of the angel and his words concerning the White Cov
And he told of his vision as it had happened and in detail, ev
as it was told to him by the angel in the night.

Giving thanks to God for sending this cowl, the archbish
went forth from the church, preceded by the deacons in h
vestments carrying tapers and singing hymns. And they p
ceeded with serenity and piety. And the people crowded roun
jostling each other and jumping so that they might see the Wh
Cowl on the archbishop's head. And all were in wonderme
Thus, in this way, thanks to the Grace of our Lord, Jesus Chri
and to the blessing of his Holiness Philotheus, Patriarch
of Constantinople, the White Cowl became a symbol upon t
heads of the archbishops of Novgorod. And Archbishop Vas
was overcome with great joy, and for seven days he feasted
priests, deacons, and clerics of the city of Novgorod the Gre
And he also offered food and drink to the poor, to monks, a
to prisoners. And he asked that the prisoners be released. Duri
the divine service he placed the holy and venerable gifts of t
patriarch in the Cathedral of Holy Sophia and with the blessin
of all clerics. And the golden salver, on which the White Co
was placed, was also deposited in the Cathedral of Holy Sopt
during the Mass.

The messengers of the patriarch who brought the Holy Wh
Cowl were also shown great honor and they received many gif
The archbishop sent gifts to the Emperor and Patriarch
Constantinople and sent the messengers forth with great hono
Thereafter, multitudes arrived from many cities and kingdo
to look upon, as if it were a miracle, the archbishop in the Wh
Cowl. And they were in wonderment about it, and told of it
many lands. This Holy White Cowl was created by the fir
pious Christian Emperor, Constantine, for Blessed Pope S
vester in the year 297 (5805). And this is the history of t
Holy White Cowl up to this day.

[11] *Ispola eti despota* is Greek for "Many years to the lord,"
more loosely translated, "Long live the bishop." The Russians us
this expression during the Church service, and it was always p
nounced in Greek.

PART III

the muscovite period

(1478–1700)

Russia Toward 1660 A.D.

MILITARY TALES

32. The Story of Stephen Bathory's Campaign Against Pskov

'OR almost two centuries the primary objective of Muscovite
Russia's foreign policy was to gain free access to the Baltic Sea
1 order to establish direct contact with the West and put an
nd to Russia's political and cultural isolation. On many oc-
asions Russian armies had tried to capture the Baltic shores,
which had been in the hands of the Teutonic Knights of the
Livonian Order since the thirteenth century. In 1558 Ivan IV
egan a military campaign against this Order, and at first he
vas successful. When Sweden and the Polish-Lithuanian Em-
ire came to the help of the Livonian Order, however, the
Russian advance lost momentum. The war then became an
xhausting, indecisive undertaking that lasted some twenty-five
ears. In its final stages Russia had to face the powerful coali-
on of Sweden, Denmark, Poland, Lithuania, and Hungary, the
ist three countries being united under the scepter of the ener-
etic King of Hungary, Stephen Bathory.[1] After 1578 Russia
ost most of the lands she had conquered earlier, and by 1581
ing Stephen Bathory was able to begin an invasion of Russian
rritory. Polish, Lithuanian, and Hungarian troops, supported
y some German mercenaries, invaded Russia and advanced on
he city of Pskov, Russia's principal stronghold in the northwest.
fter a long siege and many attempts to subdue the city, King
tephen Bathory was forced to abandon his plans for conquest,
or the heroic defense of Pskov and his failure to take the city
ad undermined both the strength and morale of his Polish-
ithuanian forces.

The Story of Stephen Bathory's Campaign Against Pskov was
vritten in the form of an epic in the late sixteenth century by a
alented and erudite anonymous writer who displays an excel-
nt command of the traditional, ornamental stylistics of his

[1] Stephen Bathory was also elected King of Poland and Lithuania
1 1575. His wife was Anna, the last princess of the Polish dynasty of
agellons. The author of this work refers to Stephen as "King of
ithuania," although Poland, Lithuania, and Hungary were all united
nder his scepter.

time. His account is at once dramatic and ironic, picturesqu
and varied. His metaphors and literary devices ideally serve h
purpose to present a solemn account of the heroism of th
Russian soldiers. With considerable mastery and pointed iron
the author describes King Stephen Bathory's campaign, h
courageous, boastful courtiers and knights who, long before th
final outcome of the battle was in sight, bragged that they woul
capture Princes Vasily and Ivan Shuysky, the valiant defende
of Pskov. This tale betrays the strong national fervor of th
writer, who was firmly convinced that God would help the "onl
truly Christian" Russian army, and grant it final victory ove
the "infidel" invaders.

The excerpts that follow were taken from the early seven
teenth-century Russian text published by V. I. Malyshev
Povest o prikhozhdenii Stefana Batoriia na grad Pskov, Academ
of Sciences of the U.S.S.R., Moscow and Leningrad, 195
pages 56, 57, 59, 60, and 65–78.

◆ ◆ ◆

Dreadful and cruel times have come. The Polish and Lithuar
ian king, Stephen Bathory, approached the borders of the Ru
sian land with numerous forces. The rumor has spread to Psko
that this Lithuanian king has already invaded the land of Psko
and has occupied the city of Voronoch, located sixty miles fror
the city of Pskov.

Similar to insatiable hell which opens its jaws to swallow i
victim, so also did the Polish-Lithuanian king prepare to tak
the city of Pskov in the pincers of his regiments. Always liveli
and swifter, this king's army, like an ominous and great serper
wriggling from its cave, moved in columns to Pskov, an
threatened the Russians with its campfires, guns, and smok
The Lithuanian king boasted that he would swallow Pskov, eve
before he reached it. He boasted that he would satiate all th
reptiles, snakes, and scorpions of his army with the rest of th
booty. This ominous serpent leaped at Pskov, wanting to hurl
to the earth with its wings and to sting the Pskovian men t
death with its stinger. He boasted that he would plunder all th
spoils of Pskov and take them to Lithuania and that he woul
swallow up the Pskovian land, dragging on its tail all those wh
remained alive to the Lithuanian land. The serpent alread
flattered itself with thoughts of victory over Pskov.

Dark smoke rose from south of the God-protected city

Pskov. The Lithuanian armies approached Pskov, and their black shadows, like a cloud, fell over the white stone walls of Pskov. Still, the whole Lithuanian land could not make the city black. Smoke began to rise from the enemy camp, which was three miles away from the city, on the river Cherekh. The tsar's officers, who scouted at this river, rushed to Pskov to inform the tsar's boyars and voevodas that the first Lithuanian troops were already at the river Cherekh. The tsar's boyars and voevodas ordered the tocsin sounded, and gave the command to burn the settlement beyond the Velikaia[2] River in order not to leave behind any quarters for the enemies. And so, on the day of the Holy Martyrs Frol and Lavr, on August 18, 1581 (7189), the siege of the God-protected city of Pskov began. The Lithuanian troops began crossing the river Cherekh, and soon afterward their regiments appeared at the gates of the city. The boyars and voevodas lead their men in a sortie against the enemy troops. But the enemy demonstrated their weakness in this skirmish, beginning the siege with methods of flight, and not daring to approach the city. And for them this was a bad omen. . . .

On Friday, September 8th, the day of the birth of the Holy Virgin, at five o'clock in the afternoon, the Polish and Lithuanian voevodas, captains, storm troops, and gaiduks[3] hurried joyfully and hopefully to storm the city of Pskov. The tsar's boyars and voevodas,[4] all warriors, and the citizens of Pskov saw from their walls that a large number of regiments were leaving the king's camp and moving toward the city with banners. The gaiduks were entering the trenches and tunnels, and the Russians understood that they were moving to storm the breaches in the fortress wall. The voevodas ordered that the tocsin, which was located on the city wall in the vicinity of the Church of Vasily the Great on the hill, be sounded to warn all people of Pskov that the Poles and Lithuanians had begun the storming of the city. The boyars and voevodas of the tsar, with all their warriors and streltsi, were ordered to their places, and stood in preparedness while the artillery received the command to open fire on the enemy regiments. The artillery fired incessantly on the enemy, destroyed many regiments, and killed many Lithuanians and Poles. And their corpses were covering the ground. Still the enemy was advancing to the fortress, fight-

---

[2] The city of Pskov is located on the Velikaia (Great) River.

[3] The Gaiduks were mercenary infantry and shock troops.

[4] The city of Pskov was under the command of Princes Ivan and Vasily Shuysky, and Prince Andrew Khvorostinin.

ing fiercely, daringly, and hopefully. The enemy advanced as if it were a great stream flowing toward the city. The enemy troops looked as terrifying as the waves of the sea. And an endless number of their sabers were glinting at the city as if they were lightning bolts.

In the Cathedral of the Life-Giving Trinity the clergy began the service, praying to God with tears and appealing to God for the deliverance of the city. The Pskovian men took leave of their wives and children, and hurried to the breaches of the fortress wall, prepared to stave off the enemy, and in their hearts they pledged to God that they would defend the Christian faith and die for each other, for the city of Pskov, for their homes, for their wives and children, and never surrender. And they did as they promised.

At six o'clock of this same day they heard a noise comparable to that of approaching gigantic waves or of powerful thunder. And the entire enemy army howled and ran to the breaches in the fortress wall, covering themselves with their shields, rifles, muskets, lances, and other weapons, and thus appearing to be under a roof. The tsar's boyars and voevodas appealed to God for help, encouraged the Russian warriors with their battle cries, and began fighting the enemies on the fortress walls. The innumerable Lithuanian troops rushed to the fortress wall like a rampaging stream. But our Christian warriors remained as firm as the stars in the sky, and did not permit the enemy to scale the walls. Like powerful thundering, there arose a din of shouts, noises of the shooting of artillery and gunfire, and battle cries of the great multitude of warriors from both armies.

The Pskovian army barred the way of the Lithuanian army, but these lawless Lithuanian warriors fiercely and daringly scaled the wall. The enemy artillery made such large breaches in the wall that even the cavalry could go through them. And at the Virgin's Veil and the Hog Gates there was not a single place safe from the enemy's artillery and guns. The Russians had begun building new wooden walls of many stories for artillery, but they could not complete them because of the heavy enemy artillery barrage. And only their foundations were completed. Thus many enemy warriors were able to climb the city walls. Many of their captains and gaiduks scaled the Virgin's Veil and Hog Towers with their banners, shooting at our defenders from the tower windows and from behind their shields. The first to scale the wall and to remain on it were the enemy's veteran soldiers who were clad in steel armor and armed with the best of weapons. The tsar's boyars and voevodas and the entire

Orthodox army resisted them firmly and unbendingly, fighting bravely and skillfully, and not letting the enemy into the city.

When the most glorified King Stephen saw that his choicest storm troops were on the walls of the city, that his captains and gaiduks had unfurled the banners of the Lithuanian army over the Virgin's Veil and Hog Towers, and that they opened fire against the city and against the Russian artillery to open the way for the taking of the city, his heart was filled with indescribable joy. And he looked hopefully forward to the taking of the fortress. He moved his headquarters closer to the city, into the church of Christ's great martyr, Nikita, which was situated one-half mile from the wall of Pskov.

His retinue, councilors, and beloved foremost aristocrats approached the king and spoke words of hope and praise to him: "Our lord and sovereign, you have done it. You are the conqueror and victorious ruler of the city of Pskov. Glory be to you. We beg you, extend your kindness to us and allow us to proceed to the fortress of Pskov, so that not only your captains and gaiduks will know the glory of having taken Pskov."

When the king heard how joyfully his noblemen and councilors expressed their readiness to fulfill his plans, joy overcame him. With a gay face and happy heart he told them, as if they were his brothers, "Well, my friends, if you show such intentions to fight, I shall also go with you and not stay behind, my friends."

But they answered: "Oh, our sovereign, King Stephen! You will make your triumphant and glorious entry into this great city of Pskov, in the same way as the great king, Alexander the Great, made his glorious and triumphant entry into the city of Rome.[5] And in the same way as Alexander's courtiers met him in the city, so also shall we, your servants, meet you in the city of Pskov with a hymn of glory. And we will prepare for you the spoils of the city. And we will meet you with the Russian commanders of Pskov, whom we shall capture! And for a particularly cherished treasure, we shall meet you with the two captured boyars and voevodas: the first commander of Pskov, Prince Vasily Shuysky, and the glorious, strong, invincible, great, and courageous second commander, Prince Ivan Shuysky. And we shall put them both in irons before you. And you, our sovereign, will do what you please with them in order that they be punished for their unruly resistance to you."

---

[5] Either the Polish nobles erred in their speeches or the author of this tale did, for Alexander the Great certainly was never at war with Rome.

Hearing this, the king permitted them to go to the walls of
the fortress of Pskov with joy, telling them the following: "I
knew, friends, that it always would happen as you used to pre-
dict, and so it will happen now. And you will accomplish what
you intend to, for no one can resist you and your brilliant mind."
And two thousand selected storm troops and personal guards
of the king began the assault of the Hog Tower, which was
already destroyed on their side, and they began shooting through
the windows of the wall at the Christian people and at the
Russian militia. Their bullets fell like drops of rain from a
storm cloud, and flooded the Russian warriors. These bullets
were killing the Christian people as if they were the stings of
serpents. Other enemy troops stormed through the break in the
Virgin's Veil Tower, and cleared the tower of Russian warriors,
preparing the way for the final taking of the city.

The Russian voevodas, their soldiers, and the Pskovian militia
firmly and courageously stood their ground. Some waited for the
enemy with lances at the foot of the wall. The streltsy shot
at the Poles with their muskets. Some of the noblemen shot
with their bows, while still others hurled rocks or defended the
city of Pskov in other ways. The artillery shot at the Russian
army from the walls and the towers and, relieving tired ones
with fresh troops, they shot incessantly and shouted, "Let's take
the city of Pskov!"

The king often sent his messenger to them, inquiring whether
the city had been taken, and ordered the commanders, captains,
and the entire army to speed the taking of the city.

In the God-protected city of Pskov the voevodas and boyars
of the tsar, with kindness and tears, urged their Christian warriors to fight heartily, and they, themselves, fought unyieldingly
at the side of their troops. It was sad to see the heads of the
Christian warriors falling to the earth like the ears of wheat torn
from the ground and lying in one heap. Many soldiers fell from
the many wounds inflicted by the enemy's weapons, from exhaustion, and from the incessant fighting. During the day it was
extremely hot because of the burning sun. Only faith in God's
protection and deliverance gave strength to the warriors.

In the city itself and in the Cathedral of the Life-Giving
Trinity the clergy incessantly prayed with tears and moaning
for deliverance of the city. When the clergy of the cathedral
learned the news that the Lithuanians were already on the walls
and in the towers, and that they had unfurled their banners and
were shooting from the walls into the city, preparing their way,
then Tikhon, the abbot of the Caves Monastery, and arch-

riest Luka, and all the deacons of the city began to weep with
oud voices, extending their arms to the most holy icon. They
ell to their knees. Like the streams of many rivers their tears
covered the marble steps of the altar, and they began to pray
with more fervor, asking the Holy Virgin to protect the city and
ts inhabitants. The noble ladies, who had gathered in the
athedral for the service, beat their breasts and prayed to God
nd the most Pure Virgin; they fell on the floor, beating the
round with their heads and crying for divine help. And in
very house of the great and God-protected city of Pskov the
omen, infants, and children who remained at home fervently
ried and prayed before the holy icons, beating their breasts
nd asking the Holy Virgin and all saints for help, and begging
od for the forgiveness of their sins and deliverance of the
ity. And in all the streets of the city there was crying, moaning,
nd indescribable wailing.

The enemy troops were incessantly and steadily advancing.
Forward, friends!" shouted their officers. "Let us slay all the
eople of Pskov for their unsubmissiveness. Not even a memory
f the Christian inhabitants of Pskov will remain. The shadow
f death will engulf them, and nothing will be able to aid them
n escaping from our hands."

> But who can speak of the power of God? Who can praise
> his glory?
> Blessed are those that fear God and follow his righteous
> ways,
> and who honestly enjoy the fruits of their labors.
> Listen, all people of the universe.
> Listen all sons of man.
> Listen all rich and poor.
> Come all saints of Russia to the Christian land to aid the
> city of Pskov.
> You have prayed for us and have helped us through your
> prayers to God.
> You protected the city of Pskov,
> which verily I say unto you is the God-protected city.
> Let us glorify and declare together the power of the Holy
> Trinity.
> God is our protection and power; God is our aid in the
> sorrow befallen us.
> Therefore, I verily say unto you,
> that we have no fear, as the voice of the prophet an-
> nounced it.

Great is God and greatly is he glorified in this city of God
We recognize God, who is on his holy mountain,
when we are in misfortune and when he intercedes for us
For our humility God did not forsake us
when the kings of the earth gathered to march on Pskov
    saying:
"God has abandoned that city. Let us hurry and take it."

O Lithuanian commander, Stephen Bathory!
Your tongue is cursed, and both you and your army are in
    sanely proud.
How can you say that no one will deliver this city?
The power of God is with us!
Our Protector is the God of Jacob, the God of the Glorifie
    Trinity,
the One God who has three names, but whom we worship
    as One,
the Father, the Son, and the Holy Ghost.
We place our hope in him and we rely upon him.
But you, Bathory, do not know him with your lawles
    Latin Heresies.
And you, Bathory, who place your own majesty before tha
    of Heaven,
hope to conquer the city of Pskov, relying on your mult
    tude of forces.
Wait, accursed one! You will see what happens to you
    forces!
You will see whether there is One who can deliver us!
And what is the worth of all your proud bragging abou
    the taking of Pskov?
Because of your pride, you will now experience humiliatior
And from the heights of arrogance, you will descend to th
    hell of shame.
And so will it happen to your army,
for the Lord has remembered us for our humility
and has delivered us from our enemies.
And the Lord has heard the prayers of his servants
and through the miracle of his unfathomable compassior
    his mercy was revealed,
and he delivered his people and showed clemency to hi
    servants.

A bomb from the great gun called the Leopard, which wa
placed upon the Praise Bastion, hit the Hog Tower squarely

And the bomb killed a great many Polish and Lithuanian warriors. At about the same time, the tsar's boyars and voevodas ordered the exploding of a large quantity of black powder under this Hog Tower. And the overproud knights, courtiers, and nobles of the king, who had begged their king for permission to take the city of Pskov and bring in the Russian boyars and voevodas in irons, as it was previously mentioned, were blasted into the air according to God's design, and were thus slain by these Russian boyars and voevodas. And the corpses were so numerous that another tower might have been built with them. And the best of the royal nobles, who had boasted that they would bring the imprisoned Russian commanders to their king, remained under the ruins of the Hog Tower, prisoners of death until the Last Judgment. And the deep Pskovian moat was overflowing with their bodies.

The king learned this, when he asked, "Are my noblemen already in the castle?"

And his courtiers told him: "No, sire, they are under the walls of the castle."

And then the king asked, "Do my nobles fight behind the walls of the city and destroy the Russian forces?"

And they answered, "Sire, all your nobles have been killed in the Hog Tower or lie burned in the moat."

And the king was so bereaved that he wanted to run on his sword, as the pagans used to do, for his heart was bursting with sorrow. And he became wroth, and ordered his captains and storm troops who were fighting at the Virgin's Veil Tower to stand firm and take by any and all means the city of Pskov.

The tsar's boyars and voevodas, seeing the heavy and uninterrupted bombardment, the incessant storming, and realizing that many of their warriors had been killed or wounded, relied only upon the help of God. They sent for the holy and miracle-working icons and for the miracle-working relics of the faithful and great Prince Gabriel[6] who had once delivered the city of Pskov from the enemy. And they ordered that the icons be brought to the breach which had been made in the wall by the Poles. Once the holy icon of the Holy Virgin of Vladimir protected the city of Moscow at the time of Tamerlane's invasion. Now another icon was brought to Pskov because of the invasion of King Stephen Bathory. Once the icon of the Virgin

---

[6] Prince Gabriel, as well as Prince Dovmont, mentioned in the following paragraph, were rulers of Pskov in the thirteenth and fourteenth centuries, and became known for their courageous defense of Pskov against the Teutonic Knights of the Livonian Order.

protected the city of Moscow from the infamous lame man [Tamerlane]. Now another icon of the Virgin, which had been brought from the Crypt Monastery,[7] helped and protected Pskov. At that time the holy icon of Vladimir was brought to Moscow on the day of the Assumption of the Holy Virgin, and Tamerlane was defeated because he became afraid of this icon of the Pure Virgin, and fled with all his army from Moscow and from Russia. This time the miracle happened in the glorious city of Pskov, on the very day of the venerable and glorious holy day of her birth.

When the holy, miracle-working icon of the Assumption of the Holy Virgin of the Crypt Monastery was brought from the Cathedral of the Holy Trinity with other icons, relics of Prince Gabriel, and other holy relics, divine protection invisibly appeared over the breach in the wall.

The Poles and Lithuanians were fiercely fighting against the Russians in the breaches of the wall and in the Virgin's Veil Tower. Together with the warriors, the Russian officers and commanders were fighting, preventing the enemy from breaking through into Pskov. And when the church procession moved from the cathedral with the icons, at the head of the procession, black-robed heralds rushed on their steeds; they were not soldiers, but the warriors of Christ. Among them were the cellarer of the Crypt Monastery, whose name was Arseny Khvostov; the treasurer of the Monastery of the Birth of the Holy Virgin in Snetegorsk, Jonah Naumov; and the abbot, Mantiry, who was known to everyone in Pskov. All three of these monks were aristocrats by birth and, before becoming monks, had been great warriors. Seeing the bloody battle, they rushed to the breach and, for the sake of God and their holy faith, called out in strong voices. And it seemed as if these voices were coming from the icons. They called to the commanders and to the whole Christian army: "Be not afraid. Let us stand firm. Let us charge against the Polish and Lithuanian forces. The Holy Virgin has come to our aid with all her mercy and protection, and with all the saints."

As soon as the words were heard that the Holy Virgin had come with all the saints to help the Russian commanders and warriors, they felt that the Holy Virgin really did give them her blessing and protection, and thus their weakening hearts became

---

[7] The Crypt Monastery mentioned here is west of the city of Pskov, and has preserved to the present its fortifications built by Ivan IV. The name of the monastery was apparently taken from the Kievan Cave (or Crypt) Monastery.

m and they became ready for heroic deeds. In their hearts
ey accepted the aid of the Holy Virgin, and all commanders,
arriors, and the aforementioned monks cried out in unison:
Oh, friends, let us die this day at the hands of the Lithuanians
r the sake of Christ's faith and for our Orthodox tsar, Ivan of
. the Russias! Let us not surrender to the Polish king,
ephen!" And they appealed also for the intercession of the
ly protectors of Pskov, late Prince Gabriel, late Prince Dov-
ont, and Nicholas, the fool in Christ. And in their hearts they
cepted their help, and the entire Russian Christian army
ormed the enemy together, and they were fighting in the
each of the wall.

Thus, with God's and the Holy Virgin's help, and with the
tercession of the holy miracle workers, the Russians expelled
e Polish-Lithuanian forces from the breach and, where re-
ntly stood the feet of the enemy, now stood the firm feet of
e Christian warriors. And they continued to defeat the enemy,
ing beyond the walls of the city, while others fought with the
thuanian troops who remained in the Virgin's Veil Tower.

When the Lord demonstrated the Christian victory over Paul
e Lithuanian, and when the Russian troops repulsed the
thuanian warriors, captains, and gaiduks from the breach in
e wall, this news of the blessing of Christ spread throughout
e entire city of Pskov, and reached the women who had been
t at home. And the word that the enemy had been stopped
rough divine help spread from house to house. And the
omen were ordered to go take the Lithuanian artillery and the
mnants of the Lithuanian and Polish troops that remained
the city, and then to gather at the breach. And all the women
Pskov, who had remained in their homes in great sorrow,
ere seized with joy, forgot their womanly weaknesses, and
ined the strength of men, hurried to the breach, and took
om their homes weapons according to their strengths. Even
fore, at the beginning of the assault, some strong young
omen had been fighting against the enemy with arms. Now
, the young, the strong, and the weak, were running with
pes to pull the artillery pieces left by the enemy into the city.
l of them rushed to the breach. And each woman wanted to
rpass the others in her speed. A multiude of women gathered
the breach, and they were great help for the Christian war-
ors. Some of them, as I mentioned above, who were young and
ong, fought with masculine courage against the Polish and
thuanian forces, demonstrating their superiority over them.
e others brought rocks so that the soldiers might hurl them at

the Lithuanians both within and outside of the fortress. Oth
helped the warriors, and brought them water to quench th
thirst, thus bringing back courage to their brave hearts.

This happened on Friday, on the holy day of the H
Virgin's Birth. It was already evening, but the Polish and Litl
anians were still fighting in the Virgin's Veil Tower and w
shooting against the Christian warriors in the city. Then
tsar's boyars and voevodas appealed to God for succor, cal
their troops together, and began the storming of the Virgi
Veil Tower. Men and women hurled themselves against t
remaining enemy troops in the tower, fighting with all t
arms given to them by God. Some shot muskets, while oth
were trying to smoke out the enemy from their hiding plac
Others threw rocks at the Poles and Lithuanians, while s
others poured boiling water upon them. Finally they put bla
powder under this tower also, and with God's help they blast
the remaining Lithuanians and Poles from the Virgin's V
Tower. In this way, with the Grace of Christ, the stone wall
Pskov was cleansed of the evil Lithuanian feet. When nig
came, God sent light, and the remainder of the enemy w
driven out from under the walls.

And then the Lithuanians and Poles began to flee from t
fortress back to their camps. The Christian Russian warrie
made sorties from the fortress, pursued them, cut them to piec
and chased the others away. Those who remained in the m
were destroyed. Many were taken prisoner and brought back
the city, to the tsar's boyars and voevodas to be interrogat
Many enemy warriors were taken with banners, drums, a
weapons. And many Russians returned to the city uninjure
and brought back with them enemy arms, special muskets, gu
and endless booty.

Thus, with God's blessing, through the infinite mercy of t
Divine Trinity, and the prayers and intercession of the H
Virgin, and in the honor of her glorious birth, and for t
sake of the holy, great miracle workers, the great city of Psk
was delivered from the Poles and Lithuanians. And at thr
o'clock in the night the Lord gave a great victory to the Chr
tian army over the proud and lawless enemy.

[The final part of this work describes the fighting arou
Pskov until February 4, 1582, the day when King Steph
Bathory lifted the siege of this fiercely embattled Russi
fortress.]

EPISTOLARY POLEMICS

33. Prince Andrew Kurbsky: First Epistle Written to the Tsar and Grand Prince of Moscow in Consequence of His Fierce Persecution

PRINCE Andrew Kurbsky's first epistle to Ivan IV is a strong protest against Tsar Ivan's autocratic rule. Wishing to destroy the old feudal system of Russia, by which the princes were practically independent rulers of their appanages, Ivan IV began a systematic purge of the aristocracy in the late 1550's and many nobles died on the scaffold or in prison.

An outstanding statesman and military leader, Prince Kurbsky was a close friend and adviser of Tsar Ivan IV until the latter began his cruel struggle against the Russian feudal aristocracy. Kurbsky then broke with the tsar and fled to Lithuania, where he settled for the rest of his life. Kurbsky had belonged to the intellectual elite of sixteenth-century Moscow and had been a pupil and friend of the famous and erudite scholar-monk, Maxim Trivolis, called Maxim the Greek, who had come to Russia in the early years of the sixteenth century. Living in Lithuania, Andrew Kurbsky became a writer and translator and participated in the revival of Russian Orthodox literature in the Russian parts of Poland and Lithuania. His best-known work is his correspondence with Ivan IV, in which he sharply criticized the tsar's autocratic policies and his persecution of the aristocracy.

This translation of the letter was made by J. L. I. Fennell and was published in *The Correspondence Between Prince A. M. Kurbsky and Tsar Ivan IV of Russia, 1564–1579*, Cambridge University Press, 1955, pages 3, 5, 7, 9, and 11.

✦ ✦ ✦

To the tsar, exalted above all by God, who appeared (formerly) most illustrious, particularly in the Orthodox faith, but who has now, in consequence of our sins, been found to be the contrary of this. If you have understanding, may you understand this with your leprous conscience—such a conscience as cannot be found even amongst the godless peoples. And I have not let my tongue say more than this on all these matters in turn; but because of the bitterest persecution from your power, with much sorrow in my heart will I hasten to inform you of a little.

Wherefore, O tsar, have you destroyed the strong in Isra
and subjected to various forms of death the *voevodas* given
you by God?[1] And wherefore have you spilled their victorio
holy blood in the churches of God during sacerdotal ceremoni
and stained the thresholds of the churches with their blood
martyrs?[2] And why have you conceived against your we
wishers and against those who lay down their lives for y
unheard-of torments and persecutions and death, falsely accu
ing the Orthodox of treachery and magic and other abuses, a
endeavoring with zeal to turn light into darkness and to c
sweet bitter? What guilt did they commit before you, O tsa
and in what way did they, the champions of Christianity, ang
you? Have they not destroyed proud kingdoms and by the
heroic bravery made subject to you in all things those in who
servitude our forefathers formerly were? Was it not through t
keenness of their understanding that the strong German tow
were given to you by God?[3] Thus have you remunerated
[your] poor [servants], destroying us by whole families? Thi
you yourself immortal, O tsar? Or have you been enticed in
unheard-of heresy, as one no longer wishing to stand before t
impartial judge, Jesus, begotten of God, who will judge accor
ing to justice the universe and especially the vainglorious to
mentors, and who unhesitatingly will question them "right to t
hairs [roots?] of their sins," as the saying goes? He is my Chr
who sitteth on the throne of the Cherubims at the right hand
the power of the Almighty in the highest—the judge betwe
you and me.

What evil and persecution have I not suffered from yo
What ills and misfortunes have you not brought upon me! A
what iniquitous tissues of lies have you not woven against m
But I cannot now recount the various misfortunes at your han

[1] The expression "the strong in Israel" echoes the current pan
gyrical political literature of the sixteenth century, extolling t
absolution of the grand prince and the supremacy of Moscow, "t
Third Rome," "the new Israel."

[2] A reference to the first wave of Ivan's persecutions which, a
cording to Kurbsky (Skazaniia Kn. A. M. Kurbskogo, ed. N. Ustrial
[St. Petersburg, 1842], "Istoria . . ." Chapter VI, page 90) beg
"shortly after the death of Alexis Adashev and the banishment
Priest Sylvester," i.e., in 1560.

[3] The "proud kingdoms" destroyed by the "strong in Israel" in t
fifties of the sixteenth century were the Tatar Khanates of Kaz
(captured in 1552) and Astrakhan (captured in 1556). The "stro
German towns" are the Baltic towns captured during the first thr
years of the Livonian War (1558–1560): Narva, Neuhausen, a
Dorpat (1558); Marienburg, Ermes, and Fellin (1560).

which have beset me owing to their multitude and since I am still filled with the grief of my soul. But, to conclude, I can summarize them all [thus]: of everything have I been deprived; I have been driven from the land of God without guilt [*lit*. in vain], hounded by you. I did not ask [for aught] with humble words, nor did I beseech you with tearful plaint; nor yet did I win from you any mercy through the intercession of the hierarchy. You have recompensed me with evil for good and for my love with implacable hatred. My blood, spilled like water for you, cries out against you to my Lord. God sees into [men's] hearts—in my mind have I ardently reflected and my conscience have I placed as a witness [against myself], and I have sought and pried within my thoughts, and, examining myself [*lit*. turning myself around], I know not now—nor have I ever found—my guilt in aught before you. In front of your army have I marched—and marched again; and no dishonor have I brought upon you; but only brilliant victories, with the help of the angel of the Lord, have I won for your glory, and never have I turned the back of your regiments to the foe. But far more, I have achieved most glorious conquests to increase your renown. And this, not in one year, nor yet in two—but throughout many years have I toiled with much sweat and patience; and always have I been separated from my fatherland, and little have I seen my parents, and my wife have I not known; but always in far distant towns have I stood in arms against your foes and I have suffered many wants and natural illnesses, of which my Lord Jesus Christ is witness. Still more, I was visited with wounds inflicted by barbarian hands in various battles and all my body is already afflicted with sores. But to you, O tsar, was all this as nought; rather do you show us your intolerable wrath and bitterest hatred, and, furthermore, burning stoves.[4]

And I wanted to relate all my military deeds in turn which I have accomplished for your glory by the strength of my Christ, but I have not recounted them for this reason, that God knows better than man. For he is the recompenser for all these things, and not only for them, but also for a cup of cold water; and I know that you yourself are not unaware of them. And furthermore may this be known to you, O tsar; you will, I think,

---

[4] Evidently one of the commonest forms of torture employed by Ivan IV. Kurbsky speaks of Ivan's torture in his *History:* "Are not the various instruments of torture of the ancient torturers the same as those used by our new torturer [i.e. Ivan]? Pans and stoves? Cruel flogging and sharp nails? Red-hot pincers for lacerating human bodies? Needles to drive under the fingernails . . . ?" (p. 145)

no longer see my face in this world until the glorious coming of my Christ. Think not that concerning these things I will remain silent before you; to my end will I incessantly cry out with tears against you to the everlasting Trinity, in which I believe; and I call to my aid the Mother of the Lord of the Cherubims, my hope and protectress, Our Lady, the Mother of God, and all the Saints, the elect of God, and my master and forefather, Prince Fedor Rostislavich, whose corpse remains imperishable, preserved throughout the ages, and emits from the grave sweet odors, sweeter than aromatics, and, by the grave of the Holy Ghost, pours forth miraculous healing streams, as you, O tsar, know well.[5]

Deem not, O tsar, and think not upon us with your sophistic thoughts, as though we had already perished, massacred [though we are] by you in our innocence and banished and driven out by you without justice; rejoice not in this, glorying, as it were, in a vain victory; those massacred by you, standing at the throne of our Lord, ask vengeance against you; while we who have been banished and driven out by you without justice from the land cry out day and night to God, however much in your pride you may boast in this temporal, fleeting life, devising vessels of torture against the Christian race, yea, and abusing and trampling on the Angelic Form,[6] with the approbation of your flatterers and comrades of the table, your quarrelsome boyars, the destroyers of your soul and body, who urge you on to erotic deeds and, together with their children, act more [viciously] than the priests of Cronus. So much for this. And this epistle, soaked in my tears, will I order to be put into my grave with me, when I [shall be about to] come with you before the judgment of my God, Jesus Christ. Amen.

Written in Wolmar, the town of my master, King Augustus Sigismund, from whom I hope to receive much reward and com-

---

[5] Fedor Rostislavich, prince of Yaroslavl, Andrew Kurbsky's paternal grandfather to the ninth degree, ruled in Mozhaisk at the end of the thirteenth century. In 1294 he received the principality of Yaroslavl after marrying the daughter of Vasily Vsevolodovich, prince of Yaroslavl. He died in 1299 and was canonized in 1463.

[6] The Russian expression "to accept the Angel's form" is the equivalent of "to take monastic vows." In certain copies of the text there exists the following marginal note: "That is to say, he abuses the Angelic Form when he flies into a rage with certain people and then forces them to accept the monastic tonsure together with their wives and children, and condemns them to everlasting imprisonment in strong monasteries and dark cells, making the holy places fortresses of hell with the approbation of certain accursed and cunning monks."

ort for all my sorrow, by his sovereign grace, and still more with God's help.

I have heard from sacred writings that a destroyer will be sent by the devil against the human race, a destroyer conceived in fornication, the Antichrist, hostile to God; and now I have seen a counselor, known to all, who was born in adultery and who today whispers falsehoods in the ears of the tsar and sheds Christian blood like water and has already destroyed the strong and noble in Israel, as one in agreement with the Antichrist in deed.[7] It is not befitting, O tsar, to show indulgence to such men! In the first law of the Lord it is written: "A Moabite and an Ammonite and a bastard to the tenth generation shall not enter into the congregation of the Lord."[8]

34. Ivan IV: Epistle of the Tsar and Sovereign to All His Russian Tsardom Against Those Who Have Broken the Pledge of Allegiance, Against Prince Andrew Kurbsky and His Comrades, Concerning Their Treacheries

THE epistle of Ivan IV, the Terrible, to Prince Andrew Kurbsky is one of the most impressive works defending the Byzantine-Russian concept of autocracy, which accepted the tsar as ruler by divine right. Ivan IV thus claimed the exclusive right to command the destinies of the state and his subjects, while considering himself responsible only to God for the fate of the state and its people. (Concerning Prince Andrew Kurbsky and the roots of this conflict, see the introduction to Prince Kurbsky's letter to Ivan.)

A cruel tyrant who was merciless to his enemies, Ivan IV was at the same time a great ruler whose policies helped determine the future of Russia. By breaking the power of the aristocracy he ended the feudal system of medieval Russia and thus laid the foundation for a unified Russian state. His successes against the Tatars opened to Russia the nearly limitless territories of the

[7] This is probably a reference to Fedor Alekseevich Basmanov, who was a favorite of Ivan's at that time. He was, indeed, renowned for his cruelty, and is alleged by Kurbsky to have murdered his father. There is, however, no confirmation of his illegitimacy.

[8] See Deuteronomy, 23: 2-3.

Tsar Ivan IV (the Terrible).
A late sixteenth-century Russian portrait.

Volga-Ural region and northern Asia, thus paving the way for future Russian expansion. Some one hundred and fifty years before Peter the Great, Ivan IV tried to open a window to Europe and to end Russia's isolation by winning an area on the Baltic shore from the Order of Livonian Knights.

Ivan IV was very well educated, was a forceful polemicist and writer, and even composed music. His style of writing is not restrained, but fierce, stinging and merciless, and he did not hesitate to insult his enemies.

These excerpts from Tsar Ivan's letter to Prince Kurbsky, which grew into a rather lengthy treatise, have been translated by Leo Wiener.

◆ ◆ ◆

Our God, the Trinity, who has existed since eternity but now as Father, Son and Holy Ghost, has neither beginning nor end; through him we live and move about, through him kings rule and the mighty write laws. By our Lord Jesus Christ the victorious standard of God's only Word and the blessed Cross, which has never been vanquished, have been given to Emperor Constantine, first in piety, and to all the orthodox tsars and protectors of orthodoxy and, insofar as the Word of God has been fulfilled, they, in eagle's flight, have reached all the godly servants of God's Word, until a spark of piety has fallen upon the Russian realm. The autocracy, by God's will, had its origin in Grand Prince Vladimir, who had enlightened all Russia through the holy baptism, and the great Tsar Vladimir Monomakh, who had received memorable honors from the Greeks, and the valiant great Tsar Alexander Nevsky, who had obtained a great victory over the godless Germans, and the praiseworthy great Tsar Dmitry, who had obtained a great victory over the sons of Hagar beyond the Don, then it passed to the avenger of wrongs, our ancestor, the great Tsar Ivan, the gatherer of the Russian land from among the ancestral possessions, and to our father of blessed memory, the great Tsar Vasily until it reached us, the humble scepter-bearer of the Russian empire.[1]

[1] Roman Emperor Constantine (306–337) granted the rights to the Christians, and summoned the first Ecumenical Council of the Christian Church. Prince Vladimir Christianized Russia in 988 or 989. Vladimir Monomakh was the last prince of Kiev (1112–1125) to be recognized as Grand Prince by all Russian princes of the Kievan era. Dmitry, Grand Prince of Muscovy, was the victor over the Tatars in 1380. "The great Tsar Ivan" is Ivan III, unifier of northern Russia (1462–1505) and grandfather of Ivan IV. Vasily—Vasily III (1505–1533)—was father to Ivan IV.

But we praise God for the great favor he has shown me in
not permitting my right hand to become stained by the blood of
my race: for we have not snatched the realm from anyone, but
by the will of God and the blessing of our ancestors and parents,
were we born in the realm, were brought up there and enthroned, taking, by the will of God and the blessing of our ancestors and parents, what belonged to us, and not seizing that
which was not ours. Here follows the command of the orthodox,
truly Christian autocrat, the possessor of many kingdoms—our
humble Christian answer to him who was an orthodox, true
Christian and a boyar of our realm, a councilor and a general,
but now is a criminal before the blessed, vivifying cross of the
Lord, a destroyer of Christians, a servant of the enemies of
Christianity, who has departed from the divine worship of the
images and has trodden underfoot all sacred commands, destroyed the holy edifices, vilified and trampled the holy vessels
and images, who unites in one person Leo the Isaurian, Constantine Kopronymos and Leo of Armenia—to Prince Andrew
Mikhailovich Kurbsky, who through treachery wanted to become
a ruler of Yaroslavl.[2]

Wherefore, O Prince, if you regard yourself to have piety,
have you lost your soul? What will you give in its place on the
day of the terrible judgment? Even if you should acquire the
whole world, death will reach you in the end! Why have you
sold your soul for your body's sake? Is it because you were afraid
of death at the false instigation of your demons and influential
friends and counselors? . . .

Are you not ashamed before your slave Vaska Shibanov,[3] who
preserved his piety and, having attached himself to you with a
kiss of the cross, did not reject you before the tsar and the
whole people, though standing at the gate of death, but praised
you and was all too ready to die for you? But you did not emulate his devotion: on account of a single angry word of mine,
have you lost not only your own soul, but the souls of all your
ancestors: for, by God's will, had they been given as servants to
our grandfather, the great tsar, and they gave their souls to
him and served him up to their death, and ordered you, their
children, to serve the children and grandchildren of our grand-

[2] Leo III the Isaurian (717–741), Constantine V Kopronymos
(741–755), and Leo V, the Armenian, were Byzantine emperors who
supported the heresy of the iconoclasts and were posthumously condemned by the Orthodox Church.

[3] Vaska (Vasily) Shibanov, a faithful servant of Prince A. M.
Kurbsky who delivered his master's letter to Ivan IV, and died after
long tortures without betraying the prince.

father. But you have forgotten everything and traitorously, like a dog, have you transgressed the oath and have gone over to the enemies of Christianity, and, not considering your wrath, you utter stupid words, hurling, as it were, stones at the sky. . . .

We have never spilled blood in the churches. As for the victorious, saintly blood—there has none appeared in our land, as far as we know. *The thresholds of the churches:* as far as our means and intelligence permit and our subjects are eager to serve us, the churches of the Lord are resplendent with all kinds of adornments, and through the gifts which we have offered since your satanic domination, not only the thresholds and pavements, but even the antechambers shine with ornaments, so that all the strangers may see them. We do not stain the thresholds of the churches with any blood, and there are no martyrs of faith with us nowadays. . . . Tortures and persecutions and deaths in many forms we have devised against no one. As to treasons and magic, it is true, such dogs everywhere suffer capital punishment. . . .

It had pleased God to take away our mother, the pious Tsarina Helen, from the earthly kingdom to the kingdom of heaven. My brother George, who now rests in heaven, and I were left orphans and, as we received no care from anyone, we laid our trust in the Holy Virgin, and in the prayers of all the saints, and in the blessing of our parents. When I was in my eighth year, our subjects acted according to their will, for they found the empire without a ruler, and did not deign to bestow their voluntary attention upon us, their master, but were bent on acquiring wealth and glory, and were quarreling with each other. And what have they not done! How many boyars, how many friends of our father and generals they have killed! And they seized the farms and villages and possessions of our uncles, and established themselves therein. The treasure of our mother they trod underfoot and pierced with sharp sticks, and transferred it to the great treasure, but some of it they grabbed themselves; and that was done by your grandfather Mikhaylo Tuchkov. The Princes Vasily and Ivan Shuysky took it upon themselves to have me in their keeping, and those who had been the chief traitors of our father and mother they let out of prison, and they made friends with them. Prince Vasily Shuysky with a Judas crowd fell in the court belonging to our uncle upon our father confessor Fedor Mishurin, and insulted him, and killed him; and they imprisoned Prince Ivan Fedorovich Byelsky and many others in various places, and armed themselves against the realm; they ousted metropolitan Daniel from the metropolitan see and banished him: and thus they improved their opportunity, and began to rule themselves.

Me and my brother George, of blessed memory, they brought up like vagrants and children of the poorest. What have I not suffered for want of garments and food! And all that against my will and as did not become my extreme youth. I shall mention just one thing: once in my childhood we were playing, and Prince Ivan Vasilievich Shuysky was sitting on a bench, leaning with his elbow against our father's bed, and even putting his foot upon it; he treated us not as a parent, but as a master . . . who could bear such presumption? How can I recount all the miseries which I have suffered in my youth? Often did I dine late, against my will. What had become of the treasure left me by my father? They had carried everything away, under the cunning pretext that they had to pay the boyar children from it, but, in reality, they had kept it back from them, to their own advantage, and had not paid them off according to their deserts; and they had also held back an immense treasure of my grandfather and father, and made it into gold and silver vessels, inscribing thereupon the names of their parents, as if they had been their inheritance. . . . It is hardly necessary to mention what became of the treasure of our uncles: they appropriated it all to themselves! Then they attacked towns and villages, tortured the people most cruelly, brought much misery upon them, and mercilessly pillaged the possessions of the inhabitants. . . .

When we reached the age of fifteen, we, inspired by God, undertook to rule our own realm and, with the aid of almighty God, we ruled our realm in peace and undisturbed, according to our will. But it happened then that, on account of our sins, a fire having spread, by God's will, the royal city of Moscow was consumed. Our boyars, the traitors whom you call martyrs, whose names I shall purposely pass over in silence, made use of the favorable opportunity for their mean treachery, whispered into the ears of a stupid crowd that the mother of my mother, Princess Anna Glinsky, with all her children and household, was in the habit of extracting men's hearts, and that by a similar sorcery she had put Moscow on fire, and that we knew of her doings.[4] By the instigation of these our traitors, a mass of insensate people, crying in the manner of the Jews, came to the apostolic cathedral of the holy martyr Dmitry of Saloniki, dragged out of it our boyar Yury Vasilevich Glinsky, pulled him

[4] Princes Shuyskys were members of an influential and wealthy aristocratic family who actually ruled in Moscow during Ivan IV's childhood.

humanly into the cathedral of the Assumption, and killed the
innocent man in the church, opposite the metropolitan's place;
they stained the floor of the church with his blood, dragged his
body through the front door, and exposed him on the marketplace as a criminal—everybody knows about this murder in the
church. We were then living in the village of Vorobievo; the
same traitors instigated the populace to kill us under the pretext,
and you, dog, repeat the lie that we were keeping from them
since Yury's mother, Princess Anna, and his brother, Prince
Mikhail. How is one not to laugh at such stupidity? Why should
we be incendiaries in our own empire? . . .

You say that your blood has been spilled in wars with foreigners, and you add, in your foolishness, that it cries to God
against us. That is ridiculous! It has been spilled by one, and it
cries out against another. If it is true that your blood has been
spilled by the enemy, then you have done your duty to your
country; if you had not done so, you would not have been a
christian but a barbarian—but that is not our affair. How much
more ours, that has been spilled by you, cries out to the Lord
against you! Not with wounds, nor drops of blood, but with
much sweating and toiling have I been burdened by you un-
cessarily and above my strength! Your many meannesses and
persecutions have caused me, instead of blood, to shed many
tears, and to utter sobs and have anguish of my soul. . . .

You say you want to put your letter in your grave: that shows
that you have completely renounced your Christianity! For God
is ordered not to resist evil, but you renounce the final pardon
which is granted to the ignorant; therefore it is not even proper
that any Mass shall be sung after you. In our patrimony, in the
country of Lifland, you name the city of Volmir as belonging to
our enemy, King Sigismund: by this you only complete the
treachery of a vicious dog![5] . . .

Written in our great Russia, in the famous, imperial, capital
city of Moscow, on the steps of our imperial threshold, in the
year from the creation of the world 1564 (7072), the fifth day of
July.

---

[5] The city of Volmir, actually Volmar, was conquered by Ivan IV
during the first phase of the Livonian War (see introduction to
Selection 32, the *Story of Stephen Bathory's Campaign Against
Pskov*), and later was claimed by the Polish King Sigismund.

HISTORICAL WORKS FROM THE
TIME OF TROUBLES

35. *Avraamy Palitsyn: Pseudo-Dmitry*

SOON after the death of Ivan IV, the Rurik dynasty, which ha
presided over Russia's destiny for seven hundred years, came
its end. Ivan had accidentally killed his eldest and favorite so
Tsarevich Ivan, and the throne was inherited by the physical
and mentally debile Fedor. After reigning fourteen years, 158
to 1598, Tsar Fedor died without leaving an heir to the thron
The dynastic crisis was aggravated by the fact that Ivar
youngest son, Dmitry, mysteriously perished in 1591. Rumo
circulated that he had been slain at the order of Boris Goduno
Tsar Fedor's brother-in-law, a brilliant but ruthless statesm
who wanted the throne for himself. Indeed, the Land Assembl
which was manipulated by Boris, elected him as Tsar of all t
Russias in 1598. His reign was not a happy one, however, f
Russia was plagued by famines and epidemics. Moreover,
1602 a mysterious impostor appeared who claimed that he w
Tsarevich Dmitry, the son of Ivan IV, declaring that he ha
escaped the knives of Boris' henchmen in 1590. The Poles, t
age-old rivals and enemies of Russia, supported Dmitry and l
claim to the Russian throne. He also received the blessing
the Pope of Rome, and in return Pseudo-Dmitry promised t
Holy See that he would convert all Russia to the Roman Cathol
faith. In 1604 he began his campaign against Tsar Boris, lea
ing both Russian and Polish troops. Upon the unexpected dea
of Boris Godunov, Dmitry entered Moscow and became tsar
1605. Hated by the boyars because of his sympathy for t
Poles and by the Russian clergy for his rapprochement with t
Catholic Church, Pseudo-Dmitry was murdered in the followi
year. For the next seven years anarchy reigned while Poli
and Swedish armies occupied a good deal of Russian territor
Even Moscow fell to the Poles, in September of 1610. Only
1613, after the election of Michael, the first tsar of the Roman
dynasty, did Russia begin its rehabilitation under a stable a
legal government.

These nine years, 1604 to 1613, years of crisis, great unre
and foreign intervention, are usually called the "Time of Tro
bles," and they left a deep and indelible impression on the mir

of Russia. Many writers who lived through these dramatic events left memoirs and analyses concerning this period. In most of them can be found a feeling of offended nationalism and fierce hatred toward the foreigners who had invaded the Russian land during these turbulent years. These writers are especially bitter toward the Poles and Catholics, who supported Pseudo-Dmitry, hoping, through him, to dominate all of Russia.

Among such writers Avraamy Palitsyn, a monk and cellarer of the powerful Holy Trinity-St. Sergius Monastery, left one of the best accounts of the events of the time. A member of a wealthy aristocratic family, Averky (Avraamy was his monastic name) was born about 1555, and, like many aristocrats of the day, served both in the civil service and in the army. In 1588 the anti-Godunov faction forced him to take monastic vows, thus excluding him for a time from political activity. As cellarer of the Holy Trinity-St. Sergius Monastery he participated in the patriotic and counterrevolutionary revival of 1610 to 1613, and as an influential leader he wrote his history (*skazanie*), which became one of the most popular accounts of the Time of Troubles, surviving in over one hundred extant manuscripts from the seventeenth century alone. Palitsyn died in the Solovki Monastery on September 13, 1627.

The translations of Chapters V and VI of his work, *A Concise History Written in Memory of Past Generations*, are given here. These translations follow the text of *Skazanie Avraamiia Palitsyna*, edited by O. A. Derzhavina and E. V. Kolosova, Academy of Sciences, Moscow and Leningrad, 1955, pages 110–115.

◆ ◆ ◆

ABOUT THE DEFROCKED MONK GREGORY AND THE DEATH OF TSAR BORIS

In the year 1605 (7113) a certain monk, whose name was Gregory and who was a scion of the Otrepiev[1] family, and who had been an addict of occult books and other evils, left Russia and went to the Polish Kingdom. Living there, he began to write subversive proclamations, sending them to all parts of Russia, in which he declared that he was the real Dmitry, son of

[1] Pseudo-Dmitry remains one of the great enigmas of Russian history. His actual identity has remained unknown to this day. However, the government of Boris Godunov, as well as other opponents of the pretender, identified him as being Gregory Otrepiev, a scion of a wealthy and noble Muscovite family.

the tsar. He would go from city to city, hiding himself and causing disturbances among the people of both realms. Then he
was joined by fugitives from western Russian and Polish cities,
by serfs whose time had arrived according to the will of the
evil spirit, and by one village after another, and by one city
after another, and finally all were tempted. However, his scheme
was evident to many. Yet, what a great amount of evil did they
cause! And until this day Russia is unable to be rid of this yoke.
He and his followers in evil have done so many base deeds in
Russia that no one could describe them all, even if he wrote for
many years. In two years this unfrocked monk Gregory succeeded in winning over one-quarter of the entire universe, the
entirety of Europe; and even the Pope of Rome wrote on his
behalf to the entire West, presenting Gregory as an exile from
his fatherland. And the Pope ordered the Polish king, Sigismund
III, to start a campaign against Russia in order to take revenge
for the impostor. Gregory joined the Catholics, that eternal
enemy of Christians, and he gave them a written promise that
he would bring entire Russia under the blessing of the Antichrist,[2] thus delivering all Russians to eternal death through the
abomination of the Catholic Communion. And he would have
done this, if the Lord hadn't overthrown his evil design. To him
refer the prophecies of Ezekiel, for it is written, "You shall be
fuel for the fire and your blood shall be in the midst of the
land" (21: 32).

Although Tsar Boris was not killed by this impostor, he died
a sudden death in the summer of 1605 (7113) during the revolt
brought about by Gregory, and all those upon whom Boris relied
were dispersed along with his household.[3]

After Boris' death, this monk ascended the throne and called
himself Tsar Dmitry. But from many witnesses we know that
this Gregory was a simple monk, despite the fact that he wanted
to become the Tsar of Russia. And he gathered together all the
relatives of the murdered Tsarevich Dmitry[4] and many other
people who had been deported by Tsar Boris. And those who

[2] In the sixteenth and seventeenth centuries the Protestant West
and the Orthodox East often called the Pope of Rome the Antichrist
and they claimed that the Pope served Satan. The Catholics, in turn,
called the Protestants the servants of Satan and the Antichrist.
[3] When Tsar Boris Godunov died, his son, Fedor II, became Tsar
of Russia. However, he was soon murdered by the impostor's supporters, and Pseudo-Dmitry ascended to the throne of Muscovy.
[4] Maria Nagoy was the last wife of Ivan IV. After the killing of
her son, Tsarevich Dmitry, Boris Godunov forced her to take monastic vows. She did so under the name of Marfa (Martha).

not wish to join him, he won over through his gifts. In such
[man]ner did he win over the nun Marfa, the mother of Tsarevich
[Dm]itry and the wife of Tsar Ivan Vassilevich, Tsar of all the
[Ru]ssias. And so she called this impostor her son. And many of
[the] people of Uglich[5] who could have exposed him and even
[his] real mother, Barbara, the wife of Bogdan Otrepiev, his
[fa]ther's widow and son, and his uncle, Smirny-Otrepiev, did
[not]. Therefore his uncle was sent to Siberia, and underwent
[man]y tribulations there. And there appeared many new mar[tyr]s: the nobleman Peter Turgenev, and Fedor Kolachev, who
[fear]lessly exposed him, were beheaded in the central square of
[the] imperial city of Moscow, after having undergone many tor[tur]es. When this Fedor Kolachev was led to the scaffold, he
[sho]uted to the crowd, saying: "You have accepted this servant
[of t]he Antichrist and you worship this messenger of Satan. But
[you] won't understand this until you have perished because of it."
[B]ut the Muscovites only abused him and answered that he
[wel]l deserved his execution. They paid no more heed to the
[exe]cution of Peter Turgenev. Soon after these executions, Prince
[Vas]ily Shuysky[6] was also condemned to death on the scaffold
[for] his exposures and intrigues, but the Poles, fearing his execu[tion], asked the impostor to pardon him.

[S]oon after, following the evil impostor's advice, all metro[poli]tans, archbishops, bishops, abbots, and all the leading clergy[me]n with Patriarch Ignaty, as well as the princes and boyars
[wit]h all the army commanders, obeyed him and signed the peti[tion] and sent ambassadors to the Polish Kingdom to ask the
[Loj]d of Sandomir to give his daughter to this impostor for his
[wif]e.[7] And all of them gave witness in their message that he was
[Dm]itry, the real son of Tsar Ivan IV.

[A]nd even those who knew that he was Monk Gregory gave
[wit]ness to this. Among them were Pafnuty, the Metropolitan of
[Kru]titsa. When Pafnuty was abbot of the Miracle Monastery,
[this] Gregory used to sing in his choir and then remained at the
[cou]rt of the Patriarch Job for one year, where he worked as a
[cler]k. Soon after, he ran away to Lithuania because his heretical
[intr]igues were exposed. And like a chariot of the pharaoh, he

---

Tsarevich Dmitry was killed in the city of Uglich in 1591, so it is
[quit]e natural that in 1605 many inhabitants of this city could have
[testi]fied that Pseudo-Dmitry was an impostor.

[A]fter Pseudo-Dmitry's death, Prince Vasily Shuysky became
[Rus]sia's tsar, ruling from 1606 to 1610.

Marina Mnishek, a daughter of a voevoda of Sandomir, became
[the] impostor's wife in 1606 in Moscow.

became involved in a plot, and after him the entire Russian s
became insane, giving in to his temptations.

Now involved in this plot, this accursed, defrocked impo
got into a conspiracy with the voevoda of Sandomir when
lived at his house in Poland. And, following an evil path,
voevoda decided to give his own daughter, Marina, in marri
[to this pretender, and took her to Moscow] to the lawless c
bration of her wedding, taking with him some six thous
selected troops. For the quartering of these Polish knights,
only were the houses of simple people taken, but even thos
officials, courtiers, and the Nagoy family, the so-called relat
of the impostor. And in all good and noble places and ho
heretical joy and violence spread.

This defrocked impostor, who was himself a sponsor of
crooked faith, feared that the same fate that befell Tsar B
would befall himself. And therefore, coming and leaving
tsar's palace, and going to walk about the city, he surroun
himself with many guards. Before him and behind him th
were marching armed soldiers with arquebuses, halberds,
other weapons. And this impostor would always walk in
center of them, while Russian courtiers and boyars had to fol
far behind. Indeed, it was terrifying to behold so many glin
arms and shining armor. He selected his personal guardsmen
well as the guards of his palace, only from among the Po
and German mercenaries. He permitted gamblers to gamble
cheat even in the tsar's palace. All his retinue and his comr
servants were clothed in finery as if they were bridegroo
though no one knew what they had to celebrate. They loite
from street to street searching for pleasure and bedecked
purple finery and with gold and silver accouterments. And w
they served the impostor, they adorned themselves with prec
stones and pearls. And they did not want to look upon any
who was humble. In such a way, the Poles were squandering
ancient treasures of Russia. And they used the silver vessels
carrying water and even in the bath, while they used silver
gold vessels for washing. And besides all this, they spread
seeds of the heretical dogma of Luther.

And no one dared to pronounce a word in the presence of
evil and fiercesome Cossacks.[8] And many an aristocrat s
tears, seeing the arrogance shown them by their serfs. The s
could always claim that their masters had called Dmitry

---

[8] Many Don and Dnieper Cossacks, among whom were many
away serfs, joined with Pseudo-Dmitry.

rocked impostor," and then such masters would always dis-
ear. In all the Russian cities and in the venerated monas-
es many laymen and monks perished. Some of them were
risoned, while others were drowned, and the belly of a huge
became their tomb. The impostor permitted both Jews and
etics to visit the holy and divine churches, and foreigners
ed to enter the Cathedral of the Assumption of Our Holy
, Honored Lady and to profane the miracle-working relics of
holy metropolitans, Peter and Jonas, leaning upon the
quaries. And the unholy Poles entered the churches even
n their weapons, but no one dared tell them a word, since
sting one of them could mean death.

oon after, the accursed Roman pope sent a missal to the
ostor reminding him of his promise to introduce into Russia
Roman Catholic form of Holy Communion and fasting on
rday. This cursed, defrocked monk attempted to do as he
ordered, but when he wed his heretical bride, they were
ried in a divine Orthodox Church. But before marrying her,
cursed man corrupted many virgin nuns and even pious
ks. And both he and the Poles were committing many
eful deeds. And the rebels and Cossacks who brought him
he throne enjoyed the fall of Christian virtues, seeing those
neful acts. And they offended people who were sad and
ved sorrowfully, calling them Jews and saying, "The tsar
s as he wants, but, like Jews, you only complain about it."
n the Muscovites trod the path of perdition, did not repent
re God, but enjoyed the gains from their speculations and,
ough bemoaning much, still cared primarily for the accumu-
n of wealth.

ecoming insanely proud, this defrocked monk and impostor
ered that his title be, "The most illustrious, invincible Caesar."
s accursed man believed that by bearing the name of the
he could win the highest and most sought-after of honors.
here was a high official at the court, whose name was
othy Osipov, who was a person of pious behavior and dis-
tion, and who gave little heed to this impostor's ambitions.
s virtuous man saw that much harm was being done by this
ocked monk and his councilors. Seeing the unnatural and
title the impostor had given himself, this man realized that
man is mortal and possessed by passions and therefore
ld not call himself an "invincible Caesar," since only God
vincible. This Timothy Osipov was a man devoted to God,
he prayed piously and the fasts were strictly kept in his
se. Once, after he had received the most wonderful and

life-giving Communion—the pure flesh and blood of Christ, (
Lord, he went to the tsar's palace and daringly exposed the
frocked monk before the people, saying: "Verily, verily thou
Grishka Otrepiev, a defrocked monk, and not an 'invinci
Caesar.' Thou art not Dmitry, the son of the tsar, but a sl
to sin, and a heretic."

The defrocked impostor could not stand such a denunciat
and shame, but ordered the man immediately executed.
ended the life and the heroic deed of this worthy martyr.

Once the impostor sent to the Khan of Crimea the most
honorable of gifts. He ordered a fur coat made of swines' sl
for the khan, and wrote him that he was preparing a campa
against the Crimea, the land of the southern sun, and that
himself would appear there soon to plunder the Crimean hon
And he ordered all Russians, as well as the Poles, to his serv
and to prepare the campaign against the city of Azov.[9] And
immediately sent a large corps of selected artillerymen to
city of Elets. He ordered that the army prepare to adva
either by boats on the river Don or on land across the prai
Rumors about these military moves spread to Constantino
and the Turks began to prepare for the spilling of Christ
blood. Some people claimed, I do not know whether it is true
not, that this defrocked monk wanted to arouse the Crim
Khan and the Turks, so that many Christian Russians wo
fall on the battlefield. It does appear that he was not re
interested in victory over the sons of Hagar, but wanted rat
to withdraw the Orthodox Russians in order that he might af
ward settle the Muscovite realm with Poles. But the Lord h
self did not allow this ambitious man's plan to come to fruit

HOW THE DEFROCKED MONK PREPARED A PLO
WITH THE POLES TO KILL MUSCOVITES, BUT WA
HIMSELF KILLED BY THE MUSCOVITE BOYARS

This enemy, the defrocked monk, plotted with the here
[the Poles] to massacre the Russian people of all ranks, be
ning with the courtiers and ending with common officers. /
he intended to have a great celebration with the shooting
artillery in the Pond Field at the Strelets Gate. And when
people went to this celebration, then he would order the ;
to be closed and all would be slain.

[9] The city of Azov, located at the mouth of the river Don not
from the Azov Sea, was an important Turkish-Tatar fortress at
time.

But this base plot did not come to fruition because two days before the celebration was to have taken place, and ten days after his improper wedding, this accursed man died an evil death, having reigned for one year. He used to say of himself that he was thirty-four years of age, but his friends, the demons, didn't give him many more years of life. And so the writing of St. John Chrysostom, "Such is the honor which demons render to those who love them," was fulfilled.

After his death, the people of Moscow gave themselves to drinking in their joy, instead of rendering thanks to God. And everyone bragged about his deeds in murdering the impostor, pseudo-Dmitry, and all boasted about their courage. But the people forgot to give thanks through prayer in the Church of the Holy Virgin for this most glorious victory. Once, a great miracle was performed by the Most Pure Holy Virgin in Constantinople, but this miracle against the Persians and the Scythians occurred on the sea and beyond the walls of the city, and not within the city walls.[10] In Moscow, however, the miracle occurred within the city. This accursed heretic was able to keep everyone firmly in tow, and he was loved by everyone. And yet, on that day, by the command of God, everyone rose against him. And a great amount of heretical [Polish] blood was spilled in the streets of Moscow. But, instead of rendering thanks to the Righteous Avenger, the people were seized by insanity and pride. And therefore the wrath of God did not subside; but we the Russians did not recognize the divine plan and designs, and were not able to realize from what evils the Lord had delivered us.

36. *Avraamy Palitsyn: Answer of the Defenders of the Holy Trinity—St. Sergius Monastery to the Polish Request of Surrender*

ONE of the most dramatic events of the Time of Troubles was the besieging of the Holy Trinity—St. Sergius Monastery by Polish and Lithuanian troops in 1609. After a long siege and many attempted stormings of the well-fortified monastery-fortress, the commanders of the Poles and Lithuanians, John Peter Paul Sapieha and John Alexander Lisowski, demanded

[10] The author refers to the so-called Miracle of the Holy Virgin's Veil which, according to the legend, protected the city of Constantinople against a Russian attack.

the monastery's surrender. The commanders of the Russian
troops defending the monastery, Prince Gregory Dolgorukov and
Alexis Golokhsvastov, together with Abbot Ioasaf and the lead
ing elders, refused to capitulate, and answered the Polish and
Lithuanian commanders in a letter that well reflects the bitter
ness, hatred, and fierce national feeling that reigned in both
camps. For the defenders of this monastery, surrender to the
Poles would not only have meant betrayal of the national cause
but also betrayal of the Orthodox Faith. There are reasons to
believe that the letter was written by Avraamy Palitsyn himself
as he was certainly the most skillful writer in the monastery at
that time.

The present translation follows the text of the letter contained
in *Skazanie Avraamiia Palitsyna* edited by O. Derzhavina and
E. V. Kolosova, Academy of Sciences of the U.S.S.R. Moscow
and Leningrad, 1955, pages 110–115.

◆   ◆   ◆

To the proud commanders Sapieha and Lisowski! Your dark
majesties and your warriors are the opposers of God, the abomi
nation of dissolution, and know that you attempt in vain to lead
us, a flock of Orthodox Christians, into temptation. You should
know that even a ten-year-old Christian youth from the Holy
Trinity–St. Sergius Monastery would laugh at your request. And
as far as your letter is concerned, we spit on it upon receiving
it. What man would, at the expense of his soul, prefer darkness
to light, a lie to the truth, honor to dishonor, and freedom to
bitter slave labor? How could we forsake our eternal, holy, and
true Orthodox Christian Faith of the Greek confession and sub
mit ourselves to the new heretical law which betrays the Chris
tian Faith and which was cursed by the four ecumenical patri
archs.[1] What would be our gain and honor in betraying our
Orthodox sovereign and tsar[2] and submitting ourselves to our
enemy, the impostor and rebel?[3] And you, people of the Latin
faith, have become like Jews, and even worse, for the Jews
didn't recognize the Lord and consequently crucified him. Yet
how can we, who know our Orthodox sovereign, concede to your

[1] The four patriarchs refers to the four patriarchs of the cities of
Constantinople, Antioch, Jerusalem, and Alexandria who broke with
the Pope of Rome owing to the latter's claim for primacy.

[2] Sapieha and Lisowski fought in the name of the second impostor
that is, the second Pseudo-Dmitry, while the monastery refused to
capitulate in the name of Tsar Vasily Shuysky (1605–1610).

[3] This refers to the second Pseudo-Dmitry.

equest to forsake our Christian tsar despite the fact that our
grandfathers were born in the vineyard of our true pastor Christ
and under the rule of a Christian tsar? And how can you at-
empt to tempt us with false kindness, vain flattery, and ill-
gained wealth. We shall remain faithful to the pledge we gave
on the cross, for we do not care for all the wealth in the entire
world.

37. *Prince Ivan M. Katyrev-Rostovsky*
A Description of the Tsars and Their Families

The Book of Annals, written by Prince Ivan M. Katyrev-
Rostovsky, gives one of the best accounts of the Time of Troubles. Others who wrote about this first great national crisis in
Muscovite Russia followed both the basic outline and the literary
style found here. Since it gives a vivid description of this difficult time, the author remaining quite unbiased and keeping to
the historical truth, it is an important source for historians. *The
Book of Annals* is also significant for several innovations, such
as the first literary portraits of the heroes of the narrative, especially of the tsars and their families. *The Book of Annals* was
as well one of the first Russian works to describe nature and the
changes of the seasons superbly; the account of the coming of
spring is particularly noteworthy. The author often used rhymed
passages, and there are many rhymed couplets to be found
throughout the text.

The reader will find in this selection from *The Book of
Annals* the portraits of the tsars and their families. The translation follows one of the earliest extant manuscripts, published in
Russkaia istoricheskaia biblioteka, Volume 13, St. Petersburg,
1912.

◆ ◆ ◆

SHORT DESCRIPTION OF THE MUSCOVITE TSARS, THEIR PHYSICAL APPEARANCES, STATURES, AND TEMPERAMENTS

[TSAR IVAN IV (THE TERRIBLE), REIGNED FROM 1533 TO 1584]

Tsar Ivan was physically unattractive, had gray eyes, a
hooked and long nose, and was tall, lean, and with broad shoulders and chest. He had great physical prowess and was a person

of great acumen, being well read, erudite, and very eloquen
He was fearsome to the enemy, and was always prepared t
fight for the fatherland. He was cruel to his subjects given t
him by the Lord, being always ready to spill their blood, an
both merciless and daring at killing. He ordered that many pec
ple be slain, from infants to the aged; he laid waste to many c
his own cities; and many clergymen were thrown into prison
and mercilessly executed at his orders. He committed man
other evil deeds to his own people, deflowering many girls an
women in his lust. This Tsar Ivan did many good things, how
ever, and he cared very much for his armies, generously reward
ing them from his treasury. Such was Tsar Ivan.

[TSAR FEDOR (IVAN'S SON) REIGNED FROM 1584 TO 1598]

Tsar Fedor was short of stature, and appeared as a man wh
constantly fasted. He was most humble, and greatly cared afte
his soul, standing before the icons and praying endlessly. H
generously gave alms to the poor. He was not taken up wit
worldly matters, but concerned himself only with the salvatio
of his soul. And so, from his infancy to the very end of his day
his life was dedicated to matters of salvation; and thus Go
gave peace to his reign, brought his enemies in tow, and grante
him a blessed epoch. Such was Tsar Fedor.

[TSAR BORIS (GODUNOV, BROTHER-IN-LAW OF TSAR FEDOR) REIGNE
    FROM 1598 TO 1605]

Tsar Boris shone in the full bloom of his handsome appea
ance, and he surpassed many people in his attractiveness. H
was of average stature. He was a man of great intelligence, ha
a marvelous power of reasoning, and was a clever polemici
and eloquent orator. He was a faithful Christian, gave gene
ously to the poor, and was a great builder. He spent much tim
on state affairs and he performed a great many marvelous deed
He had, however, two great shortcomings, for he was n
granted a certain virtue by God: he used to go too much t
doctors, and he was obsessed by an insatiable desire for powe
And he dared to slay those who should have been tsars befo
himself. And for such deeds he received divine retribution.

[TSAR FEDOR II, THE SON OF BORIS, WHO REIGNED SOME WEEK
    IN 1605]

Tsar Fedor, the son of Tsar Boris, was a marvelous youth
He was so handsome that he blossomed like a flower in th
meadow, having been created by God like a lily blooming in th

fields. His eyes were large and black; his complexion was light and white as milk; his stature was average; and his body was slightly stout. He was brought by his father to the learned books, and he was clever and eloquent in polemics. And never did any senseless or coarse words come from his lips, but he was devoted to the faith and to the reading of books.

[TSAREVNA XENIA (DAUGHTER OF BORIS AND SISTER OF TSAR FEDOR II)]

Tsarevna Xenia, Tsar Boris's daughter, was a maiden of wonderful spirit, physically very attractive, of light complexion, and had beautiful rosy cheeks, red lips, and big black eyes. From her there radiated graciousness. Being sad and shedding tears, her graciousness would become particularly radiant. Her eyebrows were thick and joined, and her body was supple, while her skin was as white as milk. She was neither too tall nor too short; her hair was black and long, covering her shoulders. She was the most distinguished among maidens, and she was accustomed to reading books. She shone by her forceful and distinguished speech, and she did well in whatever she attempted. She had a fondness for beautiful voices, and loved to listen to church music.

[PSEUDO-DMITRY, REIGNED FROM 1605–1606]

This defrocked impostor was of very short stature, but was powerfully built and of great physical strength. His face did not have the distinction of a tsar, but it was very common and his body was covered with dark spots. But he was very witty and was rather learned. He was a daring and eloquent speaker, loved horseracing, was courageous in fighting the enemy, was brave and strong, and cared greatly for warriors.

[TSAR VASILY SHUYSKY (THE HEAD OF THE POWERFUL AND ARISTOCRATIC FAMILY OF BOYARS, HE ORGANIZED THE MURDER OF THE PRETENDER, PSEUDO-DMITRY, AND WAS THEREAFTER ELECTED BY THE BOYARS TO SUCCEED HIM) REIGNED FROM 1606 to 1610]

Tsar Vasily was short of stature, physically very unattractive, and had eyes that were dull, as if he were blind. He was rather cultured, and his reasoning was sound and pointed. He cared only for those people who brought him gossip and rumors about people, and he used to receive such persons with a joyful face, and with sweet pleasure, did he listen to them. He was given to sorcery, and cared little for the military.

BIOGRAPHICAL WORKS

38. K. Druzhina-Osoryin
The Life of Yuliania Lazarevskaia

THE *vita* of Yuliania Osoryin, called Lazarevskaia after the village of Lazarevo, where she lived and died, was written in the first quarter of the seventeenth century by her son, Kallistrat Druzhina-Osoryin. Although written with the purpose of glorifying her holy life, this work is very different from the typical *vitae* of saints of medieval Russia. With the exception of the descriptions of some miracles and the appearances of demons, Yuliania's biography much more resembles a narrative from a family chronicle than a hagiographic work. The biographer gives a detailed account of the domestic relations of Yuliania's family, and often remarks that the author, himself, and his family, witnessed her works and life. Yuliania was neither a nun who spent her life in a convent, nor a princess whose Christian charity and works gave her the halo of a saintly protectoress. She spent all her life with her family, and her biography is filled with the details of every-day events. While her life was one of prayer and Christian piety, the fact that she remained all her life with her husband and children as a devoted wife, mother, and daughter-in-law distinguishes this *vita* from the usual hagiographies dealing with heroes who performed miraculous deeds or defended the Orthodox Faith, and who were usually either hermits, church leaders, or pious rulers. With this *vita* there began to appear in Russia a realistic, secular biography.

This narrative is written in plain language, completely devoid of the panegyrics, lengthy epithets, and stylistic embellishments that characterize Russian lives of saints. The present translation follows an early seventeenth-century text published by M. Skripil in *Russkaia provest XVII veka*, Moscow, 1954, pages 39–47.

◆ ◆ ◆

In the days of the pious Tsar and Great Prince Ivan Vasilie-vich[1] of all Russia, there was at his imperial court a good and

[1] Ivan IV, or Ivan Vasilievich, usually called the Terrible or Dread, reigned over Russia from 1530 to 1584.

charitable man by the name of Yustin Nediurev, a housekeeper by rank.[2] He had a wife named Stefanida, equally devout and compassionate, daughter of a certain Gregory Lukin from the city of Murom. They led a pious and virtuous life, had several sons and daughters, and possessed considerable wealth and many serfs. To them was born this blessed Yuliania.

Her mother died when she was six years of age, and Yuliania was taken to the lands of Murom by her grandmother, who raised her in piety for six years. When the grandmother died, Yuliania's aunt, Natalia, wife of Putila Arapov, took, at the grandmother's behest, the young girl to her house. As the blessed Yuliania had loved God and the Holy Virgin since her very youth, she respected and honored her aunt and her aunt's daughters. She was humble and obedient, assiduous in prayer and fasting. Because of her fasting, she was much berated by her aunt and ridiculed by her cousins, who said, "O insane one! Why dost thou exhaust thy flesh and so ruin thy beauty, while thou art so young?" They urged her to take food and drink every morning, but she did not yield to them; rather she withdrew in silence, even though she accepted everything with gratitude and was obedient to all. She also refrained from laughter and games, as from her very childhood she was meek, silent, and obedient, and never rude or haughty. Although frequently urged by her companions to take part in games and frivolous songs, she did not comply, pretending confusion in order to conceal her virtues. Instead, she applied herself with great diligence to spinning and hoop embroidery, working late into the night. She also did all the sewing for orphans and ailing widows in the village, and supplied the sick and needy with all kinds of goods. Everyone admired her wisdom and devotion.

The fear of God dwelt in her. There was no church in the village, nor any closer than within two miles; so Yuliania had no chance to go to church in her maidenhood. Neither did she ever hear the reading of the Holy Scriptures, nor any preacher teaching salvation, but God himself instructed her in virtuous ways. When she was in her sixteenth year she was given in marriage to a virtuous and wealthy man, named Georgii Osoryin. They were married by a priest, Potapy, in the church of the righteous Lazar, in her husband's estate. This priest instructed them in the law of God according to the rules of the holy fathers, and she carefully listened to the teaching and instructions, carrying them out in her deeds. Her parents-in-law were

[2] The names of the relatives and other people mentioned in this *vita* are the names of real historical personages.

still alive and, when they saw her of mature age and accomplished in virtue, they commanded her to take charge of the whole household. She humbly obeyed them in all things, never contradicting them, but respecting them and fulfilling all their orders without fail, so that all marveled at her. Many people tested Yuliania in conversation and she gave a seemly and reasonable reply to every question, so that all wondered at her good sense, and glorified God. She prayed much every evening, and made one hundred and more genuflections. Upon arising each morning, she did the same, together with her husband. When her husband would be away in the tsar's service in Astrakhan[3] for a year or two, and sometimes even for three years, she went without sleep all night, praying or working, weaving or embroidering. She would sell her work and give the price to the poor or for the building of churches; she gave many alms in secret by night. During the day she managed the household and cared for widows and orphans as a true mother, ministering to them with her own hands and giving them to drink and to eat. She provided the serfs, both men and women, with food and clothing, and assigned them work according to their strength. She called no one a rude name, nor did she command anyone to pour water while she washed her hands, or to take off her shoes, but did all this herself. She instructed and corrected foolish serfs with meekness and humility, taking the blame upon herself and denouncing no one, but placing all her hopes in God and the Holy Virgin, She called for help upon the great wonder-worker Nicholas, and he assisted her.

One night in her husband's absence, as Yuliania arose for prayer, as was her wont, she was seized with fear and great terror by the attack of demons. Being young and inexperienced, she was frightened, lay down on the bed, and fell fast asleep. Then she saw many demons coming at her with weapons, saying, "If thou wilt not cease thy efforts, we will straightway destroy thee." She prayed to God and to the Most Holy Virgin and to St. Nicholas the wonder-worker. And St. Nicholas appeared to her, holding a large book; he dispersed the demons, so they disappeared like smoke. Lifting up his right hand, he blessed her, saying: "My daughter, take courage and stand firm and do not be afraid of the demons' threats! For Christ hath

[3] All Russian nobles were supposed to serve either with the army or in the civil service. This service was not a permanent one, but each noble could be summoned into the service as soon as the necessity arose. The city of Astrakhan, where Yuliania's husband served, is located at the delta of the Volga in the vicinity of the Caspian Sea.

ommanded me to guard thee from demons and from evil men."
hen she straightway awoke from sleep and clearly saw the
oly man leaving the chamber through the door, quick as light-
ing. Rising promptly, she followed him, and forthwith he be-
ame invisible; yet the anteroom of the chamber was securely
ocked. Taking this as a message, Yuliania rejoiced, praising
od, and was more diligent in good works than before.

In a short time, for our sins God's wrath fell upon the Russian
and, and a great famine occurred, and many starved to death.
uliania gave many alms in secret; she began to accept food
om her mother-in-law for morning and midday meals, and gave
ll to the poor and hungry. So her mother-in-law said to her:
How comes it that thou hast changed thy custom? When there
as an abundance of bread, I was not able to make thee eat
arly and midday meals, and now, when there is a dearth of
od, thou eatest!" Wishing to keep her secret, Yuliania an-
wered, "When I did not bear children, I did not want to eat,
ut when I started to bear them I grew weak and I cannot eat
y fill. Not only in the daytime, but many times in the night as
ell I am hungry, but I am ashamed to ask." The mother-in-law
as glad to hear it, and sent her enough food not only in the
aytime but also at night, for in their house there was an
bundance of bread and of everything. However, while receiving
od from her mother-in-law, Yuliania did not partake of it her-
elf, but gave all to the poor. When anyone would die, she hired
omen to cleanse him, gave sheets to wrap the bodies, and
oney for the burial. When any deceased whatever were buried
a their village, she prayed for the remission of their sins.

In a short time, there was a severe pestilence among the peo-
le and many died from the plague. Many locked their doors
o that those who were afflicted would not enter their homes;
nd they would not even touch the garments of the ill. Yet,
ecretly away from her parents-in-law, Yuliania healed many of
ie afflicted, washing them in the bathhouse with her own
ands; she prayed to God for their recovery, and if they died
he prayed for their salvation, hired men to bury them, and
rdered the forty days' prayer.[4] When her parents-in-law, after
aving been tonsured,[5] died in extreme old age, Yuliania buried
iem with honor: she gave many alms in their memory, and

---

[4] In the Orthodox Church special prayers are required for the dead
r forty days after their death.

[5] It was the custom in medieval Russia, especially among the
ristocracy, to take monastic vows shortly before the approach of
eath.

ordered many forty days' prayers. She also had the Mass cele
brated for them and had meals served at her house for th
priests, monks, and beggars every day during the forty day
and sent alms to the prisons. At that time her husband wa
serving for three years in Astrakhan, and she spent a great part o
their wealth in almsgiving, not only in those days, but through
out these years, honoring the memory of her dead parents-in
law.

Having thus lived with her husband for many years in grea
virtue, according to God's commandments, Yuliania gave birt
to sons and daughters. The devil, who hateth all good, sough
to cause her strife, arousing frequent discord among the chi
dren and the serfs. Reasoning sensibly and wisely, Yuliania re
strained them all, but the devil provoked a serf to slay th
eldest son; then another son was killed in the service. Althoug
she grieved, it was for their souls, and not because of thei
deaths. And she honored them with memorial Masses, prayer
and almsgiving. Then Yuliania begged her husband to give he
leave to go to a nunnery. He did not let her go, but they agree
to live together yet have no bodily intercourse. She continue
to prepare his bed as usual, yet she herself, after long evenin
prayers, would lie down on the stove without any bedding. Sh
lay on firewood with the sharp edges against her body, and sh
put iron keys under her ribs, and on these she took little slee
until her serfs fell asleep. Then she would rise to pray through
out the night, until daylight, when she went to church fo
Matins and Mass. She occupied herself diligently with hand
work and managed her house in a manner pleasing to God. Sh
provided her serfs with sufficient food, and appointed each c
them a task according to their strength. She cared for widow
and orphans, and helped the poor in all things.

Ten years after their bodily separation, Yuliania's husban
passed away, and she buried him reverently, honoring him wit
memorial Masses, prayers, the forty-day service, and alms. Fro
then on, she rejected even more all worldly things that sh
might better care for her soul and emulate the holy women c
old and, in this way, to please God. She prayed and fasted, wer
every day to church, gave unending alms, so that ofttimes not
silver coin remained in her house and she had to borrow i
order to give alms to the poor. When winter came, Yuliani
borrowed silver from her children for warm clothing, but gav
even this money to the poor and she herself passed the winte
without any warm clothes. She wore her shoes over bare fee

using nutshells and sharp potsherds instead of inner soles so as to mortify the flesh.

Once the winter was so cold that the ground cracked from the frost, and for some time Yuliania did not go to church but prayed at home. It came to pass that once the local priest came alone to church very early and heard a voice from the icon of the Holy Virgin, which said: "Go and ask merciful Yuliania why she does not come to church and pray? Her prayers at home are also pleasing to God, but not so much as her prayers in church. However, let her be venerated, for she is already no less than sixty years of age, and the Holy Spirit resides within her!" The priest, being seized by awe, came forthwith to Yuliania, fell at her feet, asked her forgiveness, and told her of the vision. She treated him severely because he spoke of it in the presence of others. And she said, "Thou hast been tempted when thou spake of it; for how may I, a sinner, be worthy of such heavenly intervention?" And she adjured him not to tell anyone. Yet she herself went to church, prayed with warm tears, and venerated the icon of the Holy Virgin.

From then on, Yuliania even more devoted herself to God, going to church and praying every evening in the porch of the church, where there were icons of our Lady and of St. Nicholas. One evening she entered it to pray, as was her wont, and suddenly the chamber was filled with demons who wanted to kill her with various weapons. But she prayed to God with tears, and St. Nicholas appeared to her. He carried a club and chased the demons away, so that they disappeared like smoke. Yet he caught one of them, and tormented it. He blessed St. Yuliania with a cross, and forthwith became invisible. Still the demon screamed, crying: "I have always made trouble for thee: I have aroused strife amongst thy children and slaves. Yet I did not dare to come close to thee because of thy charity, humility, and prayer." (For Yuliania incessantly said Jesus' prayer with beads in her hands; and whether she was eating or drinking, or doing anything, she said the prayer incessantly; even when she was asleep, her lips moved and her soul was aroused to the praise of God; many times we saw her asleep, and her hand was moving the beads.) The demon ran away from her, screaming, "A great disaster befell me now because of thee, but I will make trouble for thee in thy old age: thou wilt starve, instead of feeding others!" But she blessed herself with the sign of the cross, and the demon disappeared. She came to us sore afraid and changed in the face. Seeing her perturbed, we questioned her, but she did not tell us anything. Yet, not too long later, she told us secretly, and bade us to tell no one.

Yuliania lived as a widow for nine years and showed great goodness to everyone. She gave away much property as alms, retaining only the essential for home needs; she rationed food year after year and gave all surplus to the needy. She lived even until the reign of Tsar Boris.[6] At that time there was a great famine in the whole land of Russia—such that, in dire need, many partook of unclean meats and of human flesh, and untold numbers starved to death. In Yuliania's house there was great scarcity of food and of all necessary supplies, for the sown spring rye never sprouted, and both horses and cattle died. She implored her children and serfs that they in no way touch anything belonging to others, nor steal, and whatever cattle and clothes and vessels were left, she sold for rye to feed the servants. She also gave considerable alms, for even in destitution she did not discontinue her customary charity, but let no one asking for help go away empty-handed. She herself came to extreme need, and not a grain was left in her house; yet she was not alarmed but placed all hope in God.

That year Yuliania moved to another village, called Vochnevo, in the confines of Nizhny-Novgorod, where there was no church closer than within two miles. Being afflicted with old age, and destitute, she did not go to church but prayed at home. That grieved her sorely, yet she remembered St. Kornily and other saints, and knew that praying at home did not harm them. When destitution increased in her house, she set the serfs free so they would not be exhausted by hunger. Those of them who were virtuous promised to endure with her, while others left, and she let them go with her blessing and prayers, being not the least angered. Then Yuliania commanded the remaining slaves to gather goosefoot and wood bark and, making bread therefrom, she lived on it with her children and the serfs. And through her prayers that bread was sweet. She continued to give to the poor and let no pauper go without; at that time the poor were innumerable. Her neighbors said to the beggars, "Why do you go to Yuliania's house? For even she herself is starving!" And the beggars told them, "We have walked through many villages and have received pure bread, but we did not relish it so much, for sweet is the bread of this widow." They called her this, for many did not know her name. And the neighbors, who

[6] Tsar Boris, brother-in-law of the last representative of the dynasty of Rurik, Tsar Fedor, ruled from 1598–1605. During his reign there were both plagues and great famines in Russia.

d plenty of bread, sent to Yuliania's house to ask for some of
rs, to try it, and they also witnessed that her bread was very
eet. They marveled, saying to themselves, "Her servants are
od at baking bread," for they did not understand that the
ead was sweet through Yuliania's prayer. Yuliania endured
is destitution for two years, and she neither grieved nor was
oubled, nor complained, and did not sin with her lips, neither
d she charge God foolishly. And she was not broken by pov-
ty, but was more cheerful than in earlier years.

As her righteous passing drew near, Yuliania became ill on
e twenty-sixth day of December and stayed abed for six days.
daytime she prayed as she lay in bed, and at night she arose
pray to God, standing without assistance and supported by
one, for, as she said, "Even from the sick God demands
ayer." At daybreak on the second day of January, she sum-
oned her confessor and received the last rites. Then, sitting up,
e summoned her children and serfs and instructed them in love,
ayer, charity, and in the other virtues. She added this also:
ince my youth and with all my heart I have desired to take
onastic vows, but because of my sins and wretchedness this
as not granted to me. I was not worthy, being a wretched and
wly sinner, God willing it so; glory be to His righteous judg-
ent." She commanded that a censer be prepared and that
cense be put in it; she kissed all those present and bade them
ace and forgiveness. She lay down, crossed herself thrice, and,
ving wound the beads around her arm, she spake her last,
ying, "Praise God in all things! Into Thy hands, O Lord, I
mmend my spirit. Amen!" And she surrendered her soul into
e hands of God, whom she had loved since her youth. And all
w a golden halo around her head, such as is painted around
e heads of the saints on icons. Having washed her, they laid
r out in a storeroom, and that night they saw there light and
urning candles, and a strong fragrance wafted from that store-
om. Having put her into an oaken coffin, they took her back
the confines of Murom, and buried her beside her husband
the wall of the church of the righteous Lazar, in the village
Lazarevo, which was three miles from the city. And this
me to pass in the year 1604 (7112), on the tenth day of
nuary.

They later erected over Yuliania a church in the name of
changel Michael. A stove happened to be over her grave and,
rough the removal of ashes, the earth above her became
icker through the years. In the year 1615 (7123), on the
ghth day of August, her son Georgii passed away, and they

started to dig a grave for him in the porch between the churc
and the stove, for that porch had no floor. They found Yuliania
coffin intact and on top of the earth. It was in no way damage
and they wondered whose it was, as for many years no one ha
been buried there. On the tenth day of the same month the
buried her son Georgii next to her coffin, and went to his hous
to offer refreshments to the burial attendants. But the wome
who attended the funeral opened the coffin and saw it to l
full of fragrant myrrh. Being seized with awe at that time, the
did not reveal anything, but after the departure of the gues
they related what had happened. Having heard this, we ma
veled. And when we opened the coffin, we saw even as th
women had told us. We ladled out a small vessel of that myr
and took it to the cathedral church of the city of Murom. I
the daytime that myrrh looked like beetroot kvass, and at nig
it thickened, looking like crimson oil. We did not dare to ope
the grave and to view all the body. We saw only her legs ar
thighs intact, yet her head we did not see, because a log fro
the oven lay on the end of the coffin.

Next to the coffin there was an opening under the stove. I
the night the coffin, by itself, moved toward the east. An
having gone the distance of two yards, it stopped at the churc
wall. This same night many people heard the ringing of th
church bell. When they arrived, they saw nothing; only a fr
grance emanated. Many people heard of it and came there
anoint themselves with the myrrh. And they received relief fro
various diseases. When all the myrrh had been distributed,
dustlike sand began to issue near the coffin. Those suffering
various ailments came and rubbed themselves with this sar
and received relief. And even to this day they do so. And v
would not dare to write this if there had been no witnesses.

39. *The Life of Archpriest Avvakum by Himsel*

A SIMILAR fate befell the most unusual literary works of bo
the Kievan and Muscovite eras of Russian literature. Because
their nonconformity with the spirit of the Russian Church, bo
the *Lay of Igor's Campaign* and the *Life of Archpriest Avvaku
by Himself* remained unavailable to the general reader, ar
therefore did not have a considerable influence on the furthe

velopment of Russian literature. Once discovered, however,
ey fascinated the Russian reading public.

Born in 1621, Avvakum became a priest at the age of twenty.
. the early 1640's he joined the revival movement of the
alots of Piety, or Seekers After God (Bogoliubtsy), which
tracted many representatives of the Russian Church at that
ne and which tried to breathe new life into Russian Ortho-
xy. For several years both the government and the Church
aders supported this movement, but when the authoritarian
d unbending Nikon became patriarch in 1652, he moved
ainst this revival because he saw in its activities a threat to
e authority of the hierarchy. Officially, the conflict arose over
e re-editing of the missal and changes in the ritual, both of
hich Nikon revised to conform to those of the contemporary
eek Church. Avvakum and his followers advocated the an-
ent texts and rites which had originally been introduced into
ussia from Greece, some seven centuries earlier. The real core
the conflict, however, was different. Nikon sought the un-
estioning submission of the Church to the authority of the
triarch, and received the support of Tsar Alexis and the state,
ce they also desired stronger controls over the Church by
th the central ecclesiastic offices and the state itself. Avvakum
d his followers, who represented the lower clergy and their
rishioners, felt that the parish priests and local laity should
ve a greater voice in Church affairs. Moreover, in opposition
domination and disciplining of the Church from above, they
oposed a genuine religious regeneration of the Church on the
cal level.

In 1653 Patriarch Nikon succeeded in deporting Avvakum,
an Neronov, and other leaders of the reform movement, and
us Avvakum spent some nine years in Siberia. He was per-
itted to return to Moscow in 1662, but his fierce defense of his
inciples led once more to his deportation to northern Russia
d, finally, to his censure by the Church council. In 1666 he
as condemned for his opposition to the ecclesiastic authorities
d for upholding the ancient traditions of the Russian Church.
e next year this condemnation was reaffirmed by a larger
urch council, in which not only the Russian hierarchs par-
ipated but also the Greek patriarchs of Alexandria, Antioch,
d Jerusalem. This time Avvakum and his followers, Deacon
dor (Theodore), the monk Epiphany, and the priest Lazar,
re deported to Pustozersk, a small settlement and fort in the
treme northeast of European Russia, about a hundred miles

from the Arctic Ocean. They remained there some fifteen yea
and during that time Pustozersk became the spiritual center
the Old Believer movement, as it was called. It was there th
Avvakum's autobiography and his many treatises and epist
were written. In 1682 the government, which was unable
curb the spread of this movement, ordered that Avvakum a
his three comrades should be burned at the stake.

The autobiography of Avvakum is certainly not the first R
sian work in which an author describes his own life and dee
but it is the most important one in old Russian literatu
Avvakum uses a simple but vigorous, clear, and laconic style
which there are hardly any of those stylistic devices of or
mentation which so characterized the literary works of his pred
cessors and contemporaries. His narration is dynamic, and
flects the active, unbending nature of the author. Avvaku
rarely used the solemn Church Slavonic literary language, b
turned to colloquial Russian. He does not hesitate to use cru
folk sayings that lend expressiveness to his style. A keen c
server and penetrating psychologist, he gives short, pointe
sometimes ironic portrayals of his contemporaries, among whi
perhaps the best are those describing his wife, Nasta
Markovna, and Tsar Alexis.

The *Life of Archpriest Avvakum by Himself* is given here
the translation by Jane Harrison and Hope Mirrlees, publish
by Leonard and Virginia Woolf at the Hogarth Press, Londc
1924. This work is given in its entirety except for the introdu
tion, which does not deal at all with Avvakum's life but consi
rather of theological arguments and considerations, and al
excepting the final section describing "The Healing of Tho
Possessed." For the convenience of the reader, the work h
been divided into chapters by the editor of this anthology. T
editor has also made some minor changes in personal and pla
names, and occasionally in wording, for a better understandir

❖ ❖ ❖

I. FAMILY BACKGROUND

I was born in the Nizhny country, beyond the River Kudn
in the village of Grigorovo.[1] My father was given to stro
drink; but my mother was given to fasting and prayer, and d
most constantly instruct me in the fear of God. Now one day
a neighbor's I saw a dead ox, and that night, rising from r

[1] The village of Grigorovo is in the Nizhny-Novgorod (presen
Gorky) region on the right shore of the Volga.

bed, I wept abundantly for my soul before the holy icons, pondering mortality and how I too must surely die; and from that day it became my custom to pray every night. Then my mother was left a widow, and I, young that I was, an orphan, and we were driven out by our kinsmen. My mother resolved that I should marry. And I prayed to the Mother of God that she would give me such a wife as should help me to win salvation. And in that village there was a maiden, she too was an orphan, who was wont to go continually to church, and her name was Anastasia. Her father was the blacksmith Marko, exceedingly rich, but when he died all his substance was wasted. So she lived in poverty and she would pray to God that he might so compass it that she should be joined to me in matrimony; and he willed that it should be so. At that same time my mother went to God, having first taken the veil, and died in the odor of sanctity. And I, because of persecution, moved to another place, and at the age of twenty I was ordained deacon and, after two years, priest. When I had been a priest eight years, I was raised to the rank of archpriest by Orthodox bishops, and this was twenty years ago. And it is thirty years in all that I have been in Holy Orders.

II. The Years of Mission with "Seekers After God" and Clashes with the Administration (1640–1652)

And when I was still but a parish priest I had many spiritual children—it would be five or six hundred souls in all. And never resting, I, miserable sinner, in churches and houses and at crossways, by towns and hamlets, even in the city of the tsar and in the country of Siberia, was diligent during a period of some twenty-five years in teaching and preaching the Word of God.

And in these days of my ministry a young woman came to confess to me, burdened with many sins, guilty of fornication and of all the sins of the flesh, and, weeping, she began to acquaint me with them all, leaving nothing out, standing before the Gospels. And I, thrice-accursed, though a leech, fell sick myself. I inwardly burned with a lecherous fire, and that hour was bitter to me. I lit three candles and fixed them to the lectern and placed my right hand in the flame, and held it there till the evil passion was burned out and, when I had dismissed the young woman and laid away my vestments, I prayed and went to my house, grievously humbled in spirit.

The time must have been midnight, and when I reached my house I wept before the icons so that my eyes swelled; and prayed diligently that God might remove from me my spiritual children, in that the burden was too heavy for me. And I threw myself upon the ground face downwards, sobbing bitterly. And as I lay I swooned and wist not how I was weeping, and in my fancy I was transported to the banks of the Volga and gazed at it with the eyes of my heart; and this is what I saw: On it were sailing two stately ships of gold, and their oars were of gold, and their masts were of gold and all was of gold; at the helm of each was sitting a man, and I said: "Whose are these ships?" They answered: "Luke's and Laurence's." Now these had been two of my spiritual children, and they had set me and my house on the path of salvation, and their end had been pleasing to God. And after that I saw a third ship, not adorned with gold, but pied with many and varied hues, red and white, and blue and black and ash, so that the mind of man would be hard put to grasp at the same time all its loveliness and excellence. And a young man, all shining, sat at the helm, and steered, and I called out to him: "Whose ship?" and he who was on her answered: "Thine. Sail away on her with thy wife and children, if thou wilt persist." And I was troubled not a little, and sitting there I pondered the meaning of the vision and of the sailing.[2]

And but a little time after this—as it has been written—*the sorrows of death compassed me, and the pains of hell gat hold upon me: I found trouble and sorrow.* A headman abducted her daughter from a widow, and I besought him to return the orphan to her mother; he scorned our prayers and raised up storms against me; he came to the church with a band of followers, and they crushed me to death. And I, having lain dead for half an hour and more, was brought to life by a wave of God's hand, and he was sore afraid and renounced the girl for my sake. Then the Devil prompted him: he came to the church, he beat me and dragged me, clad in my vestments, along the ground by the legs, and while he did it I was praying.

And likewise another headman at another time became as a wild beast against me. Breaking into my house, he beat me and gnawed the fingers of my hand, like a dog, with his teeth; and when his throat was full of blood, then he loosened his teeth from my hand and, throwing me aside, went to his house. But I, blessing God, wrapped up my hand in a cloth, and started for vespers; and on the way he leaped out on me again with two small pistols and, standing close to me, fired from one of

[2] The symbol of the ship is very common in Russian literature, and usually symbolized the life of a man. It has a biblical origin.

them and, by God's will, the powder exploded in the pan and the pistol missed fire. So he threw the pistol on the ground and in the same manner fired from the other, and God willed it should be in the same sort, for that pistol also missed fire. But I, praying diligently, with one hand signed him with the Cross and bowed low before him; then began he to snarl imprecations, but I said to him: "Out of thy mouth, Ivan Rodionovich, let blessings proceed." And next he took from me my homestead and drove me out with violence, seizing all my goods, leaving me not even a morsel of bread to eat on the road.

During that time my son Prokopy was born, the same that today lies a prisoner with his mother dug into a pit in the earth. So I took my staff and his mother took the unbaptized infant, and we set off on our wanderings, whither God should lead us, and on the way we baptized our son, even as Phillip of old baptized the eunuch.[3] And when in my wanderings I reached Moscow, I made straight for the tsar's chaplain, the Archpriest Stephen, and for Neronov, the Archpriest John, and they informed the tsar concerning me, and from that time began my acquaintance with the tsar.[4] And the reverend fathers sent me back whence I had come with royal mandates, and wearily I dragged myself home; but the walls of my house had been pulled down and I set to to rebuild them, and once again the Devil raised up a storm against me. There came to my village dancing bears with drums and lutes, and I, though a miserable sinner, was zealous in Christ's service, and I drove them out and broke the buffoons' masks and the drums, on a common outside the village, one against many, and two great bears I took away— one I clubbed senseless, but he revived, and the other I let go into the open country. And after that Vasily Petrovich Sheremetiev,[5] who was sailing up the Volga to Kazan to take over the Governorship, took me on board, and he sternly reprimanded me and ordered me to bless his son who had a shaven face.[6] And when I saw that image of shame I would not bless him, but condemned him from the Scriptures. So my lord waxed terribly wrath and ordered that I should be flung into the Volga and,

[3] The episode described in the Acts of the Apostles, 8, 27-38.
[4] Archpriest Stephen Vonifatiev was the confessor of the tsar. He and Archpriest Ivan Neronov were the leaders of the Zealots of Piety.
[5] The Zealots of Piety energetically fought these buffoons, or *komorokhs,* traveling actors, singers, and bear trainers whose performances and songs strongly reflected the pre-Christian mentality.
[6] The shaving of a beard was considered sinful in Muscovite Russia. Vasily Sheremetiev was a wealthy and influential aristocrat and high official.

having inflicted on me many hurts, they cast me aside, but in later years their rough handling turned to friendliness, for we were reconciled one to another in the antechamber of the tsar, and my youngest brother was his lady's confessor. Thus does God fashion the lives of his people.

Let us return to earlier days: again another headman became as a wild beast against me; he arrived with his folk at my homestead and attacked me, shooting from bows and muskets; and I, the while, prayed to the Lord, calling to him in a loud voice: "Lord God! Make his heart gentle, and reconcile him to me by whatsoever means thou choosest." And he fled from my yard, driven out by the Holy Ghost. And that very night his folk came running and they called out to me with many tears: "Little father! Euphemy Stepanovich is near his end and he is most inconveniently screaming; he strikes himself and groans, and of his own accord he says: 'I want parson Avvakum, God will punish me because of him.'" And I felt it to be a trap. And terror seized on the spirit within me and I prayed to God thus: "Thou, O Lord, who broughtest me out of my mother's womb and out of nothing didst create me, if they are about to strangle me, then count me with Phillip, the Metropolitan of Moscow[7] and if they are about to stab me, count me with the Prophet Zachariah[8]; and if they are about to drown me, then deliver me from their hands, as thou didst Stephen of Perm."[9] And praying the while I betook myself to the house, even to the house of Euphemy. And when they had led me into the yard, out rushed his wife, Neonila, and seized me by the hand, and she said: "Come in then, dearie, my lord, my father! Come in then, light of our eyes!" And I answered: "Strange! Before it was 'Son of a whore'! and now it's 'My Father!' Christ wields a crueler scourge than he. Your good man has not taken long to own himself in fault." She led me into the bedroom. Euphemy leaped out of the feather bed, fell down at my feet, and howled and blubbered confused words: "Forgive me, my lord! I have sinned before God and before thee"; and he was all of a tremble. And said in reply: "Dost thou wish to be healed?" and he, lying on the ground, answered: "Aye, good father!" And I said: "Stand up, God pardons thee." But he, sorely stricken, could not rise by himself, so I lifted him and laid him on his bed, and con-

[7] Phillip, Metropolitan of Moscow, was imprisoned and then slain by the order of Ivan IV.

[8] According to biblical tradition, Prophet Zachariah was slain in 520 by his enemies whose immorality he denounced.

[9] For Stephen of Perm, see introduction to Selection 26.

fessed him and anointed him with sacred oil, and his sickness departed. So Christ willed it. And the next morning they sent me back with honor to my home, and he and his wife became my spiritual children, excellent servants of Christ. Thus doth the Lord harden his heart against the proud, but he showers blessings on the meek.

And but a little time after this I was once again driven out of this place, so I betook me to Moscow and by God's will the tsar was pleased to appoint me Archpriest of Yurievets-on-the-Volga.[10] But I did not stay there long, but a matter of eight weeks. The Devil prompted the priests and the peasants and the good wives; and they came to the patriarch's chancellery where I was occupied in business of the church and dragged me out of the chancellery (there would be nigh two thousand of them), and in the middle of the street they beat me with cudgels and stamped on me, and the good wives beat me with shovels; and, for my sins, they flung me into a corner of a house. The captain of the troops came rushing up with his soldiers, and seizing me they galloped on their horses to my little home; and the captain placed the soldiers round the house. But the folk came up to it, and raised an outcry through the town, especially the Jack priests and their Jills, whom I had rated for their whoring ways, and they howled: "Death to the thief, to the son of a whore, and we'll fling his body into the ditch, for the dogs." And, on the third day, by night, after a short rest, I left my wife and children and with two others made for Moscow by way of the Volga; I would have taken refuge in Kostroma,[11] but, lo! there too they had driven away their Archpriest, Daniel. Ah, lack-a-day! The Devil leaves no man in peace! I reached Moscow; and went to Stephen, the tsar's chaplain; and he grumbled at me: "Why," says he, "have you abandoned your minster church?" And more trouble was awaiting me. In the middle of the night the tsar came in to his chaplain for his blessing and he saw me there;—more vexation: "And why have you abandoned your town?" And there were my wife and children and household (some twenty souls in all) left behind in Yurievets and I not knowing if they were alive or dead—yet another burden on my heart!

[10] Yurievets-on-the-Volga used to be an important market city in the province of Nizhny-Novgorod.

[11] Kostroma was an important merchant city on the Volga. Archpriest Daniel was the leading member of the Zealots of Piety in that city, and he met with considerable difficulties there because he denounced the morality of the city's people.

III. Conflict with Nikon, and the Rout of the "Seekers After God" (1652–1653)

After that, Nikon, our friend, brought down the relics of the Metropolitan Phillip from the Solovki Monastery,[12] and before his arrival, Stephen, the chaplain, with the brotherhood[13] and I with them, passed a week in prayer and fasting, concerning the patriarchate, even that God might give us a shepherd fitted to the saving of our souls. And the Metropolitan of Kazan and I, we signed our names to a petition and gave it to the tsar and the tsarina, concerning the chaplain Stephen, that he might be made patriarch. But he did not wish it for himself and named the Metropolitan Nikon. And the tsar hearkened to him and wrote to Nikon to greet him on his arrival. "To Nikon, the Right Reverend Metropolitan of Novgorod and Velikie Luki and of all Russia, greetings,"[14] and so forth. And when he arrived he played the fox with us, and it was bowings and scrapings and "Good morrow to you!" For he knew that he was to be patriarch and wished to remove all obstacles thereto. But I'll not waste my time telling all these cunning machinations. And when he became patriarch he would not so much as allow his friends into the room of the Cross,[15] and now at last belched forth his venom.

In Lent he sent a pastoral letter to St. Basil's Church, to John Neronov. Now the latter was my spiritual father and I was lodging in his presbytery; and when he was absent I took the services; and at the time there was some talk of making me the successor to Silas, God rest his soul, at St. Saviour's, but God willed not that it should be so and I myself was not over eager concerning it; I was well content to continue at St. Basil's: I used to read godly books to the flock, and they would come in great numbers. Nikon inscribed his letter with the year and the date, "According to the tradition of the holy Apostles and the Fathers, it is not seemly to make obeisance in church to the knee, it should be no lower than the girdle, and moreover it behooves you to sign yourselves with three fingers."[16] We met

---

[12] In 1652 Tsar Alexis sent Nikon to bring the relics of Metropolitan Phillip from the Solovki Monastery to Moscow.

[13] When speaking of brotherhood, Avvakum refers to the main group of the Zealots of Piety in Moscow.

[14] Before becoming patriarch, Nikon was Metropolitan of Novgorod and Velikie Luki.

[15] Room of the Cross—the official reception room in the patriarchal palace.

[16] As previously mentioned, the conflict between the Zealots of

together and took counsel. It was as if winter was of a mind to come; our hearts froze, our limbs shook. Neronov entrusted his church to me and shut himself up in the Miracle Monastery, and he spent a week praying in a cell, and one day a voice came from the icon of the Saviour: "The hour of tribulation has come; it behooves you to suffer and be strong." And, weeping, he recounted these words to me and to Paul, the Bishop of Kolomna, the same that afterwards Nikon was to burn in the Novgorod country[17]; and then to Daniel the Archpriest of Kostroma, and also to all the brothers. Together with Daniel I wrote out excerpts from the Fathers concerning the manner to be used in crossing oneself and making obeisances, and we gave them to the tsar. And many were the excerpts we had made. But he hid them, we know not where; I am of opinion that he gave them to Nikon.

And a little later Nikon seized Daniel in the monastery outside the Tver Gates, and sheared him monk in the presence of the tsar, and tearing off his cassock and insulting him the while, had him taken to the Miracle Monastery and put in the bakehouse, and when he had suffered grievously there, he sent him to Astrakhan; and there they placed a crown of thorns on his head and cast him into a dungeon, where he died. After the shearing of Daniel, they seized another Daniel—he also was an archpriest, of Temnikov—and they confined him in the monastery of New St. Saviour's. And in the same way with the Archpriest Ivan Neronov, Nikon took off his biretta in church and had him confined in the monastery of Simon, and later banished him to Vologda, to the walled monastery of St. Saviour's, then to the fortress of Kola,[18] and in the end, after having suffered exceedingly, he recanted—poor soul; he signed himself with three fingers, and so died a heretic. Woe is me! Let every man stand firm and be ever on the watch lest his foot shall stumble. In the words of the Scriptures, these are surely evil days when even the elect yield to the blandishments of Antichrist. It behooves us to be exceeding strong in prayer to God, and he will save us and help us, for he is merciful and loves mankind.

Piety, which was later to grow into the movement of Old Believers, and Patriarch Nikon originally grew out of the latter's changes in the Russian rites and missals. One of the most important changes was that of the two-fingered sign of the cross to a three-fingered one.

[17] Bishop Paul of Kolomna was a staunch upholder of old traditions and a resolute enemy of Nikon. Nikon deported him to the Novgorod region, and, according to rumor, had him burned.

[18] The city of Vologda is located in northern Russia. The fortress Kola is located in the extreme north not far from the Arctic Ocean.

And I, too, while I was celebrating vespers, was arrested by Boris Neledinsky and his musketeers, and together with me they arrested nigh on sixty souls and took them off to prison, and me they fastened with a chain for the night in the patriarch's court. And when the Sabbath dawned they placed me in a cart and stretched out my arms and drove me from the patriarch's court to the monastery of Andronicus, and there they put chains on me and flung me into a black dungeon, dug into the earth, and there I lay for three days, and I had nothing to eat or to drink in the darkness, as I sat there bowing myself to the earth against my chains, though I knew not, as I made my obeisances, which was east and which was west. No one came to me but mice and black beetles, and the crickets chirped, and of fleas there was abundance. And on the third day I was famished, that is to say, I wanted to eat, and after vespers someone was standing before me, I knew not whether he was man or angel, and to this day I know not. I only know this that he said a prayer in the darkness and, taking me by the shoulder, led me on my chain to a bench and seated me on it and put a spoon into my hands and gave me a little bread and some cabbage soup to sup—Oh, but it was tasty!—and he said to me: "Enough, let that serve you as restorative." And, lo, he was gone! The door had not opened and yet he was gone! Were he a man, it were a miracle; but were he an angel? Then were there no cause for wonder, because for such as he there are no barriers. In the morning came the archimandrite[19] with the brothers, and they led me away; they spoke to me coaxingly, that I should yield to the patriarch, but I thundered against them from the Scriptures and snarled at them. They took off the big chain and put a small one on me in its place, and set a monk as jailer over me; they ordered that I should be dragged to church. In church they pulled my hair and poked my ribs and pulled at my chain, and spat in my eyes. May God forgive them in this life and the next! It was not they themselves that did it, but Satan in his malice. I remained there four weeks.

After me they next seized Login, the Archpriest of Murom. In the monastery church, in the presence of the tsar, they sheared him monk at mass. At the time of the carrying round of the Host, the patriarch seized the paten from the head of the Archdeacon and placed it on the altar, together with Christ's body and the chalice. Meanwhile, Therapont, the archimandrite of the Miracle Monastery, was standing outside the choir before

[19] This refers to Therapont, the archimandrite, or abbot, of the Miracle Monastery.

he King's Gates. Woe is me that Christ's body should be
rendered, more impiously than ever by the Jews! When they
had shorn him they tore from him his kaftan and his outer garment. But Login was consumed with the zeal of God's fire; and
he defied Nikon and spat across the threshold to the altar
straight into his eyes; loosening his girdle, he tore off his shift
and flung it into the altar, into Nikon's face, and, oh, wondrous
to tell, the shift spread itself out and fell on the altar in such
a way that it covered the paten as though it had been the corporals. And the tsarina was in church at the time. They put a
chain on Login and, dragging him from the church, beat him
with brooms and whips to the monastery of the Epiphany, and
thrust him into a dungeon for the night and set musketeers to
guard him strictly. But lo! in the night God gave him a new fur
cloak and a biretta; and in the morning they told Nikon, and
he, laughing, said: "*I know that breed of sham saint!*" and he
took from him the hat, but left him the fur coat.

At that time they led me again from the monastery on foot
to the court of the patriarch's palace; and then again, spreading
out my arms and wrangling much with me, they took me away
from there also. And on St. Nikita's day there was a procession
with crosses, and as they were driving me in a cart we met the
crosses. And they drove me to the monastery church, that they
might shear me, and during Mass they kept me for a long time
at the threshold. The tsar rose from his place and going up to
the patriarch entreated him that he should not shear me, and
they took me away to the Siberia Office and handed me over to
the scribe, Tretiak Bashmakov, the same that today is suffering
for Christ—the elder Savvaty (for he took the cowl), he lies in
the monastery of New St. Saviour's in a dungeon dug into the
earth: may God have mercy on his soul! and even in these days
he entreated me kindly.

IV. Deportation to Tobolsk (1653–1655)

So they sent me then to Siberia with my wife and children, and
of the many and great privations on the way, had I the time there
would be much to tell. Dame Avvakum bore a child, and, she
being unwell, we transported her in a cart to Tobolsk; it was a
journey of 3,000 versts, and for some thirteen weeks we dragged
along in carts and by water and half of the way in sledges.[20]

The archbishop got me a church in Tobolsk. And there in

[20] One verst is about five-eighths of a mile. The city of Tobolsk is
situated in western Siberia.

that church great afflictions found me out; in one and a ha
years five times were the *Tsar's Words*[21] called out against m
and a certain member of the archbishop's household, the scrib
Ivan Struna, outraged me. The archbishop was away in Moscov
and in his absence he, taught by the Devil, fell on me. He wa
minded to torment without cause Anthony, the clerk of m
church. He, Anthony, gave him the slip and fled to me, i
church. But this Ivan Struna, having collected some other
came to me that same day in church—I was singing vespers
and came leaping into the church and seized Anthony in th
choir by the beard. I, in the meantime, had shut the churc
doors and would let no one in, so Struna was alone and kep
twirling round like an imp of hell; and I, when I had finishe
vespers sat him down, Anthony lending a hand, in the middle
the church on the floor and thrashed him soundly with a leath
strap for having made a riot in church; and the other rogue
some twenty in number, fled, every man of them, driven awa
by the Holy Ghost. And Struna having declared that he r
pented, I let him go in peace. But Struna's kinsmen among th
priests and monks raised the whole town against me, so th
they might compass my death. And in the middle of the nig
they drove up in sledges to my homestead and broke into n
house, being of a mind to take and drown me; but a terror fro
God fell upon them and drove them hence, and they fled awa
For a month was I tormented by their tricks, for they wou
attack me in secret; and sometimes I would take refuge by nig
in the church, and sometimes with the governor, and I wou
beg that for safety I might be put in prison—but this they wou
not do. Matthew Lomkov—the same that as a monk was call
Mitrophan, and later in Moscow was apparitor to the Metr
politan Paul—he kept close to my side; it was he that afterwar
sheared me in the monastery church together with the deac
Afanasy: but at that time he was a just man, though the Dev
has now swallowed him. Then the archibishop returned fro
Moscow, and, as was but meet considering his offense, thru
Struna into prison with chains on him. For a certain man h
lain with his own daughter, and he, Struna, had accepted fi
kopeks from the fellow and had let him go without punishme
And the lord bishop ordered him to be fettered, and he t
thought him of that affair with me. For he, Struna, went to t

---

[21] The expression "Tsar's Words" meant that one person accus
another and, pointing to him, claimed he was involved in a c
spiracy against the tsar. It always led to the arrest of the accus
man.

governor and his men in their office, and said the *Tsar's Words* against me. And the captain allowed a petty squire, Peter Beketov, to go bail for him. Woe is me! Misfortune entered the gates of Peter's dwelling place, and it grieves my soul. The archbishop took council with me, and, in accordance with the rubric, on the first Sunday in Lent he started cursing Struna for the sin of incest in the great church. And that same Peter Beketov came to church, and rated the archbishop and myself, and within an hour, on his way home from church, he went mad, and he died a bitter and an evil death. And his grace and I, we ordered his body to be flung into the street to the dogs, and the townsfolk mourned him and his sin; for three days they importuned God diligently that on the Day of Judgment he might be pardoned. Through pity for Struna he had brought this dire calamity upon himself, and on the third day his grace and I read the office over his body. But enough of this woeful business!

V. The Hardships of Traveling to Dauria (1655)

At this time an edict arrived, ordering that I should be taken from Tobolsk to the Lena, in that I had condemned Nikon from the Scriptures and pronounced him a heretic.[22] At that time a letter came from Moscow telling how two brothers, who lodged in the tsarina's apartments at the top of the palace, had both of them died of the plague, together with their wives and children, and many also of their friends and kinsfolk; God was pouring forth the vials of his wrath on the kingdom. But they, wretched men, knew not this and continued making disturbance in the church. Then Neronov spoke to the tsar, saying: "The visitation for schism is threefold: plague, the sword, and division." And thus has it come to pass in our days, even now; but the Lord is merciful. When he has punished us to bring us to repentance, than has he mercy on us and, driving away the ills of our souls and bodies, he giveth quietness. I preach Christ and my hope is in him; I confidently await his mercy and I believe in the Resurrection of the Dead.

So once more I got into the boat that had been assigned me —as I have said before—and sailed towards the Lena. And when I reached Eniseysk I was met by another edict, wherein I was ordered to get me to Dauria[23]—it would be more than twenty thousand versts from Moscow—and to give myself over to

[22] This was the result of Struna's *Tsar's Words* against Avvakum.
[23] Dauria was a region in eastern Siberia in the vicinity of Lake Baikal and which the Russians intended to conquer.

Afanasy Pashkov as chaplain to his troops that numbered six hundred men, and, for my sins, he was a fierce hard man, and it was ever his custom to burn folk and torture them, and beat them, and many times did I try to persuade him to desist, and now I was in his hands, and from Moscow came an order from Nikon that I was to be tormented.

On our journey from Eniseysk, it would be on the great Tunguska River, a storm sank my raft. It foundered completely in midstream and it was full of water and its sail was in tatters, only the deck remained above water, all the rest was under water. My wife, bareheaded[24] as she was, managed, I know not how, to drag the children out of the water on to the deck, but I, looking up at the sky, cried out: "O Lord! Save us! O Lord! Help us!" And by God's will we were driven to the shore; but why multiply words?

From another raft two men were wrenched away and drowned in the water. After that, when we were come to ourselves, we set out once more on our way.

VI. First Difficulties with Pashkov (1655–1656)

When we came to the Shaman rapids, diverse folk came sailing out to meet us, and with them were two widows; one of them was aged about sixty; and the other was older, and they were traveling by boat to a nunnery where they were to take the veil. And this Pashkov was minded to send them back, and to give them by force in marriage; and I said to him: "It is against the canons of the church to give such women in marriage." And in lieu of heeding my words and letting the widows go, he waxed angry and devised how he might torment me.

In other rapids—called the long rapids—he set about driving me from the raft. "You bring bad luck," says he, "to the raft. You're a heretic," says he; "off with you to the mountains! It is not for such as you to keep company with Cossacks." Alackaday! The mountains were high, the ravines impassable, there was a stone crag that stood there like a wall—you'd crick your neck before you saw its top. In these mountains great serpents were to be found, and in them dwelt geese and ducks with red feathers, and black crows, and grey jackdaws; in these mountains were also eagles, and hawks, and gerfalcons and guinea fowl and pelicans, and swans and other wild things in plenty every variety of bird. Moreover, on these mountains many wild

[24] It was unseemly for a married woman to be without a kerchief on her head.

...sts wandered at liberty: wild goats, and deer and bison,
...d elk, and boars, and wolves, and wild sheep—clearly to be
...n but not to be caught.

...Pashkov was of a mind to turn me out into these mountains
...live with beasts and birds, and I wrote him a little letter that
...gan thus: "O man! Fear God who sits on the Cherubim and
...zes into the abyss; before him tremble the celestial powers
...d every creature including man; thou alone despisest him and
...est things that are not seemly," and so forth. It was a long
...ter; and I sent it to him. And some fifty men rushed on me;
...y seized my raft and hastened towards him, who was distant
...ne three versts; and I stood there, boiling some porridge for
... Cossacks and I fed them with it; and they, poor souls, ate
...it and trembled, and some of them, looking at me, began to
...ep for me. They dragged up the raft; the executioners seized
...and led me before him. He was standing with drawn sword,
...king with rage; he began to speak to me, saying, "What are
...? A parson, or an unfrocked one?" And I answered, "I am
...vakum, the archpriest; speak! what is your business with me?"
...en he roared like a wild beast, and struck me a great blow
...t on one cheek and then on the other, and then again on the
...d, and knocked me off my feet; and seizing his leather
...rd-strap struck me, where I lay, thrice on the back, and
...n, tearing off my shift, gave me seventy-two strokes on my
...ed back with the knout. And I kept saying, "O Lord Jesus
...rist, Son of God! Help me!" And this I kept repeating with-
...pause, so that it was bitter to him, in that I did not say,
...ave mercy." At each stroke I said a prayer, but in the middle
...the flogging I screamed to him, "You've beat me enough, I
..."; so he ordered that it should stop. And I said to him, "Why
...you beat me—do you know?" And he ordered them to beat
...again on the ribs; and then they stopped; and I was trem-
...ng all over, and I fell. And he ordered them to drag me off
...the raft that carried the money bags: they put fetters on my
...ds and feet and flung me on to the deck. It was autumn,
...rain fell on me all night, and there was a pool where I was
...g. When they were beating me it did not hurt because of
...prayers I was saying; but now, as I lay, the thought came
...ne: "Son of God, why didst thou permit them to beat me so
...ly? Look thee, Lord, I was championing the widow, conse-
...ted to thee. Who shall judge between thee and me? When
...as living as an evil man, thou didst not chastise me thus;
...now I know not in what I have sinned." Ay! There was a
...teous man for you, another dungfaced Pharisee, wishing,

forsooth, to judge the Almighty! If Job spoke in that fashion
was because he was a perfect and an upright man; and, mo:
over, he knew not the Scriptures, for he dwelt outside the L:
in a barbarian land, and it was through Creation, not throu
Revelation, that he learned to know God. But I, in the fi
place, was a sinful man, and, in the second place, I was learn
in the Law and the Prophets and was fortified by the Scriptu:
in all my goings: *"We must, through much tribulation, en*
into the Kingdom of God"; and yet had I reached such a pit
of folly. Woe is me! How came it that the raft did not foun
with me in the water? Then my bones began to ache, my ve
to grow rigid, my heart to palpitate, verily, I was dying; t
water began to splash into my mouth, then I heaved a si;
yea, I repented before the Almighty, for, verily, the sweet Lo
of compassion remembers not against us our former transgr
sions when once we have repented of them; and once more
ceased to feel the pain.

In the morning they flung me onto a small craft and carri
me away. Then we came to the great rapids of the Padw
where the river is a verst in breadth, and there are three excee
ing steep reefs stretching across the whole of the river, an
except you find the passages between them, your boat will
shattered into splinters. They brought me into the rapids: abc
was rain and snow, and they flung over my shoulders nought l
a mangy little kaftan; the water flowed over my belly and »
spine—my poor body was in sorry plight. The took me out
the raft and, skirting the rapids, they dragged me over 1
stones in fetters. Verily I was in a sad plight, but with my s«
it was well; I was no longer peevish with God. Once again the
came into my head the words spoken by the Prophets and :
Apostles: *"My son, despise thou not the chastening of the Lo*
nor faint when thou art rebuked of him.

"For whom the Lord loveth he chasteneth, and scourg
every son whom he receiveth. If ye endure chastening, C
dealeth with you as with sons; for what son is he whom :
father chasteneth not?"

And with these words I comforted myself.

And after that they brought me to the fortress of Bratsky, a
flung me into a dungeon, and gavè me straw to lie upon. A
there I lay till Advent, in a freezing tower; these are the seas«
when winter reigns, but God kept me warm, and that with«
garments. Like a poor dog I lay on the straw; and sometir
they fed me, and sometimes they did not; there were many m
and I would strike at them with my biretta—the fools had :

en me a stick; I lay all the time on my belly, my back was
vered with sores, and of fleas and lice there was abundance.
vould fain have cried on Pashkov to pardon me; but it would
ve been contrary to God's will, it was ordained that I should
dure. Then they moved me to a warm hut, and there I dwelt
fetters with hostages and dogs the whole winter; and my wife
d been sent with the children some twenty versts away. And
the winter her serving-wench, Xenia, tormented her with her
trums and complaints. After Christmas my son Ivan, who was
l but a little lad, stole away from home that he might dwell
th me; and Pashkov ordered him to be flung into the freezing
ngeon where I lay; dear little lad, he spent the night there and
s nigh froze to death; and in the morning Pashkov ordered him
ck to his mother and I saw him no more; it was all he could
to drag himself home to his mother from the frostbite on his
ads and feet.

VII. The Dauria Campaign (1656–1662)

n spring we set out once more. There remained but scant
vision, for the first store had all been robbed—books and
ments and other sundries had all been taken; but the second
re remained. I came near again to drowning on the lake of
kal; I was made to pull a towing rope on the Khilok River,
d upstream it was mighty hard going. And there was no time
eating nor for sleeping; for a whole year I suffered from the
dships of water-travel; the folk kept dying, and my feet
d belly were blue. For two summers we journeyed by water
d in the winter we were towed along by haulage. And, as I
ve said, on this same Khilok for the third time I came nigh to
wning. My boat was sucked by the current from the shore,
d the boats of the other folk stayed where they were, but
ne was caught up and carried away. My wife and children
d remained on shore, and the boat bolted with the steersman
d me! she was pitched and tossed on the swirling water, but
limbed onto her and cried out, "Help, Blessed Virgin! Thou
our Hope and Defense. Let me not be drowned!" Sometimes
feet would be in the water and sometimes I would scramble
he top; she was carried on for a verst and more, and then the
stopped her and she was shattered to fragments. Ay, what
ld one do if Christ and the Immaculate Mother of God so
ed it? And I climbed out of the water laughing, but the
were weeping, and they spread out my garments on the
hes—cloaks of satin and taffetas, and sundry trifles: for I still
a store of such things in chests and coffers, but from that

day they were rotted. But Pashkov was fain to give me anot
flogging. "You're making yourself a laughingstock," said
And once again I importuned the sweet Mother of God: "(
Lady! Soothe thy fool!" And she, our Hope, did soothe him, a
he began to concern himself about me.

Our next stage was the Lake of Irgen. There is there a ha
age and in the winter we began hauling; he took from me
workmen, and would not permit me to hire others, and we l
small children—many mouths and none to fill them; this p
hapless wretch of an archpriest set to fashion a dog-sleigh
himself and started hauling. That spring we began to sail dc
the Ingoda River—it was the fourth summer of my journey fr
Tobolsk. They were floating logs for the building of houses a
towns. There began to be nothing to eat, the folk began to
of hunger and from ceaseless working in the water; shallow v
the river, heavy were the rafts, merciless were the taskmaste
stout were the sticks, gnarled were the cudgels, cutting w
the knouts, cruel were the sufferings—fire and rack; the l
were so spent with hunger that let him, Afanasy, but start
menting one of them, and lo! he was dead on his hands. Ah, v
What a time! It would almost seem that he was out of his mi
There remained to Dame Avvakum one Moscow gown that l
not been rotted with damp. It would have fetched twenty-
rubles and more in Moscow; but in these parts they gave
four sacks of rye for it, and we dragged on for another y
living on the Nercha River, and keeping ourselves alive v
the roots and herbs that grew on the banks. One after anot
the folk died of hunger, and he saw to it that none of them
away, and they were circumscribed within a small space, a
they would wander over the steppes and fields, digging
grasses and roots, and we with them. And in winter we wo
live on fir cones, and sometimes God would send mare's fle
and sometimes we found the bones of stinking carcasses of v
beasts left by the wolves, and what had not been eaten up
the wolves that did we eat; and some would eat frozen wo
and foxes—in truth, any filth that they could lay their hands
A mare foaled, and, in secret, the starving folk devoured
foal together with the caul. And Pashkov got wind of it, and
flogged them with his knout to the point of death. And anot
mare died, and desperation seized them all, inasmuch as t
had pulled the foal out of her, stealing a march on nate
When nought but the head had as yet emerged from the wor
they tore it out, yea, and they began to eat the blood that ca
away with it. Ah, me! What a time! And two of my little s

died from these sore straits, and roaming the hills and the sharp rocks with my children that survived, naked and barefoot, living on grass and roots, what did I not endure? And I, sinful man, partook willy-nilly of mare's flesh and foul carrion and the flesh of birds. Woe for my sinful soul! Who will pour water on my head and unseal for me the fountain of tears, even that I may weep for the poor soul that is mine, which I have been destroying with my daily appetites? But in Christ's name a great lady helped us, the captain's daughter-in-law, Eudokia Kirilovna, and also his, Afanasy's, wife, Thekla Semenovna; in secret they would give us some comfort against a death from starvation. Without his knowledge they would sometimes send us a piece of meat, sometimes a circular loaf, sometimes flour and oats, as much as ever they could, and sometimes one of them would save up ten pounds of flour and some coins and sometimes twenty pounds and hand it over to us, and sometimes she would take out the chicken's food from the trough. My daughter, the hapless lass Agraphena, would go in secret under her window. And it was both pitiful and laughable! Sometimes, without the lady's knowledge, they would chase the child from the window, and sometimes she would come home burdened with a nice little store; at that time she was still but a child, but now she is twenty-seven. My poor little maid! She dwells unwed with her younger sisters by the Mezen, living from hand to mouth and weeping; and their mother and brothers lie buried in a dungeon in the earth. But what would you? Let every man endure great tribulation for Christ's sake! With God's help let even that which has been ordained come to pass, and let us suffer tribulation for the sake of the Christian faith. The archpriest used to love keeping company with the great but love in place of that, poor wretch, to endure even to the end; for it is written: *"Better is the end of a thing than the beginning thereof."* Enough of this: let us return to the previous matter.

We continued in the land of Dauria in dire straits some six or seven years, but during some of these years there would at times be some little balm, and he, Afanasy, slandering me, ceaselessly sought my death. And during these lean years he sent me of his own accord two widows—they were servants in his house and dear to him—Mary and Sophia, clothed about with an unclean spirit; many times had he tried spells and incantations upon them, but it had availed him nought; and tongues had begun to wag concerning the matter, whereupon the imp of hell would start tormenting them most cruelly, and they would twist themselves and shriek. He summoned me and, bowing to me, said, "I pray you take them home with you and physick them with prayer to God; God will hearken to you." And I answered him, "My Lord! What you ask of me is beyond my powers. By the prayers of the holy Fathers of our Church all things are possible to God." So I took the poor souls home—if it was presumptuous in me may I be forgiven. I had had some experience in such matters in Russia. Three or four persons possessed by an unclean spirit had, in former times, been brought to my house, and with the prayers of the holy Fathers I had cast out the imps of hell by the action and will of the living God and of our Lord Jesus Christ, Son of God, Light of the World. I had sprinkled them with tears and with water and anointed them with oil, chanting prayers the while, in the name of Christ, and the holy magic of these things had driven the imps out of these persons, and they had been healed—not by any virtue in me—by no means; but by their own faith. Of old time an ass was made the instrument by which a blessing came to Balaam,[25] and by a lynx a blessing came to Julian the martyr and by a stag to Sisinius: they spoke with a human voice. God whensoever he chooses triumphs over Nature's laws. Read the life of Theodore of Edessa; there will you find that a harlot raised a man from the dead; in the *Christian's Pilot*[26] it is written: *"Not for all men are the gifts of the Holy Ghost, but all men can he leaven, excepting only heretics."*

So they brought me these two women that were possessed and I, as the custom is, myself fasted and would not let them eat, and I prayed and anointed them with oil and tried every remedy I knew. And the good wives returned to health and to their right minds; and I confessed them and administered the Sacrament to them; and they tarried in my house, praying to God, for they loved me and would not go home. And it came to his knowledge that they had become my spiritual daughters and he was angered against me, more fiercely than before, and he was fain to burn me alive. "You have wormed out of them in the confessional," said he, "private matters concerning me. And how, forsooth, can one administer the Sacrament to a man if one has not first confessed him? And if you do not administer the Sacrament to the possessed, you'll in no wise succeed in casting out of them the imps of hell. A devil is not a mujik, forsooth, that he should fear the stick; what he fears is the Cross of Christ, and holy water and holy oil, but before the Body of

[25] See the Book of Numbers, Chapter 22.
[26] The *Christian's Pilot* was a Byzantine codex of canon law.

hrist he flies. Without the Blessed Sacrament I cannot heal; in
ur Orthodox faith there is no Communion without Confession;
the Roman faith they pay no heed to Confession; but to us,
e Orthodox observers, this is not seemly, and for us the Sacra-
ent of Penance must ever first be sought. And if in your need
ou cannot have a priest, then confess your sins to some discreet
other, and, beholding your contrition, God will pardon you;
nd then, having read through the Canon of the Mass before
ommunicating, keep by you some reserved sacrament. And,
hensoever you are away on a journey or engaged in traffic or
hatever it may be that takes you far from a church, if you
ave first given sighs of contrition to the Lord and have con-
ssed to your brother, as has been said above, then may you
artake with a clear conscience of the Blessed Sacrament and all
ill be well, if you have first fasted and read through the Canon
the Mass: take then a little casket and spread a napkin in it,
nd light a candle, and pour a little water into a cup, and ladle
ome out in a spoon, and place with prayer a portion of Christ's
ody in the water in the spoon, and sense it all with a censer;
nd weeping say out loud the whole of the prayer that begins:
Lord! I believe and confess that thou art Christ, the son of
e living God." (It is written in the Canon of the Mass.) Then,
rowing yourself on the ground before the icon, ask for for-
veness and, standing up, kiss the holy image; and, having
gned yourself, communicate with prayer, and drink a little of
e water and pray again to God, saying, "Now glory to Christ!"
ven if you die the minute after, it will be well with you.
nough of that matter, you yourselves know that it is good
ounsel. Now I shall go on with the story of the women.

Pashkov took the poor widows away from me, and in lieu of
ratitude he gave me harsh words. He hoped that Christ had
ttled the matter once and for all; but they began to rave
orse than before. He shut them up in an empty outhouse and
lowed no one access to them; then he summoned a monk to
em, but they flung logs at him, and he scuttled away. I sat at
ome weeping, and I knew not what to do. I did not dare to
o up to the big house, for he was mighty wroth with me; so
a secret I sent them holy water, and told them to wash them-
lves and drink a little of it, and, poor souls, their sufferings
ere eased a little. And in secret they stole off to me, and I
ointed them with oil in the name of Christ, and once again
od granted that they should be healed, and they returned
ome; and by night they would escape to me in secret to pray
God. And they became exceeding good churchwomen; they

put aside vanities and began to follow all the observances of th
Church; and afterwards in Moscow they went with their lady ₁
dwell in the nunnery of the Ascension. Glory to God for then

And then from the Nercha River we began to journey bac
to Russia; for five weeks we traveled on the naked ice in sledge
I was given two sorry nags for my children and my baggag
while myself and Dame Avvakum, we made our way on foo
stumbling over the ice. The country was barbarous, the nativ
were hostile, so we feared to get separated from the others, an
yet we could not keep up with the horses—for we were
hungry, weary pair; and my poor old woman tramped alon
tramped along, and at last she fell, and another weary so
stumbled over her, and he fell too; they both screamed, an
were not able to get up. The man cried out, "Oh, good wif
Oh, my lady! Your pardon!" and my old woman answered, "Fi
gossip! Would you crush me to death?" And I came up, and sh
poor soul, began to complain to me, saying, "How long, arc
priest, are these sufferings to last?" And I said, "Markovna! t
our death." And she, with a sigh, answered, "So be it, Petr
vitch; let us be getting on our way."

VIII. The Story of the Black Hen

And we had a pet, a black hen, and she laid two eggs a da
to feed the children, by God's will, helping us in our need;
was God's doing. But when they were carrying out the baggag
to the dog sledge, she was crushed to death, for our sins, an
to this day whenever I think of that hen my heart aches for he
I know not if it were a hen or miracle: all the year round sh
laid two eggs a day, and we would not have taken a hundre
rubles for her—nay, we would have spat on them! mere dros
And that hen, God's living creature, fed us, and she would tak
her meals with us, pecking at the porridge of fir cones in th
caldron, and pecking at the fish, and in exchange she gave ι
two eggs a day. Glory to God, who fashions all things well! An
we had come by her in no ordinary way. My lady's hens had on
after another turned blind, and they began to die, whereupo
she gathered them into a basket and sent them to me. "And ma
it please you, Father," said she, "to pray over the hens." And
considered: she was a lady bountiful to us, she had childre
and she had need of the hens. So I chanted a prayer and blesse
some water and sprinkled the hens and censed them. Then
went to the forest and fashioned them a trough from whic
tᵒ ₑat, and sprinkled it with holy water, and sent the whol
baggage back to her. And by a wave of God's hand the hen

were healed, because of her faith. And it was from that same brood that our hen came; but enough of this matter; it was not the first miracle that Christ had brought to pass. Already Kosma and Damian had blessed and healed both men and cattle in the name of Christ.[27] God has a use for everything: cattle and fowls —they were created for the glory of his pure majesty, and also for the sake of mankind.

IX. At Lake Irgen

So we made our way back to Lake Irgen. My lady had pity on us and sent us a little basket of wheat, so we had our fill of frumenty. Eudokia Kirilovna was a lady bountiful to me, but the Devil set her quarreling with me in this manner: she had a son whose name was Simeon; he had been born in that place. It was I that had churched the mother and baptized the child, and every day they would send him to me for my blessing and I, having signed him with the Cross and sprinkled him with holy water, would kiss him and send him home; he was a fine healthy child and I loved him like my own. But the little lad began to ail, and I was away from home. And in a moment of pettiness of spirit she was vexed with me and sent the child to a medicine man. And I, when I learned of it, was angry with her, and a wide breach came between us; the little boy began to ail still more, and his right hand and foot dried up, so they were like little sticks. She grew ashamed; but she knew not what to do, and God oppressed her still further. The little one became sick unto death, and the nurses came to me weeping and I said to them, "If the goodwife is a baggage, then let her keep herself *to* herself." For I was waiting that she should repent. I saw that the Devil had hardened her heart, and I bowed down before the Lord God, praying that he might bring her to her right mind. And the Lord, the God of Mercy, softened the rich soil of her heart, and early next morning she sent to me her second son, Ivan; with tears he begged forgiveness for his mother, walking round the stove and bowing before me; and I was lying on the stove, naked, under a covering made from birch-bark, and Dame Avvakum was lying within the stove, and the children anywhere. It was raining at the time; we had no covering, and our winter quarters were dripping, so we were in sorry straits. And I said to him, bringing him low, "Tell your mother that she must ask forgiveness of Aretha, the medicine

[27] Kosma and Damian were considered the saintly protectors of men and cattle, and possessing miracle-working powers for healing.

man." Then she brought the sick child to me and I ordered her to lay him before me, and they were all weeping and bowing themselves. And I arose and got me my stole out from the mess and dirt and found some holy oil, and, praying to God, I censed the boy and signed him with the sign of the Cross. And God granted that the child was healed, both in his hand and foot. And I sprinkled him with holy water and sent him to his mother. Consider, thou who hearkenest to my story, what great things were compassed by a mother's penitence; it both physicked her own soul and healed her child. What then? It is not only today that God is with penitents. On the morrow she sent us fish and pies; and they were apt to our need, for we were starving; and that day we made our peace, she and I. When we had journeyed back from Dauria, she, sweet lady, died in Moscow, and I buried her in the nunnery of the Ascension.

And Pashkov himself learned of the affair with the boy, for she told him. I went to him and, bowing low before me, he, Pashkov, said, "God bless you! You have acted like a true priest; remember not our sins against us." And at that time he sent us no small store of food.

X. THE TRIBULATIONS OF THE MONGOLIAN EXPEDITION (1661)

But in a very short space he was minded to torture me—hearken how it came about. He was sending his son, Eremy, off to fight in the kingdom of the Mongols, and with him some seventy-two Cossacks and some twenty natives. And he made a native to *"shamanit',"*[28] that is to say, to tell their fortune, as to whether they would prosper and return home victorious. And in the evening that wizard—it was near my winter quarters—brought a live sheep and began to work magic over it: he rolled it to and fro for a long space and then he twisted its head and flung it away. Then he began to jump and dance, and invoke devils, and, giving great screams the while, he flung himself upon the earth, and foamed at the mouth; the devils were pressing him, and he asked them, "Will the expedition prosper?" And the devils said, "It will return with much booty, having gained a great victory." And the captains were glad; and all the folk, rejoicing, cried, "We will come home rich!" Oh, lackaday! It was bitter then, and even now it is not sweet to think upon. I, a bad shepherd, made my sheep to perish; from vexation of

[28] *Shamanit':* the Shamans were Siberian pagan priests and medicine men. Avvakum gives to this word a verbal infinitive ending, thus *shamanit'* means to perform pagan rites.

spirit I forgot the words of the Gospel, when the Sons of Zebedee counseled our Lord concerning the stubborn villagers, saying:—

"Lord, wilt thou that we command fire to come down from heaven and consume them, even as Elias did?"

But He turned and rebuked them, and said, Ye know not what manner of spirit ye are of.

For the Son of Man is not come to destroy men's lives, but to save them. And they went to another village.

But I, accursed, did not so. In my poor room I cried with a great cry to the Lord, "Hearken to me, my God! Hearken to me, King of Heaven! Sweet Lord! Hearken to me! Let not one of them return home; and dig a grave for every one of them yonder! Lay on them an evil fate, O Lord! Bring them to destruction, so that the Devil's prophecy may not be fulfilled." And many like words did I say, and in secret I prayed to God concerning it. They told him that I was praying thus, but he did but snarl abuses at me. Then he sent off his son with the captain; they rode off at night, directing their course by the stars. And I was seized with pity for them, for my soul foresaw that they would perish; nevertheless, I continued praying for their destruction, and some of them, as they passed, called out goodby to me, and I called back, "You will die yonder." And, as they rode off, the horses under them began to whinny, and the cows that were there to low, and the sheep and goats to bleat, and the dogs to howl, and the natives to howl, like the dogs. Terror seized them all. With tears Eremy sent me word, "that it may please my lord and spiritual father to pray for me." And I was seized with pity for him, for he had been my secret friend and had suffered for my sake. When his father was flogging me with the knout, he had tried to dissuade him, so that his father had chased him with drawn sword. And when they arrived after me, at other rapids, those of the Pandun, forty rafts all got through the straits in safety; but his, Afanasy's own raft, though her rigging was excellent and six hundred Cossacks had been set to build her, yet were they not able to get her through: the waters overcame them, or rather God was punishing him: all the crew were sucked into the water, and the raft was hurled against a rock; the waters splashed up against it, but did not flow into it. It is marvelous to watch God's lessons to the foolish! He himself was on the shore, and his lady was on the raft, and Eremy began to speak, saying, "Father! God will punish you for your sins; you flogged the archpriest with that knout unjustly; it is time to repent, my lord!" But he roared at him, like a wild beast, and Eremy, dodging behind a fir, clasped his hands and repeated the *Lord have mercy upon us*. But Pashkov, having seized a ringed musket, one that never missed, from an attendant, took aim at his son and pulled the trigger, and by God's will the weapon missed fire. Then, having adjusted the powder, he fired again, and again it missed fire. And he did the same a third time, and the third time, also, it missed fire. So he flung it on the ground, and the attendant picked it up and threw it out of the way, and it went off of its own accord.

And Pashkov sat him down on a chair and, leaning on his sword, he came to his right mind, and beginning to weep, he said, "I have sinned, accursed that I am, I have spilled innocent blood, I flogged the archpriest unjustly, God will punish me." It was strangely, strangely in accord with the words, *God is slow to anger and swift to hearken*. For because of his repentance the raft floated away from the reef; its prow was toward the water; and they pulled it from the shore and it leapt out into a lower level of the water. Then Pashkov called his son to him, and entreated him, saying, "Forgive me, Eremy, you spoke truly!" and he, running up, and bowing before his father, said, "It is God, my lord, that will forgive you; for I myself am guilty before God and before you." And he took his father's hand, and led him away. Eremy was a righteous-minded man, and a virtuous one; already was his own beard grey, and yet he honored his father exceedingly, and feared him, and according to the Scriptures it is seemly so to do, for God loves the children that honor their fathers. Come then, hearkener to my story! Is it not true that Eremy had suffered for my sake, and for the sake of Christ and his Law?

And all this was recounted to me by the helmsman of his, Afanasy's raft, by name Gregory Tielnoy. Let us return to the previous matter.

They went away, then, from me, and rode off to the wars; and pity seized me for Eremy, and I began to importune God Almighty that he might protect him. Time passed and they were expected home from the wars, and the day came fixed for their return, but they came not; and during three days Pashkov refused me admittance to his house. And at last he prepared a torture chamber, and had a fire kindled; he wished to torture me. And I was repeating prayers for my latter end, for I knew what manner of cook he was and that few came out alive from his roasting. And I sat waiting in my house, and I said to my wife, who was weeping, and to my children, "God's will be done! For whether we live, we live unto the Lord; and whether

ve die, we die unto the Lord." And lo! at that moment I saw
wo executioners come hurrying in to seize me. Marvelous are
he acts of the Lord, and unspeakable the counsels of Almighty God! Suddenly Eremy himself, wounded, comes riding
along by the little path that goes past my house and garden,
and he calls out to the executioners, and makes them turn back
with him; and he, Pashkov, left the torture chamber and came
toward his son, staggering like a drunk man from grief. And
Eremy, bowing low to his father, acquainted him with all that
had taken place: how all his troops had been slaughtered, no
single man surviving; and how a native had led him, through
wild and lonely places, away from the Mongolian people; and
now, without food, they had wandered over stony mountains
and through the forest for seven days, having nought to eat but
one squirrel; and how a man in my image had appeared to him
in a dream and had shown him the path, and whither he must
journey; and how he had leaped up and gone on his way rejoicing. When he had recounted all to his father, then I came in to
greet him. But Pashkov rolled his eyes at me—the very spit of a
white polar bear, and he would have gobbled me up alive, only
the Lord did not grant that it should be so—and, drawing in his
breath, he said, "What think you of your handiwork? How many
men, think you, have you caused to perish?" But Eremy said to
me, "Father Avvakum! for Christ's sake, get thee gone, and do
not bandy words with him." And I went.

For ten years he had tormented me, or I him—I know not
which. God will decide on the Day of Judgment.

A change of post came for him, and for me a letter; we were
ordered back to Russia. He went away and did not take me
with him, for in his heart he was saying, "If he travels back
alone, then surely the natives will slay him." He and his guns
and his folk, they sailed away on rafts, and, on my own journey
back, I learned from the natives that they were a timid, trembling crew. And I, a month afterwards, having assembled the
aged, and the sick, and the wounded, whatever there was
here of useless folk (there would be ten of them, and I with
my wife and children would bring it to seventeen), got into a
boat, and, putting our trust in Christ and fixing the Cross to our
prow, we started on our way, wherever God should lead us,
fearing nothing. I gave the book, the *Christian's Pilot*, to the
clerk, and he gave me a fellow for steersman in exchange; and
he manumitted my friend Basil, the same that was wont to de-
nounce folk to Pashkov and was the cause that much blood was
shed, and he sought my life also. And at one time, having

flogged me, he fastened me to the stake, but once again God
kept me safe; and when Pashkov was gone the Cossacks wished
to flog him to death, but I begged him off for Christ's sake and
gave the money for his manumission to the clerk, and carried
him back to Russia, from death to life. Poor soul, may he repent
his sins! Ay, and I took back with me another lousy spy of the
same kidney; him they did not wish to give up to me, and he
fled from death to the forest, and, coming upon me on the path
he flung himself into my boat, for he was pursued and had no
where to turn. And I, forgive me, acted cunningly. As Rahab
the harlot of Jericho, hid Joshua the son of Nun, so did I hide
him, making him lie down at the bottom of a chest, and I flung
a coverlet over him, and ordered my wife and daughter to lie on
the top of him; they sought him high and low, but they would
not disturb my wife from her place, and all they said was, "Rest
in peace, Mother Avvakum! You have had enough to endure, as
it is, my lady." And I—for God's sake forgive me—I lied that
day, and I said, "He is not here"—I was loth to give him up to
be slain. And when they had searched they went away empty
handed, and I carried him back to Russia. Elder and servant of
Christ![29] Forgive me, then, in that I lied that day. How think
you, it may be that it was not a very grievous sin? It would
seem that Rahab the harlot did likewise, and the Scripture
praise her for it; give judgment, then, for God's sake: and if I
acted sinfully, then pardon me; but if I acted in accordance
with the traditions of the Church, then is it well. See, I have left
a space for you, and do you, with your own hand, write in either
forgiveness or penance for me and my wife and my daughter,
for we all three shared in the cheat—we saved a man from death
that he might repent before the Lord. Judge us then so that we
shall not be judged for it by Christ on the Day of Judgment:
write in a few words, I pray you:—

God pardons thee and blesses thee in this life and the life to
come, together with thy helpmeet Anastasia, and thy daughter
and all thy house: thou hast acted rightly and justly. Amen.[30]

So be it then, my elder. God bless you for your graciousness.
But enough of this.

The clerk gave us sacks of corn to the value of thirty silver
pieces, and a cow, and five or six sheep, and dried meat, and

[29] These words are addressed to Avvakum's cellmate and spiritual
father, Epiphany.
[30] This last passage is written into the manuscript by Epiphany,
who read the manuscript and made some addenda.

this we fed on for the summer, as we sailed on our way. The clerk was a good soul; he had been sponsor to my daughter Xenia, who had been born in the days of Pashkov, but Pashkov would not give me myrrh and oil, so she had to stay long unchristened; but when he was gone I christened her (I myself churched my wife and baptized my children),[31] and the clerk and my eldest daughter were the gossips, and I was the parson. In this manner, then, I also christened my son Afanasy, and both confessed my own children and administered the Sacrament to them during the Mass I said at Mezen, and I myself communicated, but I did not administer it to my wife: there are instructions concerning this in the rubric, wherein we are bade so to do. But as to my excommunication, it came from heretics and, in Christ's name, I trample it under foot, and the curse written against me—why, not to mince my words, I wipe my arse with that; if the heretics curse me, the saints of Moscow—Peter, and Alexis, and Jonah, and Phillip—*they* bless me; and in accordance with their books, with a clear conscience I believe in and serve my God; but the apostates I loathe and curse: they are God's enemies and, living in Christ, I do not fear them. Were they to heap stones on me then, secure in the tradition of the Fathers, I would lie in peace beneath these stones—how much more so beneath the thorny, knavish curses of Nikon! Tush! Why multiply words? All we need do is to spit on their doings and their ritual, and on their newfangled books, then all will be well. Our following discourse will be pleasing to Christ and the Immaculate Mother of God, so enough of their knavery. Pardon me, good Nikonites,[32] for having abused you; live as ye will. As for me, I am now about to take up again my tale of woe, so go your ways in peace. For twenty years God has willed that I should be tormented by you, and should it be for twenty more, then will I endure it, in the name of the Lord our God and of our Saviour Jesus Christ. Enough of this. I have wandered, as it is, far enough from my story—let us return to it.

So I left Dauria; the food began to grow scarce, so I prayed together with my company, and Christ gave us a roebuck, a huge beast, and on him we lived till we reached Baikal. There, by the lake, we came on Russian folk—a settlement of sable-hunters and of fishermen; they were right glad to see us, dear souls, and we them, and they dragged us and our boat to shore, and led us far inland to the hills. There was a dear lad called

---

[31] Under ordinary circumstances, it was prohibited by the canons of the Orthodox Church to baptize one's own children.

[32] Nikonites: refers to the supporters of Nikon.

Terenty, and he and his comrades gazed on us, and we on them —dear souls—with tears of joy. And they snowed meat and drink on us, as much as ever we needed. They brought me some forty freshwater sturgeons, saying, "There, Father! God sent them into our fishery for you. Take them all." I, bowing to them, blessed the fish and bade them take them back, saying, "What need have I of so many?" They entertained me there and, from dire need, I accepted from them some provision. Then, having repaired our boat, we let out our sails, and prepared to cross the lake. But the lake grew rough, so we took to our oars. In that place the lake is very broad—it must be a hundred or at least eighty versts. When we stood to the shore there sprang up a tempest and we were forced to find a shelter from the waves on the shore. The place was surrounded by high mountains: I have wandered over the face of the earth 20,000 versts and more, but never have I seen their like. On their summit are tents and earthen huts, portals and towers, stone walls and courts, all neatly fashioned. Onions grow of them and garlic, bigger than the Romanov onion, and exceeding sweet to the taste; there also grows wild hemp, and in the gardens fine grass and exceeding fragrant flowers, and there is great quantity of birds—geese and swans that fly over the lake like snow. And there are fishes—sturgeon and trout, sterlet and salmon-trout and whiting and many other kinds; it is fresh water and in that mighty ocean lake there are sea-calves and great sea-hares. I saw none such during all the time that I was living on the Mezen,[33] and the fish in it are of a great weight, the sturgeon and salmon-trout are exceeding fleshy—they are not for frying, for it would be naught but fat. And all this has been fashioned by our sweet Christ for man, so that, with a mind at last at rest, he might give praise to God. But such is man that he is given to vanity, and his days go by like a shadow: he leaps, like a goat; he blows himself out, like a bubble; he rages, like a lynx; he seeks to devour, like a serpent; when he looks on the comeliness of his neighbour he neighs like a foal; he is crafty, like a fiend; when he has eaten his fill then, like an heathen, he falls asleep, without saying his prayers; he puts off repenting till his old age and then he vanishes; we know not where,— whether it be to light of darkness: it will be shown on the Day of Judgment. Forgive me; I myself have sinned more than other men.

[33] Mezen was a small city in northern Russia to which Avvakum was deported in 1664, remaining there until 1665.

XI. THE STAUNCH PROTOPOPITSA[34]

So we reached Russian settlements, and I was informed con-
ºrning the Church, and like Pilate, I saw that I *"could prevail
ºthing, but that rather a tumult was made."* My mind was
ºubled and, sitting down, I began to ponder what I should do
ºhould I continue preaching God's Word or should I hide
ºyself? For I was tied by my wife and children. And seeing
ºat I was troubled, my wife came up to me, timidly, delicately,
ºd said, "How comes it, my lord, that you are troubled?" And
ºcquainted her with all my thoughts. "Wife! What must I do?
ºe Winter of Heresy is at the door; am I to speak or to hold
ºy peace? I am tied by you!" And she said to me, "Lord have
ºrcy! What are you saying, Petrovitch? Have I not heard, have
ºu not read, the words of the Apostle: *Art thou bound unto a
ºfe? seek not to be loosed. Art thou loosed from a wife? seek
ºt a wife.* I and the children, we give you our blessing, con-
ºue preaching the Word of God as heretofore, and take no
ºought for us until such time as shall seem good to God; when
ºat times comes, remember us in your prayers; Christ is strong
ºd he will not abandon us. Get thee gone, get thee gone to
ºurch, Petrovitch! Unmask the Whore of Heresy!" And I bowed
ºyself to the earth before her, and shook myself free from the
ºindness of a troubled mind and began once more to preach
ºd teach God's Word in the towns and in all places until such
ºe as I could boldly tear the mask from the heresy of Nikon.
ºIn Yeniseisk[35] I wintered, and having sailed through the sum-
ºer again I wintered in Tobolsk; and on my way as far as
ºoscow I cried aloud in every town and in every village, in
ºurches and in marketplaces, preaching the Word of God and
ºaching and laying bare the snares of the ungodly. And thereon
ºame to Moscow. Three years was I in coming from Dauria,
ºd it took me five years traveling upstream. We journeyed ever
ºstward amid native tribes and habitations. Much might be
ºid of that. Sometimes we fell into the hands of the natives;
º Ob, the mighty river, in my presence they put to death
ºenty men who were Christians. And they were minded to do
ºe like to me, but they let me go altogether. And again on the
ºysh River there was standing a company of them—they were
ºing in ambush for our men of Berezov to slay us—but I knew
ºnot and I went up toward them. And when I was come up to

---

[34] Protopopitsa: the wife of a protopope, or archpriest.
[35] Yeniseisk: a Russian outpost and merchant city in central Siberia
the Yenisei River.

them I put in to the bank. In a moment they were round abc
me with their bows, and I, I tell you, went forth to embra
them as though they were monks and I spoke and said, "Chr
be with me and with you too." And they entreated me kinc
and they brought their wives to my wife. And my wife d
sembled with them, as in the world they are wont to empl
flattery; and the womenfolk were kindly and we felt it: wh
the womenfolk are good, then under Christ all is well. The m
hid their bows and arrows. I bought some bear's flesh from the
and they let me go free. As I was saying, I was come to Tobols
And the folk were astonished thereat, for Bashkirs and t
Tatars were scouring all Siberia. But I, trusting in Christ, we
through their midst. And when I had reached Verkhoturie
Ivan Bogdanovitch, my friend, was astonished at me. "How d
you ever get through, archpriest?" And I made answer, "Chr
brought me through, and the all pure Mother of God broug
me through. I fear no man, only Christ do I fear."

XII. BACK IN MOSCOW: JOYS AND DISPUTES (1664)

Thus did I come to Moscow, and as though I were an ang
of God the tsar and all his boyars received me gladly. I we
to see Theodore Rtishchev,[37] he came himself from his te
received my blessing and began to speak of many things: f
three days and three nights he suffered me not to go home, a
thereafter he informed the tsar concerning me. His Majes
gave command to place me at his side and spake kindly to m
"Art thou well in health, archpriest?" said he. "God bade
see thee again." And I in answer kissed his hand and pressed
and myself said, "God lives and my spirit lives, your Majes
but for what is before us that God will ordain." And he sigh
softly and went whither he had need. And other things ha
pened, but what need to speak of it? That too passed by. I
bade them place me in the guesthouse of a monastery in t
Kremlin, and when he passed my door going out on expeditio
he often gave me greeting, bowing low, and himself would sa
"Bless me," said he, "and pray for me"; and one time he to

---

[36] Verkhoturie was a Russian city in western Siberia almost in t
foothills of the Ural Mountains.

[37] Theodore (Fedor) Rtishchev was a statesman and person
friend of Tsar Alexis. He actively participated in church affairs a
from 1645 to 1653 was a member of the Zealots of Piety. He
mained faithful to Nikon after the latter's break with this moveme
He was well known for his support of the arts, learning, and cha
table activities.

fur cap from his head and let it fall as he was riding on
‑seback. He used to slip out of his carriage to come to me
l all his boyars kept bowing and scraping, crying, "Archpriest,
ss us and pray for us." How shall I not grieve for such a tsar
l such boyars? It grieves me to think how good they were,
y gave me place wheresoever I wished, and they named me
ir confessor, that I might be made one with them in the faith.
t I held all these things to be but vanity. And I gained Christ
l was mindful of death, how all these things pass away.
And this was revealed to me in Tobolsk when I was half
eep. "Watch, I bid thee, that thou be not a branch cut off."
‑aped up and fell before the icon in great terror, and I spake
l said, "Lord, I will not go when they chant in newfangled
hion; my God." I was at early Mass in the cathedral on the
ne day of the tsarina. I was jesting with them in that Church
the presence of the officials, and from the moment of arrival
ook notice whether they mixed the elements in triple or in
ofold wise, and standing at the altar by the sacrificial table I
used them, and with time I got used to them, so I ceased from
using them. Such was the bitter spirit of Antichrist that stung

Thus did our sweet Christ make me afraid and said to me,
fter so great suffering wilt thou perish? Watch, lest I hew
e off as a dry branch." I went not to Mass, but I went to sup
h the prince, and I told him all, every word. A kind boyar
nce, Ivan Andrew Chelkov, began to weep. Woe is me, ac-
rsed one, that I forget so great mercy of God!
When I was at Dauria and I labored as a fisherman, I went
the winter to my children, and I went along the lake on snow-
oes; there was no snow but great frosts, and the ice froze
ll-nigh the thickness of a man. I began to want to drink,
d I suffered much from thirst. I couldn't go on, I was midway
the lake, I couldn't get to the water; the lake was eight versts.
egan to look up to heaven and to say, "O Lord, thou didst
use water to flow in the desert for the thirsty people of Israel,
n and now art thou; give me to drink by whatever means
em good to thee. O Lord my God! Woe is me. I know not how
pray, forgive me for the Lord's sake. Who am I, a dead dog?"
e ice gave a crack beneath me and split up to either side
ross the whole lake and came together again, and a great
untain of ice rose up, and while this was going on I stood
my accustomed place, and looking toward the east, I bowed
ice or thrice, pronouncing the name of the Lord in a loud
ice from the depths of my heart. God had left me a small hole

in the ice, and I, falling down, slaked my thirst. And I we
and was glad, praising God. After that the hole in the ice join
up and I, rising up, bowed down to the Lord and then ag:
ran along the ice whither I must needs go to my children. A
in my other wanderings it often happened to me like this. I w
either walking along, dragging my sledge or catching fish
cutting wood in the forest, or whatsoever I might be doing
always recited my office at the regular time, whether it w
morning Mass or evening, at the hours it was the custom; i
chanced to be among other people none could hinder me, bu
would stand upright and none of my companions with me,
they did not love my office, and when they were there it w
impossible for me to carry it out, and I, going away from amo
men, would go through it in a shortened form, either under
hill or in a wood, beating with my head against the earth, a
sometimes I would weep and feel wounded. But if there shou
be people with me I would place the icon on the sledge-rail a
I would recite the office right through, and some would pr
with me, but others would cook their porridge; and when I :
going in my sledge on Sundays to the guesthouses I sing t
whole church service, and on festival days when I am driving
a sledge I will sing, and often on Sundays as I go along I wou
sing. And when I do it very persistently, sometimes I wou
grumble though only a little, for my body was ahungered a:
would fain eat, and was athirst and would fain drink, and lik
wise my spirit, O Father Epiphany, desires spiritual food: It
not the hunger for bread that destroys a man nor the thirst f
water, but the great hunger of a man when he lives witho
praying to God.[38]

If thou art not weary of listening to this thy servant of Chri
I, a sinner, will make known to thee this too, how often in t
land of Daur, from loss of strength and from hunger I could n
keep my rule, only a little of it could I keep, only the eveni
psalms and the midnight office at the first hour, but more th:
that I could not: I dragged myself about like a poor beast. I w
grieved about that office of mine, but I could not take it up. Y
see by now I had got so weak. But sometimes I went to t
forest for wood, and while I was away my wife and childr
would sit on the ground by the fire, my daughter with h
mother, and they would both cry. Agraphena, my poor unhap
one, was then not yet grown up. I came back from the wood

---

[38] Another direct address to Epiphany, Avvakum's confessor a:
fellow inmate in Pustozersk.

the child was sobbing hard. She could not speak for her tongue was fast bound, but she sat there and whimpered to her mother, and the mother looked at her and cried. But I breathed heavily and came near to the child with a prayer and said, "In the name of the Lord I bid thee speak to me and tell me why thou weepest." And she jumped up and bowed before me and began to speak clearly thus, "I do not know who it is, my Lord father, but there is a Shining One within me and he held me by my tongue and he would not let me speak to mother, and because of it I cried. But he said to me, 'Tell your father that he should recite his office as he used to do, and then ye all go forth again to Russia, but, if he does not keep his rule, about which he is himself troubled, then in this place ye shall all die, and he shall die with you.'" At that time another thing of that sort was said to her, that there would be an edict to fetch us, and how that many of our friends had perished in Russia; all this came to pass. I was to say to Pashkov that if he sang the morning and evening office then God would give fair weather, and the corn would grow and there would be constant rain, and they sowed wheat on a small plot a day or two before Peter's day, and immediately it sprouted and was all but rotted by the rains. I spoke to him about the evening and morning office and he set to do this. God sent fair weather, and the corn ripened immediately. What a miracle! It was sown late but it ripened early.

And again, poor man, he began to practice cunning arts about God's doings—the following year he sowed much, but an unwonted rain poured down, and the water overflowed from the river and drowned the plowed fields and washed everything away, and it washed away our hut, and until that time there had never been water there, and the natives wondered. Mark you, as he went his way, so God moved in his mysterious way. At first he laughed at the news, but afterward, when the child wanted to eat, he betook him to tears—and then I sought not to slacken about my office. Enough of this have I spoken; let us return to our first subject. We must needs remember all these things and not be forgetting them, so as not to lay aside any of God's doings in negligence and waste and not to alter them for the pleasure of this age of vanity.

Now I will tell of what was done at Moscow. They said that I was not at one with them. His Majesty bade Rodion Streshnev[39] persuade me that I should hold my peace. And I did his

[39] Rodion Streshnev: a relative of the tsar's wife and his councilor in Church affairs.

bidding. The tsar is set over us by God, and at this moment was kindly disposed towards me. So I hoped that little by little he would come to a better mind. They promised me on Simeon's day to place me at the printing office to correct books, and I was exceedingly glad, for that pleased me better than to be the tsar's confessor. I wanted something better than the confessional. I waited on him. He sent me ten rubles and the tsarina sent me ten. Luke, the confessor, sent me ten, and Rodion Streshnev also ten, and our old friend Theodore Rtishchev then ordered them to slip into my hat sixty rubles from his official salary, but about that I was to say nothing! Each man put his hand in his pocket and brought out every manner of thing. I lived in the house of my dear one, Theodosia Prokofievna Morozova,[40] and didn't go out inasmuch as she was my spiritual daughter. And her sister, Princess Eudoxia Prokofievna, was my daughter also. My dear ones, martyrs for Christ! And I was ever in the house of Anna Petrovna Miloslavskaia.[41] God rest her soul! And I went to Theodore Rtishchev's house to dispute with the apostles, and so lived about the space of half a year. And I saw that I prevailed nothing but that rather a tumult was made; again, I began to grumble, and I wrote to the tsar many things to the effect that he should earnestly seek for the ancient piety and defend from heresy our common mother holy Church, and on the patriarchal throne he should place a shepherd of the orthodox faith in place of the wolf and apostate Nikon, him that was an evildoer and a heretic. And when I had got ready the letter I had no more strength left in me: and I sent it forth on the journey to the tsar by my spiritual son Theodore, the Fool in Christ, which Theodore they strangled at Mezene, hanging him upon the gallows-tree. Now he in all boldness approached the tsar's carriage, and the tsar bade him sit down with the letter near the great entrance: he did not perceive that the letter was from me. And afterward, having the letter from him he bade let him go. And he—God rest his soul!—after staying a while with me again went into the church in the presence of the tsar and began to play the fool as though he was half-witted. The tsar was angry and bade them send him away to the

[40] Theodosia Morozova—a lady-in-waiting to the tsarina, and widow of an influential boyar. She remained a faithful supporter of Avvakum. She and her sister, Eudoxia Urusova, were arrested in 1670 for their support of the Old Believer movement, and both died in prison in 1672.
[41] Anna Miloslavskaia: a relative of the tsarina, and an influential supporter of Avvakum.

Miracle Monastery. There Paul the archimandrite bade them put fetters on him, and by the will of God the fetters brake to pieces upon his legs before the people. But he, God rest his soul! my friend! crept into the burning stove in the bakehouse after the loaves and sat on the grating with his naked rump and picked up the crumbs in the stove to eat of them. Then the monks were affrighted and told the archimandrite Paul that was now metropolitan. He acquainted the tsar with this, and the tsar came to the monastery and ordered them to let him go with honor. He again came to me, and from that day on the tsar began to look askance at me. He was ill pleased that I began again to speak. He would have liked me to hold my peace but that was not my way. And the bishops, like goats, began to leap up against me, and they plotted to send me in banishment from Moscow, for many of the Christians had come to me and perceiving the truth they would not walk in the service of a lie. And from the tsar there came to me the accusation, "They tell me that the bishops bring complaint against thee; they say because of thee the churches are empty. Go again," said he, "into banishment." Thus spake the boyar Peter Mikhailovich Saltykov.[42] And they brought me to Mezen, and many good people gave me this and that in the name of Christ. And everything remained, only they took me with my wife and my children and my household. From town to town I taught the people of God and denounced them, the spotted beasts. And they brought us to Mezen.

Having endured for half a year, they took me again without my wife to Moscow, and my two sons journeyed with me, Ivan and Prokopy. But my wife and the rest were all left at Mezen. And having brought us to Moscow they took us at first away to the Pafnutiev Monastery,[43] and there they sent us a letter, and they spake thus and thus: "Wilt thou so long vex us? be reconciled to us, dear old Avvakum!" But I refused as though they were devils. And they flew in my face.

Then I wrote them an answer with much violence of words, and I sent it by Kosma, a deacon of Yaroslavl, by the subdeacon of the patriarchal court—Kosma in public tried to overpersuade me, but in private he upheld me, speaking thus, "Archpriest, do not desert the ancient rites; a mighty man wilt thou be with Christ if thou wilt endure to the end—do not look to us for we

[42] Peter Saltykov was a boyar who energetically opposed Avvakum and his movement.
[43] Pafnutiev Monastery: a monastery in the vicinity of Moscow that often served as a prison for clergymen.

are ruined." And I to him made answer that he should again
stand for Christ. And he said, "I cannot. Nikon has led me
astray." And to speak shortly, he had denied Christ before
Nikon, in that he had no strength to stand firm, my poor Kosma
I fell to crying; I blessed him, unhappy one—after that I had no
more dealings with him; let God deal with him as seems good
to him.

XIII. Preparations for the Trial (1664–1666)

Thus having remained ten weeks in Pafnutiev in chains, they
took me again to Moscow, and in the room of the Cross the
bishops held disputation with me. They led me to the Cathedral
church, and after the Elevation of the Host they sheared me and
the deacon Theodore, and then they cursed us and I cursed them
back. And I was heavy at heart for the Mass. And after I had
stayed for a time at the patriarchal court, they took us by night
to Ugresha,[44] to the monastery of St. Nicholas—and the enemies
of God shaved off my beard. What would you? It is like unto
wolves not to pity the sheep; they tore at my hair like dogs and
only left one forelock—such as the Poles wear on their fore
heads. They did it carrying me not along the road to the mon
astery but by the marshes and the quagmires that people might
not see me. They themselves saw that they were behaving as
fools but they did not wish to cease from their folly; the devil
had darkened their minds, why should one reproach them? It
was not them or they would have been otherwise. The time had
come spoken of in the Gospel. "*It must needs be that offences
must come*," and another Evangelist saith: "*It must needs be
that offences come, but woe unto him by whom offence cometh.*"
Look thou that readest! Our misery was of necessity, we might
not escape it! For this cause God doth let loose offenses and
even that the elect may be inflamed and that they may be made
white, even that temptations be made manifest in us. Satan has
asked and obtained from God our bright shining Russia, that
he might purple it with martyr's blood. Well, hast thou imagined
this, O devil, and to us it is sweet to suffer for our Sweet Lord
They kept me at Nikolas's in a cold room for seventeen
weeks. There I had a visitation from God; read of it in the letter
to the tsar. And the tsar came to the monastery and paid a visit
to my prison cell and gave a groan and then left the monastery
it seems from that that he was sorry for me, the will of God lay
in that. When they had shorn me there was a very great dis

---

[44] Ugresha: a village in the vicinity of Moscow.

turbance among them with the tsarina, God rest her soul! She, sweet lady, detected me at that time and asked to have me released from prison, as to which there is much to be said; God forgive them! As to my sufferings I do not hold them answerable, neither now nor hereafter; it sufficeth me to pray for them, be they alive or be they dead. The devil set discord between us but they were ever good toward me. Enough of this.

And poor Prince Ivan Vorotynsky[45] came there without the tsar to pray, and he asked to be admitted to my prison cell. But they would not let the hapless man in. I could only, looking through the window, weep over him. My sweet friend feared God, he was Christ's orphan. Christ will not cast him away. Thus always was Christ on our side, and all the boyars were good to us, only the devil was malicious and what could we have done if Christ had left us? They beat my dear Prince Ivan Khovansky[46] with rods and they burnt Isaiah,[47] and the lady Theodosia Morozova they brought to ruin, and they killed her son and tortured her and her sister Eudoxia, beating them with rods; and they parted her from her children and divorced her from her husband, and him they say, Prince Peter Urusov,[48] they married to another wife. But what was there to do? Let them torture those dear ones, they will go to their heavenly bridegroom. In every wise God will cause to pass this troublesome time and will call to himself the bridegroom to his heavenly palace, he the true Sun, our Light and our Hope. Let us turn again to the one first matter.

After this they took me again to the monastery of Pafnutiev, and there, having shut me up in the dark room, and put fetters on me, they kept me for well-nigh a year. There the cellarer Nikodemus was good to me at first, but he, poor fellow, smoked of tobacco more than that sixty poods the which they seized when they searched the house of the Metropolitan of Gaza,[49] and they seized a lute too and other hidden things of the monastery on the which they played and made merry withal. It is a

[45] Prince Ivan Vorotynsky: member of a wealthy aristocratic family who supported Avvakum and his movement.

[46] Prince Ivan Khovansky: a member of a conservative family that lent its support to Avvakum.

[47] Isaiah: the majordomo of the boyar, Peter Saltykov. He was burned for his faithfulness to the Old Belief.

[48] Prince Peter Urusov: the husband of Princess Eudoxia Urusova, and brother-in-law of Theodosia Morozova.

[49] Metropolitan Paisy of Gaza (Palestine): a Greek bishop who came to Russia in 1662 and became very influential at the court. He was the ideological leader of the opponents of Avvakum and the Old Believers, and was well known for his lack of scrupulousness and his participation in suspicious mercantile operations.

sin to speak of it, forgive me; it was not my business, let him look to it, to his own Lord he must stand or fall. This is just by the way. With them there were well-beloved teachers of Holy Writ. I asked of this Nikodemus, the cellarer, on Easter Day, in order that I might rest because of the holiday, that he would bid them open the door that I might sit on the threshold, and he abused me and refused me savagely as he willed. And after that he came into my cell he fell suddenly ill, they anointed him with oil and gave him the last sacraments and then and there he died. That was on Easter Monday, and before, on the night of Tuesday, there had come to him a man in the semblance of myself with a censer, and in shining vestments, and having censed him and taken him by the hand he moved himself and was healed. And he came to me with the servitor by night into the dungeon. And as he came he said, "Blessed is this dwelling —what a dungeon doth it contain—how blessed is this dungeon —what sufferings doth it hold! blessed are those bonds. . . ." And he fell before me and clasped my chain and said, "Forgive me, for God's sake! forgive, I have sinned before God and before thee. I have insulted thee, and for this God hath punished me." And I spake, "How hath he punished thee? Instruct me!" And he, "Thou thyself," said he, "didst come to me and didst cense me; thou didst have pity on me and didst raise me up. Why dost thou deny it?" And the servitor standing there said, "Yes, my Lord and Father, he took thee by the hand and led thee from the cell, and bowed down before thee, and thou didst go hence." And I charged him that he should say nothing to any man concerning this secret thing. And he questioned me how henceforth he might live for Christ. "Ah," said he, "dost thou charge me to go forth into the desert?" But I forbade him and would not suffer him to give up his stewardship, if only in secret he would preserve the ancient tradition of his fathers. And he bowed low and went away to his own place and on the morrow at meat he told it to all the brotherhood. And the people ceaselessly and with boldness pressed in to see me, asking for a blessing and for my prayers, and I taught them from Holy Writ and I healed them by the Word of God. At that time I had some enemies, but these were reconciled to me. Alas, when shall I quit this life of vanity? It is written: "Woe to him when all men speak well of him." In very truth I know now how I may endure to the end; of good deeds there are none now; but I glorified God. That he knows and with him it rests.

Thither there came to me in secret Theodore with his children; he that was strangled, God rest his soul! and he questioned me thus: "How wouldst thou have me walk? Shall I go in my shift in the old fashion or shall I put clothes upon me? The heretics," said he, "are seeking me, they would fain bring me to ruin. I," said he, "was at Riazan under guard at the archbishop's palace at the court, and he, Hilarion,[50] did grievously torment me: there was scarce a day when he did not beat me with cords and he kept me bound in iron fetters, compelling me to partake of the new communion of Antichrist. And I said, 'I could not,' and I prayed in the night and wept and spake, 'O Lord, if thou dost not save me, they will cause me to commit abomination and I shall perish. What can I do?'" And weeping much he said suddenly, said he, "My father, all my chains fell rattling from me, and the door was opened of its own motion. And I," said he, "bowed down to God, and I went forth. I came to the outer gates and the gates were opened. I went straight forth along the road to Moscow. It was scarce daylight," said he, "when they gave chase on horseback; three men passed quickly by me and they did not see me, and I," said he, "trusting in Christ, went on my way onwards. But," said he, "very soon they came upon me and they were snarling at me; said they, 'The son of a whore has escaped, where may one take him?' And again," said he, "they passed by me and did not see me. And I," said he, "again betook me to thee and asked whether I should go again to be tortured or whether I should don clothes and live in Moscow." And I, a sinner, bade him don clothes and not to hide himself from the hands of the heretics. They strangled him in Mezen, hanging him upon the gallows-tree. Eternal be his memory together with Luke Lavrentievich. My well-beloved children! They suffered for Christ. Glory to God for them. And Theodore accomplished an exceeding mighty deed above measure; by day he played the Fool of Christ, and all night long he wept and prayed. I know many good men, but I had never yet beheld such an ascetic. He lived with me in Moscow about half a year, but I was still ill—two of us lived in the same chamber with him and at the most he would lie an hour or two and then he would get up, and then he would go through a thousand genuflexions and would seat himself on the ground, or else, standing up, he would weep for some three hours; meantime I would continue lying and sometimes sleep, but sometimes I was restless, and when he had his fill of violent weeping then he would come up to me and say, "How long

---

[50] Hilarion, Bishop of Riazan: a former friend of Avvakum's who became a staunch supporter of Nikon and the modernists.

wilt thou continue lying? Come to thyself. Thou art a priest. How art thou not ashamed?" And I could not rise though he lifted me up saying, "Stand up, my sweet father!" And he pulled at me somehow or other. And he bade me say prayers as I sat, and he kept bowing down instead of me. He *was* my friend in very truth! He was sore vexed by his sufferings. At one time his intestine issued forth from him three yards in length, and at another five yards, and his guts were measureless—and it was both pitiful and laughable. At Ustiug for five years he froze barefoot in the frost with only his shift. I saw him myself. Then he became my spiritual son, and when I came from Siberia he ran up to my stall in the church in order to pray: he spoke thus: "When," said he, "one first began to thaw after the frost and get warm, my father, it was very hard to bear"; said he, "one stamps with one's feet on the brick floor as though they were wooden legs, and on the morrow they did not hurt."

He had with him there in his cell a psalter of those newly printed. He knew but little as yet of those newfangled things. But I told him all, word by word, concerning the new books—and he snatched at the book and hurled it into the stove. And he cursed all these newfangled ways. And he was exceeding zealous for the faith of Christ. But why speak many words? As he began, so he ended. And his great virtue lay not in idle words, as is with me, miserable man, for whom he died pleading to God.

A good man, too, was my dear old Afanasy, my spiritual son —his name in religion was Avraany—whom the apostates baked to death in Moscow on the fire, and like unto bread of sweet savor he was offered to the Holy Trinity. Until he took the cowl, he went about barefoot with only his shift, both winter and summer, only he was milder than Theodore and fell short of his asceticism. He dearly loved weeping, and weeping he would go about and with whomsoever he spoke his words were soft and sweet as though he wept. Theodore was very zealous and suffered much concerning the work of God. In every way he would weary himself to bring sin to light and to destroy it. But enough of them! As they lived, so they died, with Christ Jesus our Lord.

XIV. The Church Council of 1667 and the Final Schism

I will tell you yet more of my wanderings when they brought me out of the Pafnutiev Monastery in Moscow and placed me in the guesthouse, and after many wanderings they set me down in the Miracle Monastery, before the patriarchs of all Christen-

om, and the Russian Nikonites sat there like so many foxes. I
poke of many things in Holy Writ with the patriarchs. God did
pen my sinful mouth and Christ put them to shame. The last
ord they spoke to me was this: "Why," said they, "art thou
ubborn? The folk of Palestine, Serbia, Albania, the Wallachians,
ey of Rome and Poland, all these do cross themselves with
ree fingers, only thou standest out in thine obstinacy and dost
oss thyself with two fingers; it is not seemly." And I answered
em for Christ thus: "O you teachers of Christendom, Rome
ll away long ago and lies prostrate,[51] and the Poles fell in the
ke ruin with her, being to the end the enemies of the Christian.
nd among you orthodoxy is of mongrel breed; and no wonder
if by the violence of the Turkish Mohmut you have become
ipotent, and henceforth it is you who should come to us to
arn. By the gift of God among us there is autocracy; till the
ne of Nikon, the apostate, in our Russia under our pious
inces and tsars the Orthodox faith was pure and undefiled,
id in the church was no sedition. Nikon, the wolf, together
ith the devil, ordained that men should cross themselves with
ree fingers, but our first shepherds made the sign of the cross
id blessed men as of old with two fingers, according to the
adition of our holy fathers, Meletina of Antioch, Theodoret,
e blessed Bishop of Cyrene, Peter of Damascus and Maxim
e Greek;[52] and so too did our own synod of Moscow, at the
ne of the Tsar Ivan, bid them, putting their fingers together
that wise, make the sign of the cross and give the blessing,
of old the holy fathers Melety and others taught. Then in the
ne of Ivan, the tsar,[53] there were the standard-bearers, Gury
d Varsanophy, wonder-workers of Kazan, and Phillip the
bbot of Solovki among the Russian saints."[54] And the patriarchs
ll to thinking, and our people began to howl like wolf cubs
id to belch out words against their fathers saying, "Our Rus-
in holy men were ignorant, and they understood nothing, they
e unlearned folk," said they. "How can one trust them? they
ive no letters." O Holy God! How hast thou suffered so great
viling of thy holy ones? I, miserable one, was bitter in my

---

[51] Here Avvakum quotes The *Tale of the White Cowl* (see Selec-
on 31), which became one of the ideological foundation stones of
e Old Believer movement.
[52] Maxim the Greek was a Greek scholar whose writings were often
oted by the Old Believers.
[53] This refers to Tsar Ivan IV.
[54] Sts. Gury and Varsanophy were Orthodox missionaries among
e Tatars after the taking of Kazan. St. Phillip, Abbot of Solovki,
er Metropolitan of Moscow.

heart, but I could do nothing. I abused them as hard as I could
and I spake as follows: "I am pure, and the dust that cleave
to my feet do I shake off before you, as it is written—'bett
one if I do the will of God than a thousand of the godless.'
Then louder than before they began to cry out against me
"Away with him, away with him; he hath outraged us all"; an
they began to thrust at me and to beat me. And the patriarch
themselves threw themselves on me; about forty of them I thir
there must have been. Great was the army of Antichrist th
gathered itself together. Ivan Uvarov seized me and dragged
me, and I cried aloud, "Stop, do not beat me!" Then they a
sprang back and I began to speak to the interpreter, the arch
mandrite, thus: "Say to the patriarch, the Apostle Paul write
'For such an high priest became us, who is holy, harmless, an
so forth,' but ye, having sorely mishandled a man, how then ca
ye straightway perform your office?" Then they sat down. I wer
away to the door and lay down on my side. "Ye sit down,"
said to them, "but I lie down." At that they laughed. "The arch
priest," said they, "is a silly fellow, and does not show hon
to the patriarchs." And I said, "We are fools for Christ's sak
Ye are great and we without honor; ye are strong and we a
weak." After that, again, the authorities came to me and beg
to talk with me on the question of the Alleluias: Christ put it
my heart and I put them to shame for their Romish heres
through Dionysios the Areopagite, of whom mention has bee
made before. And Euphemy, the cellarer of the Miracle Mo
astery, spake: "Right art thou," said he, "there is no more to
said." And they took me along to chain me.

Then the tsar sent an officer with musketeers and they too
me to the Vorobiev hills.[55]

There was the priest Lazar and the monk Epiphany,
elder.[56] They had been shorn and were ill treated as though th
were village peasants, my dear ones. A wise man when he d
but see them must needs fall aweeping when he looked at ther
Well, let them suffer! Why grieve for them! Christ was bett
than them, and against him, our sweet Lord, evil was wroug
by the forebears of the Nikonites, Annas and Caiaphas. No wo
der, for they followed after an exemplar—we must grieve f

[55] Vorobiev, or Sparrow Hills—hills in the vicinity of Mosco
where Moscow University is now located.
[56] Father Lazar and Monk Epiphany were condemned, togeth
with Avvakum, by the Council of 1667. Both of them, as well
Avvakum and Deacon Fedor (Theodore), were deported to Pustozer
and burned in 1682.

hem, poor things! Woe to the hapless followers of Nikon! They nave perished of their own wickedness and their stubbornness of soul!

Then they brought us from the Vorobiev hills to the guesthouse of the Andreevsky Monastery to the Savin suburb, and as though we were robbers, followed after us and left us not, nay, even when we relieved nature. It was both pitable and laughable, as though the devil had blinded them.

Then again we were taken to the St. Nickolas Monastery at Ugresha. And there the tsar sent to me the officer Yury Lutokhin, that I might bless him, and we had much converse concerning his and that.

Then again they brought me to Moscow, to the guesthouse of he Nikolsky Monastery, and they demanded of us yet again a tatement of the true faith. After that there were sent more than once to me gentlemen of the bedchamber, diverse persons, Artemon and Dementy.[57] And they spake to me in the name of he tsar: "Archpriest!" they said, "I see thy life that it is pure and undefiled and pleasing unto God, I and the tsarina and our children, be entreated of us." The envoy wept as he spake, and for him I weep always. I was exceeding sorry for him. And again he spake: "I beg of thee, hearken to me. Be thou reconciled with the patriarchs." And I said, "Even if God will that I should die, I will not be joined together with apostates. Thou art my tsar, but they, what have they to do with thee? They have lost their tsar and they have come here to gobble you up. I—say I—will not cease to uplift my hands to heaven until God give thee over to me."

The last word I got from the tsar was, "Wherever," said he, "thou shalt be, do not forget us in thy prayers." And I, sinful one, now, as far as I may, pray to God for him.

XV. BANISHMENT TO PUSTOZERSK

After scourging my friends, but not me, they banished me to Pustozersk. And I sent from Pustozersk to the tsar two letters, he first not long but the other longer, what I had said to him, that I wrote also in the letters, and also certain signs of God, which had appeared to me in my prison. Who reads will understand. Also a letter written by the deacon was sent to Moscow by me and the brotherhood as a gift to the True Believers. The

[57] This refers to Artemon Mateev and Dementy Bashmakov, who were important bureaucrats and close councilors of Tsar Alexis. The atter was the head of *Tainy Prikaz* (Department for Secret Affairs) under Alexis.

book was an answer of the Orthodox and was a conviction of the
heresy of the apostates—in it was written the truth concerning
the dogmas of the Church. Further, two letters had been sent by
the priest Lazar to the tsar and the patriarch, and of all this we
got a present. In Mezen of my household they hanged two men,
my spiritual children, the aforenamed Theodore, Christ's Fool
and Luke Lavrentievich, servants of Christ. Luke was a dweller
in Moscow, the only son of his mother, who was a widow; he
was of the guild of banners, a youth in years about fifteen. He
came to Mezen, to his death, with my children. And when there
was a general slaughter in my house, Pilate asked him, "And
how do you, my man, cross yourself?" And he made answer with
all temperance: "I do believe and do cross myself so, placing my
fingers as doth my spiritual father, the archpriest Avvakum."
And Pilate ordered them to put him in the dungeon, and there
to put a noose round his neck, and he hanged him on a railing
And so he passed from earth to heaven. Greater than that what
could they do for him? And if he were but a youth, he acted
like an old man. He went his way to the Lord. Well were it ever
for an old man did he win through like that.

At this time the order was given to hang my two sons after
the flesh, Ivan and Prokopy, but they, miserable ones, were
weaklings and never thought them to lay hold on the crowns of
victory. Being soon afraid of death they made submission, and
so they buried them alive in the earth with their mother for
third. There was a death without death for you. Repent as ye
sit there, while the devil concocts something else! That death
be terrible is not wonderful! Time was when even Peter, dear
friend of Christ, made denial and went out and wept bitterly
and for his tears he was forgiven, and for my children it is no
wonderful that, because of my sins, weakness was permitted
them. Well and good! So be it! Christ is mighty to save us all
and to have mercy upon us.

At this time the deputy, Ivan Elagin, was with us in Pustozersk
having come from Mezen, and he received from us a statement
and this was it: "Year and month," and again: "We keep the
tradition of the holy Fathers unaltered, and we proclaim as
accursed Paisy the Patriarch of Palestine with his fellows as an
assembly of heretics," and besides there were said there a few
words about Nikon, the fabricator of this heresy. For this they
brought us to the scaffold, and when they had read the sentence
they took me away without scourging me to the dungeon. They
read me the edict: "Let Avvakum be put into an underground

son within the palisade and let there be given to him bread
l water." But I spat on this and I desired to die, refraining
m food, and I ate nothing for about eight days or more. But
n my brethren bade me eat.

At the same time they took the priest Lazar, and cut out his
ole tongue from his throat, but little blood flowed and soon
pped. And he spoke again without his tongue. Moreover,
ving placed his right hand upon the scaffold, they cut it off at
wrist, and the hand that had been cut off, lying upon the
und, of its own motion placed its fingers after the ancient
, and lying thus long time before the people, the poor thing
de confession, and even unto death did not betray the sign
salvation. Even I am amazed at that; the lifeless thing con-
ts the living. And on the third day I felt in his mouth with
hand; it was all smooth, and there was no tongue, but it did
hurt. God had granted that with good hap it had healed up.
Moscow they had cut out his tongue and then there was some
it left, but now it was all cut away. But he spoke clearly for
space of two years as though he had a tongue. And when he
l completed two years there was another wonder—in the
ce of three days his tongue grew again to its full size, but
t it was a little stumpy, and again he spake, instantly praising
d and railing at the apostates.

At this time they seized a hermit priest, an anchorite of strict
, Epiphany, an elder, and cut out the whole of his tongue.
l they cut off four fingers of his hand. And at first he spoke
kly, and at this time he prayed to the Virgin, the Mother of
l, and there appeared to him in the air two tongues, that of
scow and the present one. Now he, taking up one, put it in
mouth, and from that moment began to speak purely and
rly, and the whole tongue fitted itself into his mouth. Great
the works and unspeakable are the judgments of the Lord!
sendeth forth his judgments and again he healeth and hath
cy. But what availeth many words? God is an old hand at
acles. Out of nothing he brings life, and shall he not at the
t Day raise up all flesh in the twinkling of an eye; and who
y discern concerning this thing? God is after this wise: he
ateth what is new and he reneweth that which is old. In all
gs glory be to him!

At this time they seized the deacon Theodore. They cut out
whole of his tongue, but left a little bit in his mouth, having
it slantways across his throat. It healed just as it was at the
e, but later on it grew again as it was before. It stuck out a

little way from the lips, but stump-like. And they cut off
hand across the palm. By the gift of God it all healed, and
spake clearly and cleanly as before.

Then they covered us up with earth. There was a framew
in the earth, and above the earth a second framework, and t
again round the whole of it was a fence with four locks,
they set a watch to guard all the doors. Now we, both here
everywhere in dungeons, sing songs before the Lord Christ,
Son of God, such as Solomon sang when he beheld his mot
Bathsheba: *"Thou art good, my fair one, thou art good, my
loved. Thine eyes burn like a flame of fire, thy teeth are as wl
as milk; the shining of thy face is brighter than the sun's r*
and altogether thou shinest like unto the day in its strength.

Then Pilate journeyed from us, and having settled his b
ness at Mezen he returned to Moscow. And others of us w
burned and baked. They burned Isaiah to death and afterwa
burned Avraamy and other defenders of the Church—the m
of them did he undo. God will count the number of them
wonder is it that they would not come to their right mind. T
think to establish the faith by fire or the knout and gallows-tr
Which of the Apostles taught them that? I know not. My Ch
did not teach his Apostles that fire and knout and gallows-t
should lead to the faith. But it was said to the Apostle by
Lord thus: *"Go ye into all the world and preach the Gospel*
every creature; he that believeth and is baptized, the same sl
be saved." See now, my reader, Christ calls us to come if
will, but he does not bid the Apostles to burn with fire and
hang on the gallows-tree them that are disobedient. The T
god Mahmud[58] in his books wrote thus: "We bid ye lay low w
the sword the heads of them that obey not our law and tra
tion." But Christ never gave such like command to his discip
and these teachers, it is plain, are themselves Antichrists; th
who, leading men to the faith, destroy them and give them o
to death—they bring forth works like unto their faith. I
written in the gospels: *"A good tree cannot bring forth evil fr*
neither a bad tree good fruit. Every tree is known by its fru
But why speak many words? "No Cross, no Crown." He t
will be crowned, for *that* he had not need to go to Persia.
have our Babylon at home. Come, True Believer! Name t
the name of Christ, standing in the midst of Moscow, cross t
self with the sign of the Saviour our Christ, with two fing
as we have received from the holy Fathers. Lo! here at ho

[58] This refers to Muhammad, the Prophet of Islam.

thee is thy Kingdom of Heaven. Glory to God! Suffer tor-
s for the placing of thy fingers, reason not much, but I with
am ready to die for this and for Christ. If I am a foolish
and one without learning, yet this I know, that all the tradi-
s of the Church, handed down to us by the holy Fathers,
holy and incorrupt. I keep them even unto death, as I reed them. I will not falsify the eternal boundaries—that which
laid down before our days, let it so remain to all eternity,
O thou heretic, do not tamper with things, touch not the
ifice of Christ, lay not thine hand on the cross, nay, stir not
the corporals! And they have planned with the devil to
print books and falsify everything, and to alter the sign of
cross in the church, and on the wafers. Within the altar they
banished the priestly prayers, they have altered the "Lord
mercy upon us," and in baptism they bid to invoke the
One. I would fain spit in his eyes and in theirs! And round
ut the font the Evil One leads them against the course of the
and in like fashion they consecrate the church, and when
solemnize marriage they lead the married counterclockwise;
nly they do this in hostility. And in baptism they do not ab-
the Evil One. How should they? They are his children and
do not desire to abjure their father. But why multiply
ds? Woe is me for the True Believer! Every spirit that is
ted is brought low. As Nikon, the hound of hell, spake, so
he do. Print the books, Arsen,[59] anyhow, only not after the
ient fashion. And so he did! More than that, one cannot alter
gs. It behooves every man to endure for this, even unto
th. May these damnable ones be accursed, with all their
ilish imaginations: and to them whom they made to suffer in
r souls, may theirs be threefold eternal remembrance.

or this I ask forgiveness of every True Believer. Some things
I have said were perhaps best unsaid—but I may read
ugh the Acts of the Apostle and the epistles of Paul. The
stles proclaimed concerning themselves that God was work-
through them. *"Not unto us but to our God be the praise."*
I I am of no account. So spake I again and again. I am a

Arsen, a learned Greek, came to Moscow in 1649, and was
ted to become a professor there. However, it was soon discovered
he had managed to become a Catholic three times, once a
lem, and then, finally, Orthodox. For these successful conversions
was deported to Solovki Monastery. In 1652 Nikon invited him
evise the Russian missal, and this participation by Arsen in the
diting of the holy books was largely responsible for the disrepute
which Nikon's reforms fell.

man that is a sinner. Wanton am I and a ravisher, a thief an
robber, the friend of publicans and sinners, and to every ı
am I a hypocrite accursed; forgive me and pray for me; to
who read me and who hearken am I bound more than to ɛ
I know not how to live and what I am doing that I tell to n
What matter that they talk vanity of me, in the days of ju
ment they shall all know of my deeds, whether they be good
evil. But if I be unlearned in speech, yet am I not in thou;
I am untaught in rhetoric and in dialectic and in philosophy,
the mind of Christ is our guide within us, as the Apostle sa
though I be rude in speech yet not in knowledge. [A fragm
on "The Healing of the Possessed" has been omitted.]

XVI. Concluding Remarks to the Monk Epiphany

And now, my Elder, thou hast heard full much of my b
bling, and I bid thee, in the name of the Lord, write thou ɛ
for thy servant in Christ, how the Mother of God kneaded
devil in her hands and gave him over to thee, and how the ɛ
ate thee in thy secret parts, and how something devilish set
to the Word and how the cell was burnt to ashes, but all wit
it were safe and sound. And how thou didst cry aloud to heav
and other things thou dost remember to the glory of Christ ɛ
the Mother of God. Hearken to what I say; if thou dost
write to me I shall be sorely angered! Thou lovest to hear
me; of what thou art ashamed, tell me if even a little. ʹ
Apostles, Paul and Barnabas, were wont to set forth, in the
sembly at Jerusalem, before all, what sights and wonders (
had wrought by them among the Gentiles (see Acts 34 ɛ
42), and the name of the Lord Jesus was magnified. And m
who believed came to them, making confession and telling tʰ
deeds. And much of this is written by the Apostles and in
Acts. Fear not to tell me, only keep thy conscience straitly; s
not thine own glory, but speak thou for Christ and the Mot
of God. Let thy servant in Christ read and rejoice. When
die, then shall this be read and we be remembered before G
and we will pray to God for them who read and who heark
They shall be our people. They shall be there with Christ, ɛ
we shall be theirs for ever and ever. Amen.

SECULAR TALES

40. Shemiaka's Judgment

Shemiaka's Judgment is one of the oldest Russian satirical stories with a purely fictitious plot. Indeed, the name "Shemiaka" can be traced back to the middle of the fifteenth century when Dmitry Shemiaka, prince of the northern city of Galych (not to be confused with Galich, capital of the southwestern province of Galicia), waged his endless feud against his cousin, Vasily III, Great Prince of Muscovy. The proper name "Shemiaka," however, subsequently became quite popular in Muscovite Russia, and there is no definite indication that the hero of the tale can be actually identified with Prince Dmitry Shemiaka or any other real historical figure.

The language and structure of the tale, its elements of popular satire and folk riddles, bring *Shemiaka's Judgment* somewhat closer to the oral folk tales (*skazki*) than to any literary narrative. Many Russian, Bielorussian, and Ukrainian tales and fairy tales about an unjust judge commonly employ the same motifs of crimes and court decisions that can be found in this tale. *Shemiaka's Judgment* satirizes Russian court mores of the sixteenth and seventeenth centuries, when judges often thought that their decisions should be a source of personal income. In those centuries this tale became extremely popular, and there have been preserved innumerable prose and verse versions of it.

The present translation follows the text of a seventeenth-century manuscript published by M. Skripil in *Russkaia povest XVII veka*, Moscow, 1954, pages 140–142.

◆ ◆ ◆

In a village of Russia there lived two peasant brothers. One was rich and the other poor. The rich one for many years lent money to his poor brother, but could not end his destitution.

Once the poor brother came to the rich one and asked him to lend him his horse because he hadn't one for bringing in wood. The rich brother did not want to give him the horse, and said, "On many occasions I have lent you money, but I cannot improve your condition." But he did lend him the horse, and then the poor brother asked to borrow the harness. The rich brother

felt offended, and began to abuse his brother, saying: "You! You
don't even have your own harness," and he didn't give him the
harness. The poor man left the house of the rich brother, took
his own sledge, and attached it to the horse's tail. He then
went to the forest and later returned to his house, but he forgo
to take out the gate spike. The sledge got caught on the spike
and could not move. He flayed the horse with the knout, and
the horse pulled with all its might, finally tearing away its own
tail. When the poor brother brought back the horse and the rich
brother saw that it no longer had a tail, he began to abuse hi
poor brother for having ruined his horse. And he refused to take
the horse back, but went to the city to lodge a complaint with
the judge, Shemiaka.

And the poor brother, seeing that his brother went to court
followed him, because he knew that if he did not come of hi
own volition, he would be obliged to pay an additional fee to
the court messenger.

And both of them stopped for the night in some township no
far from the city. The rich brother went to pass the night with
the parson of the township because the parson was an acquaint
ance of his. The poor man also came to the parson's, and, ar
riving there, went to sleep in an upper bunk. The rich brothe
began to tell the parson about the misfortune concerning hi
horse, and explained why he was going to the city. And then
the parson began to sup with the rich brother. The poor one
however, was not invited. As the poor hungry brother looked
from the upper bunk to see what the parson and his brothe
were eating, he fell from the upper bunk, accidentally crashing
onto the cradle of the parson's infant son, killing him.

And then the parson went with the rich brother to the city
to sue the poor brother for the death of his infant son. As they
came to the city wherein lived the judge, the poor one wa
following them. They were walking over a bridge to the city
At that time one of the inhabitants of the city was transporting
his father in a cart to a steambath under the bridge in order to
wash him. The poor brother, who knew that he must expec
the worst from his rich brother and from the parson, decided
to commit suicide. He jumped from the bridge into the moat in
order to kill himself; but the moat was dry, and in jumping he
accidentally fell on the old man and killed him. He was seized
and brought before the judge.

The poor man began to think how to avoid the misfortune o
a penalty and how to bribe the judge. But since he couldn't find
anything in his pocket, he took a stone and wrapped it in a

erchief and put it in his hat and presented himself to the
idge. And now the rich brother lodged his complaint against
im, requiring a compensation for his horse, and began to ex-
lain the case to the judge. Shemiaka listened to the complaints,
nd told the poor man, "Answer." The poor brother didn't know
vhat to say. He took out of his hat the wrapped stone and
nowing it to the judge, bowed deeply. The judge, thinking the
oor man promised him a bribe, told his rich brother: "Since he
ore away the tail of your horse, don't accept the horse from
our brother as long as the tail will not grow back. But as soon
s the tail grows back, at that time take from him your horse."

And then began the second trial. The parson began to sue the
oor brother for the death of his infant son, because the poor
nan had crushed his son. The poor brother once more took from
ne hat the same bundle and showed it to the judge. The judge
nw it, and thought that in the second trial the poor man
romised another bundle of gold. And he told the parson: "Since
e crushed your son, give him your wife until a child is born
om him. And at that time take back from him your wife and
ne child."

And then began the third trial, for the crushing of the son's
ld father by jumping from the bridge. The poor one, taking
ne wrapped stone from his hat, showed it for the third time to
ne judge. The judge, hoping that the poor man was promising
im a third bundle of gold for this, the third trial, told the son
f the old man: "Go onto the bridge, while the man who killed
our father remains under the bridge. And you must jump down
om the bridge and kill him in the same way in which he
illed your father."

When, after the trial, the plaintiffs left the court with the
efendant, the rich brother began to claim his horse from the
oor brother. But the latter told him: "According to the judge's
ecision, as he told you, I will return the horse to you when its
iil grows back." So the rich one gave him five rubles in order
o get back the horse, even though it had no tail. The poor
rother accepted the five rubles, and returned the horse to him.

Then the poor one, according to the decision of the judge,
laimed from the parson his wife in order to have a child with
er, and having had the child, to return the wife with the child
o the parson. But the parson began to beg him not to take his
ife. For this concession the poor man took ten rubles from the
arson.

Then the poor one told the third plaintiff: "According to the
idge's decision, I will stand under the bridge while you go on

the bridge and jump on me in the same manner in which
jumped on your father."

And the plaintiff thought, if I jump on him, probably I w
not crush him but myself," and he began to plead with the poc
man, and gave him some money in order not to be obliged
jump on him. In this way the poor man got money from all thre
of them.

The judge sent a servant to the defendant, ordering him
get from the latter the three bundles that had been shown hin
The servant told him: "Give me that which you showed to th
judge from your hat. He has ordered me to take it from you

And the latter, taking the wrapped stone from under h
hat, showed it to the servant. "Well, but that is a stone," sai
the servant.

The defendant said: "Yes, it is for the judge. I would hav
killed him if he hadn't tried me to my advantage."

The servant came back and told everything to the judge. An
the judge, after listening to the servant, said: "I thank and prais
God that I tried him to his advantage. If I had not done so, h
would have killed me."

And the poor man returned home, being overjoyed and prais
ing God.

41. *The Tale of Savva Grudtsyn*

THE *Tale of Savva Grudtsyn* is a work characteristic of a transi
tional period when the new currents that were appearing i
Russian literature modified previously well-established pattern:
The story of Savva's life, which describes his adventures, hi
illicit affair with the wife of his father's close friend, and his mil
tary deeds during his service in regiments commanded by foi
eign soldiers according to Western tactics, reflects the new wa
of life and the new mentality of Muscovite Russia. Still, som
elements of the earlier Russian hagiographic tradition persist
especially at the conclusion of the tale.

The basic theme of this work is the struggle between goo
and evil, illustrated by the fall of a man and his eventual re
demption through repentance. Thus the *Tale of Savva Grudtsy*
has several thematic parallels with the poetic tale of *Misery*
Luckless-Plight. The style of *Savva Grudtsyn* is equally transi

tional, combining the solemn, archaic language and syntax with new, colloquial expressions and idioms.

It is worth noting that this tale begins in the Time of Troubles, when the Poles' intervention in Russia during the period 1605 to 1613 undermined the foundations of the old order in Russia. As in other Russian tales of the seventeenth century, most of the characters belong to well-known aristocratic and merchant families. The Grudtsyn-Usovs and the Vtorys were important merchants in northern Russia; the boyars Streshnev and Shein are well known from Russian history; and, finally, the tsar himself shows interest in Savva and actually influences the hero's destiny. The plot is certainly fictional and complex, but it does give vivid and realistic details of the life of a patriarchal Russian family of that time, of the life of the military, and of the mores of Muscovite society. The author was decidedly not a member of the literati of that period, for, despite the use of both archaic and colloquial expressions, his art is rather limited, and he often repeats word for word certain descriptions, speeches, and conceptions.

The translation follows an early eighteenth-century manuscript published, with some corrections, by M. Skripil in *Russkaia povest XVII veka,* Moscow, 1954, pages 82–102.

◆ ◆ ◆

This is a most truthful and true tale which has come to pass in these days and which reveals how God, who loves man, revealed his love to the Christian people. I wish to tell you, brethren, this most wonderful tale which is filled with awe and horror, which deserves inexplicable astonishment, and which explains the patience of our man-loving God who, awaiting our conversion, brings us to salvation through the most inexplicable of deeds.

On a day in 1606 (7114) God allowed, because of the multiplication of our sins, the God-offending apostate, heretic, and unfrocked monk Grishka Otrepiev[1] to attack the Muscovite state and to win the throne of the Russian land in a most robberlike, untsarlike manner. Also, at that time Russia was invaded by the

---

[1] Grishka, or Gregory, Otrepiev was a pretender to the Russian throne who claimed to be Prince Dmitry, the son of Ivan IV. See introduction to Selection 35. At that time Poland and Lithuania were united into one dominion, which explains the author's calling the foreign troops Polish in one case, Lithuanian in another.

increasing bands of faithless Lithuanians and Poles who performed all kinds of base deeds and who caused great misfortune to the Russian people in Moscow and in other cities. Because of these Lithuanian and Polish attacks, many people abandoned their homes and fled from city to city.

In the year 1606 (7114), in the city of Great Ustiug,[2] there lived a citizen named Foma, by surname, Grudtsyn-Usov, whose descendants still reside in that city. Seeing much anarchy and base deeds of the lawless Poles in Russia, this Foma decided to forsake the city of Great Ustiug, to live no longer in his home, but to migrate with his wife to the city of Kazan on the lower Volga, for in this city on the lower Volga there were no base Lithuanians or Poles.

And Foma and his wife lived in the city of Kazan until the beginning of the reign of the God-fearing sovereign, Grand Duke, and Tsar of All Russia, Michael Fedorovich. Foma had an only son, Savva, who was twelve years old. It was Foma's custom to make frequent business trips, traveling up and down the Volga, sometimes going to Solikamsk,[3] sometimes to the city of Astrakhan, and sometimes beyond the Caspian Sea to the land of Persia. He also taught his son, Savva, so that he might learn to attend to his business promptly and diligently, since after Foma's death his only son would inherit his estate.

After some time, Foma decided to sail to Persia and began the loading of his goods into the usual ships. He also loaded other boats with customary goods and ordered his son to sail to Solikamsk, there to learn the merchant's trade with all diligence. Having bidden farewell to his wife and son, Foma set out on his journey. Some days later, his son, Savva, sailed to Solikamsk in the ships his father had ordered loaded. Having reached the city of Orel, which is in the Usolsk region, he docked and, following his father's orders, went to live at the inn of a certain respectable man. The innkeeper and his wife, remembering the loving kindness of Savva's father, for he had done them many favors, cared with diligence for the son, rendering him many services and even treating him as their son.

In this city of Orel there lived a citizen, Bazhen Vtory by

[2] The city of Great Ustiug is located in northern Russia, between Moscow and the White Sea, and in the seventeenth century was an important merchant city.

[3] Solikamsk and Orel are located in the same region as Great Ustiug. The city of Atraskhan is located at the delta of the Volga, and was the main trading center for commerce with Persia and other countries of the Near East.

name, who was both famous and well known. He was already old in years and was known in many cities for his virtuous way of life and for his wealth. He had befriended and was well acquainted with Savva's father. Having learned that the son of Foma Grudtsyn had come to this city from Kazan, he thought to himself: Since his father and I share much love and friendship, why should I neglect the son by not inviting him into my home, to live with me and to eat at my table?

Having come to this conclusion, when Bazhen saw Savva walking in the street he invited him to his house, saying: "My dear friend, Savva, do you know that your father and I share much love and friendship? Why did you neglect me by not coming to abide in my home? This time, do not disobey me, but come and live in my house and break bread with me. And, for the love of your father, I shall receive you even as if you were my own son."

Hearing these words from Bazhen, Savva was very happy to be received into the house of such a famous man, and he bowed low before him, and made haste to move from the inn to Bazhen's house. And there he lived, enjoying all the comforts, and rejoicing.

This old man, Bazhen, had a young wife who had never been married before, but who was Bazhen's third wife. The Devil, that enemy who hates all things not vile in the human kind, having seen this man's virtuous way of life, decided to bring strife into his house by inducing Bazhen's wife to have sinful relations with the young man. Thus the wife began to seduce him into sin with tempting words. Human nature knows how to lead the mind of a young man into iniquity. And thus Savva, influenced by the flattery of this woman, or, better to say, by the Devil's envy, was led to the sin of adultery. They sinned endlessly, but still they were unable to satiate their desires. And Savva remained for a long time in such a sinful relation with her. They sinned even on Sundays and on holy days and, having forgotten all fear of God, they wallowed continuously, like swine, in the filth that is sin. And for a long time they remained in such insatiable lust, like beasts.

When the holy day honoring the Ascension of our Lord Jesus Christ neared, Bazhen Vtory took the young man and went to vespers in the holy church, this being on the eve of that holy day. Then they went home again and, after the usual supping, went each to his own bed, giving thanks to God. As soon as the God-loving man, Bazhen Vtory, had fallen soundly asleep, his wife, incited by the devil, got up secretly from her couch, went to the young man's bed, woke him, and compelled him to wicked adultery. Though young, Savva was seized by the fear of God, as if pierced by an arrow. And, fearing God's judgment, he began to ponder, asking himself, How could I do such a wicked deed and on such a great holy day?

And having thought thusly, he wished to be rid of her and, taking an oath, said to her, "I do not want to lose my soul forever by profaning my body on such a great holiday."

But she, in the grip of an insatiable carnal desire, tried to force him by her caresses and threats to submit to her. But try as she would, she could not force him to yield to her desire. And some kind of divine power helped him. When this evil woman saw that she could not bring the youth to do her bidding, she at once became seized by a wicked rage. Hissing like a fierce serpent, she went away from his bed. Then she began to ponder how she might destroy him through a magic potion. And she decided to fulfill her evil intention of destroying him without delay.

And she did as she had decided. When the bells announced matins, God-loving Bazhen quickly got up from his bed, woke the young man, Savva, and went with him to the morning service to glorify God. They listened to the liturgy with attention and with the fear of God, and then they returned home. When the hour of the sacred liturgy arrived, they returned to the holy church with joy so that they might hear the glorification of God. In the meantime, this accursed woman carefully prepared a magic philter for the youth, for she, like a serpent, wanted to spit poison at him.

When the holy liturgy was ended, Bazhen and Savva left the church, intending to go home. However, the voevoda of the city invited Bazhen to take dinner with him. And he asked, concerning the youth, "Whose son is this and where is he from?"

Bazhen answered that he was Foma Grudtsyn's son from Kazan. Thereafter, the voevoda invited the young man to his home, for he had known Savva's father well. So they went to the voevoda's house and, as was the custom, ate together with the others, and afterward returned home.

Arriving home, Bazhen ordered that wine be brought out so that they might drink in his home to honor the holy day. He was not in the least aware of his wife's evil scheme. When the wine had been brought in, she poured it into a cup and offered it to her husband. He drank it and gave thanks to the Lord. Then she poured more and drank it herself. Then she poured out the poisoned philter she had prepared, and offered it to Savva. He rank this base potion without any apprehension or hesitation, or he expected no evil deed from her, thinking that she arbored no ill will toward him. But as soon as he had drunk it, fire began to burn in his heart. And he thought to himself: I ave drunk many drinks in my father's house, but never such a 'ine as this one.

When he had finished the drink, he began to grieve in his eart and to long for a woman. The wife, like a fierce lioness, ooked furiously at Savva and showed him not the least friendli- ess. But she began rather to slander the young man to her hus- and, saying base words and ordering her husband to drive the outh from their house. God-fearing Bazhen, although he took ity on the young man, was finally ensnared by his wife's cajol- ry and ordered the youth out of his home, accusing him of arious failings. And the youth went away from the house with reat sorrow and grief in his heart, lamenting and grieving the vil deeds of that woman.

He went back to the house of the innkeeper where he had reviously lived, and the innkeeper asked him by what fault he ad left Bazhen's house. And Savva answered, "I did not wish o live longer with those people, for I did not have enough to at."

But he continued to grieve for and long after this woman. nd, because of his grief, his handsome face began to wane nd his flesh to waste away. Seeing the youth so grieving and menting, the innkeeper could not ascertain what had happened.

Now in the same city there was a magician who, through orcery and charms, could tell why and to whom sorrow had ome. He was also able to divine who would live and who ould die. The innkeeper and his wife, who were sensible and ared greatly for the young man, summoned this sorcerer ecretly, for they wished to learn why the youth grieved so. The orcerer came and, consulting his book of magic, told them the uth: "The youth has no sorrow for himself, but longs only for e wife of Bazhen Vtory, since he has fallen into sinful adultery ith her. But he became ashamed of her, and since that time e has grieved, longing for her."

The innkeeper and his wife, hearing this from the sorcerer, id not believe him, because they knew Bazhen Vtory to be a ious and God-fearing man who could not be involved in such affair. Savva, however, continued to lament incessantly and long for that accursed woman. And from day to day he asted away, as if he were afflicted by some overwhelming ereavement.

Once, Savva left the city and went into the fields, wishin
to take a walk to alleviate his longings and grief. He went wall
ing alone, seeing no one before him nor no one behind him, an
thinking of nothing in particular, but only grieving and lamen
ing his separation from that woman. Then there came into h
mind an evil thought, and he said to himself: "If someone, ma
or devil, would do something so that I might take sexu
pleasure with this woman, then would I serve even the Devil

And coming to such an idea, as if he had lost his mind, h
continued walking through the field, but a short distance behin
him he heard a voice that called him by name. He turne
around and saw a youth who was dressed in fine garments an
was running swiftly toward him, entreating him with his han
to wait. And the youth came up to Savva. It must be said tha
this was not a youth, but the Enemy and the Devil who searche
for ways to destroy human souls.

The youth came up to Savva and, after they had bowed t
each other, said: "Brother Savva. Why did you run from me?
have awaited you a long time, hoping that you would come t
me and would have brotherly love for me. I have known you fe
a long time, and I know that you are of the Grudtsyn-Uso
family of the city of Kazan. And if you wish to know me, I ma
say that I am also from the city of Great Ustiug. And since, b
birth, I can be considered your brother, you should become m
brother and friend from this time on. And never leave me, s
that I can be of help to you in all things."

Savva, hearing such words from his false brother, that is t
say, from the Devil, became very happy to find a relative i
such a distant and unknown land. And they kissed each othe
with love and went together through the wilderness. And th
Devil said to Savva: "Brother Savva, wherefore do you grieve
Why do you destroy your youthful beauty?"

Savva avoided the questions, however, telling him that h
was afflicted by a malady.

The Devil cunningly smiled and said: "Why do you conce
the truth from me? I know your ailment, but what would yo
give me if I were to cure you of it?"

And Savva answered: "If you actually know the affliction
bear in my heart, then I shall believe that you can help me."

The Devil replied: "In your heart you long for the wife of
Bazhen Vtory, since you are deprived of her love. What woul
you give me if I once more united you with her and she on
more loved you?"

Savva answered: "In such a case, I shall give you all the merchandise and wealth of my father and all my profits! Only cause me to be once more with this women."

The Devil laughed and retorted: "Why do you tempt me? I know that your father actually is very rich. But you are not aware that my father is seven times richer than yours. What are your goods to me? Only give me a short note, and I shall fulfill your desire."

The youth was very happy, thinking to himself: The wealth of my father will remain intact, and I shall give him the letter and write whatever he wants.

The youth did not know what misfortune he was bringing upon himself. Actually, he did not read or write well. Oh, the madness of youth! Thus he was ensnared by a woman's treachery and, for her sake, he was going to the Devil.

Hardly had the Devil spoken these words about the letter, when the youth happily promised to give him the letter. The false brother, that is to say, the Devil, quickly took paper and ink from his pocket, gave them to the youth, and ordered him to write the letter. Savva still did not fully know what he was writing, but began to write senselessly. And by this letter Savva renounced Christ, the True God, and gave himself in the service of the Devil. Having written the letter in which he rejected God, he gave it to the Devil, his false brother.

Thus, they both arrived in Orel. Then Savva asked the Devil, "Tell me, my brother, where you live, so that I may know your house."

The Devil laughed, and said: "I have no particular house anywhere, but wherever it is convenient, there do I spend the night. However, if you wish to see me often, look always for me in the Horse Market, since I sometimes live there when buying horses. Now, go to the shop of Bazhen, and I know that you will be gladly invited to live in this house."

Savva, following the words of his brother, the Devil, happily ran to Bazhen's shop. Bazhen, upon seeing Savva, eagerly invited him into his house, say to him: "Master Savva! What a wrong I have done you? Why did you leave my house? I pray you, come back now and live in my house. I am truly happy, for the love of your father, to have you here as if you were my own son."

Hearing such words from Bazhen, Savva was overcome with joy, and quickly entered Bazhen's house. And when the youth had entered, the wife, being incited by the Devil, met him with

joy and greeted him, giving him a welcoming kiss. The youth
was ensnared in the woman's flattery, that is to say, by the
Devil, and was once more drawn into the sinful net with that
accursed woman. From that time on, he remembered neither
the holy days nor Sundays. He lost his fear of God, and wallowed with her constantly in the sin of lechery, as if he were a
swine.

After quite a time had passed, there came a rumor to Savva's
mother in the city of Kazan to the effect that her son was living
an unrighteous and sinful life and that the father's wealth that
was with him had all been squandered in lechery and drunkenness. Hearing such things about her son, the mother began to
grieve profoundly, and wrote him a letter in which she urged
him to return to his father's house in the city of Kazan. When
the letter arrived, he read it, and laughed, paying it no heed.
The mother sent him a second and a third letter in which she
besought and entreated him to return home immediately from
Orel to the city of Kazan. Savva, however, did not obey his
mother's commands and entreaties, but, paying no heed to anything, continued only to persevere in his sinful passions.

Some time later, the Devil took Savva and went with him
beyond the city of Orel into the fields of the countryside. As
soon as they had left the city, the Devil said to Savva: "Do you
know who I am? You were fully convinced that I am of the
Grudtsyn family, but it isn't so. Now, out of love, I shall reveal
the truth to you. Don't be afraid, and be not ashamed to call me
your brother, for verily I do love you as a brother. But if you
wish to know who I am, I am the son of a king. Let us go
farther, and I shall show you my glory and the wealth of my
father!"

Having said these words, he lead Savva to a certain hill and
showed him a fine city a short distance away. Its walls and roofs
were of pure gold, and gleamed.

And the Devil said to Savva: "This city is the work of my
father. Let us go and bow down before my father. And now,
take the letter you gave to me and present it to my father, and
you will be given a great honor by him."

And having said these words, the Devil returned the letter in
which Savva had renounced God.

Oh, the madness of youth! Didn't he know that there was no
kingdom near the Muscovite state that was not under the sway
of the tsar? If only he had made the sign of the cross, then all
these devilish temptations would have vanished like a shadow.

When they approached this chimerical city and came up to

e city gates, they were met there by youths with dark faces
d in vestments and belts decorated with gold. These youths
wed to them, rendering honor to the king's son, who was
tually the Devil, and also greeting Savva. When they entered
e courtyard of the Kings' palace, they were met there by more
uths, who wore still more brilliant raiment than the first ones
ey had met. And these youths also bowed to them. Then they
tered the King's palace and were met by still more youths,
ho surpassed each other in their proud dignities and their
agnificent vestments. And they also rendered honors to the
ng's son and to Savva.

Entering the palace, the Devil said: "Brother Savva, wait here
r me awhile. I shall go and announce you to my father, and
shall later take you to him. When you appear before him,
ink of nothing and have no fears; only give him the letter."
aving said this, he passed into the inner chambers, leaving
vva alone. In a short while he returned, came to Savva, took
m by the hand, and let him before the Prince of Darkness.
e Prince of Darkness was sitting on a high throne embellished
th gold and jewels. He was distinguished by his proud glory
d his magnificent raiment. Round his throne, Savva noticed
large number of winged youth, the faces of some being blue,
ile the faces of others were red, and still others had faces
black as pitch. Savva appeared before the King, fell to the
or, and genuflected before him.

The King asked him: "From whence do you come? What is
ur plight?"

The senseless youth presented him with his God-rejecting
ter, and said, "I have come, great King, to serve you."

That ancient serpent, Satan, accepted the letter, read it,
ned toward his dark-faced warriors, and said, "Although I
cept this youth, I know not whether he will remain faithful
me." Then he summoned his son, Savva's false brother, say-
g to him, "Go to another room, and have dinner with your
other."

Both bowed to the King, went to another room, and began
dine. They were served unimaginably aromatic dishes, and
e same kind of drink. Savva marveled, and said that he had
ver partaken of similar dishes or of similar drinks in his own
her's house.

After the meal, the Devil took Savva, and together they left
st the King's courtyard and then the city. And Savva asked
brother, the Devil, "Tell me, brother, who were those
nged youths who surrounded your father's throne?"

The Devil smiled and answered: "Aren't you aware that ma
nations serve my father—the Indians, the Persians, and mar
many others. Don't wonder about this and don't hesitate to c
me your brother. From now on I will be your younger broth
However, when I tell you to do something, you must obey m
And I shall render you all kinds of good deeds."

Savva promised to be obedient, and the Devil became so co
fident that, when they had arrived back in the city of Orel,
left Savva alone and went away. Savva still went to the hou
of Bazhen Vtory and continued to indulge in his sinful leche

In the meantime, Savva's father, Foma Grudtsyn, return
to Kazan from Persia, having been very successful in his bu
ness. As usual and as is due, he gave a kiss to his wife a
then inquired about their son, asking whether he were s
alive. And she answered him, saying: "I have heard from ma
people about him. After you left for Persia, he went to So
kamsk, and from there to the city of Orel. And since then,
sins and, as people say, has squandered all our wealth and h
dissipated his health in drunkenness and in lechery. And
many occassions I have written him asking that he return hor
from there. But not once has he answered my letters, and so
don't know whether he is alive or not."

Hearing this from his wife, Foma was in a quandry. Then
sat down and penned a letter to Savva, beseeching him to retu
without delay to the city of Kazan. "I would like, my chil
he wrote, "once again to see your handsome face, for I have
seen you in a long time."

Savva, having received and read the letter, paid it no he
and did not even think of returning to his father. He wish
only to indulge in his insatiable lust. Foma, seeing that his lett
had accomplished nothing, ordered boats and goods prepar
for sailing, and began his travels to Solikamsk, telling his wi
"I shall myself look for our son, and bring him back to c
home."

As soon as the Devil learned that Savva's father was traveli
to Solikamsk, he decided to take Savva to Kazan. So he t
Savva: "Brother Savva, how long are we going to remain in tl
small town? Let us visit other cities and have a good time the
Then we can return here."

Savva did not contradict him, but said: "You are rig
brother. Let us go. But we should wait for a short while, sin
I want to obtain some money for my merchandise."

But the Devil prevented him from doing so, and sai
"Haven't you looked upon my father's glory? Aren't you awa

t he has estates everywhere? Wherever we go, we shall have
much money as we need."

Thus they left the city of Orel, and their departure was known
no one, neither to Bazhen Vtory nor to Bazhen's wife. In one
ht Savva and the Devil covered the distance of two thousand
es, from the city of Solikamsk to the city of Kozmodem-
sk[4] on the river Volga. And the Devil said to Savva: "In case
1 should meet someone you know, and this person should
: from whence you have come, you should answer that you
ne from Solikamsk and have spent three weeks traveling to
s place." And Savva did as he was told, following the Devil's
er.

They passed several days in the city of Kozmodemiansk, and
n the Devil and Savva covered the distance from the city
Kozmodemiansk to the village of Paul's Ferry (Pavel's
evoz) on the river Oka in one night. They arrived there on
ursday, which was the market day. Walking through the
rket, Savva noticed a very old beggar who stood dressed in
ulsive rags. This man observed Savva carefully, and then
;an to weep. Savva left the Devil's side for a short time and
nt up to the old man, wishing to learn what caused him to
. Approaching the old man, Savva asked him: "Wherefore
you grieve? Why do you weep so incessantly?"

And the beggar, who was a holy elder, answered: "My child,
ry because you have lost your soul. You don't realize that you
ve lost it, but you have voluntarily turned to the Devil. Do
1 know, my child, with whom you walk and whom you call
ur brother? It is not a man, but the Devil who walks with you
l who hopes to bring you to the very pit of hell."

As soon as the old man had spoken these words, Savva turned
ward his false brother, or, better to say, to the Devil. The
vil was standing a short way from him and was threatening
rva and gnashing his teeth. The youth left the holy elder and
nt up to the Devil. The Devil began abusing him, and said:
hy do you talk with such an evil destroyer of souls? Aren't
1 aware that this base elder has brought many people to their
wnfall? He noticed your Sunday clothes and wanted to win
u by flattery, to take you away from the crowd, and then to
angle you with a cord and steal your clothes. You will be lost
hout me, if I abandon you."

After saying these words, the Devil took Savva from that

The city of Kozmodemiansk is located on the Upper Volga,
th of Moscow.

village. He went with him to a city called Shuya,[5] and t
remained there together for a time.

In the meantime, Foma Grudtsyn came to the city of C
and began inquiring about his son's whereabouts, but no
was able to give him any information. Everyone had seen
son in the city before Foma had arrived, but then he sudde
disappeared without telling anyone of his departure. Some s
that the son was frightened by the father's arrival, because
had squandered his father's wealth, and had therefore
appeared. Especially astounded by Savva's departure w
Bazhen Vtory and his wife. And Bazhen told Foma: "He sp
the night at our place and the next morning he went away.
waited for him to come to dinner, but since that morning he
not reappeared in this city. And neither myself nor my v
knows where he has disappeared to."

Foma shed many tears, and lived for a time in Orel wait
for his son, but since his expectations went unrequited, he
turned home. And he told of the unhappy case to his w
Together they grieved and lamented the disappearance of t
only son. Foma Grudtsyn grieved for a long time, and then
entered into his Father's House. And his wife remained a wid

While the Devil and Savva were living in the town of Shu
the pious and great sovereign, Tsar, and Grand Duke, Mich
Fedorovich, the Autocrat of All the Russias, sent his ar
against the city of Smolensk[6] to fight the King of Poland.
cording to the tsar's decree, soldiers were to be recrui
throughout all Russia. For the recruiting of such soldiers, Sto
Timothy Vorontsev was sent from the city of Moscow to Shu
And he recruited soldiers and drilled them everyday accord
to military regulations. Savva and the Devil used to go
watch the drills. Once the Devil told Savva: "Brother Sav
would you like to serve the tsar? Let us volunteer for the arm

Savva answered: "Well, brother, you are right. Let us serv
And so they joined the ranks of the army and began to go
gether for drilling. The Devil gave Savva such a talent

---

[5] The city of Shuya is located between Moscow and Nizh
Novgorod (which is now called Gorky).

[6] The city of Smolensk, some 250 miles west of Moscow, was
important fortress on the Russian-Polish frontier in the seventee
century. It was lost to Poland during the Time of Troubles. In
years 1632 to 1634, Russia was at war to win back this import
city. The Russian armies were under the command of Boyar B.
Shein. The author erroneously called him Feodor Ivanovich Sh
Tsar Michael Fedorovich, the first Romanov to be tsar, reigned fr
1613 to 1645.

The siege of Smolensk by the Poles, 1604–1610. An early seventeenth-century engraving.

military studies that he very soon surpassed the old soldiers
and even the commanders. The Devil himself served as Savva's
orderly, and cared for Savva and carried his weapons.

When these recently recruited soldiers were transferred from
Shuya to Moscow, a German colonel continued their training.[7]
When this colonel came to inspect the newly recruited soldiers
during drill, he noticed a very young man who behaved most
properly, who acted by the regulations, and who was faultless in
his military deportment, and who surpassed many old soldiers
and commanders in his studies. He was astounded by Savva's
acumen, called him aside, and inquired about his background.
Savva told him the whole truth. The colonel took a liking to
Savva, called him his own son, and gave him his hat, decorated
with precious stones, from off his head. And he entrusted to
Savva three companies of recruits. And so Savva began to drill
and to instruct them in place of the colonel.

The Devil secretly approached Savva and told him: "Brother
Savva, in case you don't have sufficient money to pay your
soldiers, tell me and I shall bring you as much as you need, so
as to prevent complaints and dissatisfaction among your troops."

And all Savva's soldiers were always quiet and peaceful, while
in other companies there were complaints and disorder because
the soldiers were dying of starvation and from the lack of
clothing and provisions. Among Savva's troops the soldiers were
peaceful and well organized, and everyone marveled at Savva's
acumen.

Once, the tsar himself learned of Savva. At that time in
Moscow was the very powerful boyar and brother-in-law of
the tsar, Simeon Streshnev.[8] When this boyar learned of Savva,
he ordered that he be brought to him.

When Savva came, Boyar Streshnev asked him, "My youth,
do you want to be received in my house and to receive considerable honors from me?"

Savva bowed and replied: "I have a brother, my lord; I will

---

[7] Since the sixteenth century, the Russians had begun hiring
foreign instructors to drill and equip their armies according to the
requirements of contemporary military science. They preferred to hire
German and English instructors because they were Protestants and
not Roman Catholics. They preferred Protestants because Russia was
constantly at strife with Poland, which for centuries had been an
outpost of Catholic expansion.

[8] Boyar Simeon Streshnev was a well-known Russian statesman of
the second half of the seventeenth century. The author of this tale
erroneously ascribed to him an active part in the first half of the
seventeenth century.

ask him. If he orders me to do so, I will serve you with pleasure." The boyar had no objections, and permitted Savva to go and ask his brother.

When Savva came and told everything to his false brother, the Devil, the Devil answered him angrily, saying: "Why do you wish to disregard the tsar's service and become a servant of the tsar's servant? You are now in an important position and you have become favorably known to the tsar. No, you mustn't do this, but let us rather serve the tsar. When the tsar learns of your faithful service, you will be promoted by him to the higher ranks."

By the order of the tsar, all recruits were distributed among the regiments of streltsy[9] in order to swell their ranks. Savva was quartered in the city at the house of Jacob Shilov, a streltsy captain of the Zimin regiment. His house was located in the Stretenka neighborhood of the Earthen City. This captain and his wife, who were pious and decent people, highly respected Savva for his acumen.

The regiments were readied in Moscow for the campaign, when one day the Devil came to Savva and told him: "Brother Savva, let us go ahead of the regiment to Smolensk to see what the Poles are doing there, how they have fortified the city, and what kind of weapons they have." In one night they went from Moscow to Smolensk. Coming there, they remained in the city for three days and three nights, being invisible. There they saw and inspected all things and saw how the Poles were fortifying the city and how they were placing grenades in the places of possible storming. On the fourth day in Smolensk, the Devil revealed himself and Savva to the Poles. Upon seeing them, the Poles became alarmed and began to chase after them, trying to catch them. The Devil and Savva escaped from the city, fled to the river Dnieper, and the river parted before them and they crossed the river as if it were dry. The Poles opened fire on them, but did not succeed in injuring them. And they marveled, saying, "They, who have sojourned in our city, are demons in men."

However, Savva and the Devil returned to Moscow and once again were quartered with this same Captain Shilov. When, at the tsar's command, the regiments marched from Moscow against Smolensk, this Savva and his brother went with the soldiers. The commander over all regiments was Boyar Feodor Shein.

[9] Streltsy (sing., strelets) were professional infantrymen who were armed with muskets, halberds, and sabers. This standing infantry was first organized by John IV.

On the way to Smolensk, the Devil told Savva: "Brother Savva, when we arrive in Smolensk a giant Polish knight will ride out from the city, and will challenge one of our soldiers to a joust. Don't fear him, but go against him. I know and I assure you that you will defeat him. The next day there will come another giant from the Polish ranks who will seek to joust. Once again you must go against him, and I know that you will defeat him also. When the third day comes, the third Polish knight will ride forth from Smolensk. Don't fear him, but go against him, and you will defeat him. You will be wounded by him, but I shall cure you of your wounds." So Savva was advised. And the regiments came to the city of Smolensk and set up camp in a good place.

As the Devil had said, there rode forth from the city of Smolensk a most terrifying warrior who rode on his horse and looked through the Muscovite ranks for an adversary. But no one dared to oppose him. But then Savva announced that he would do so, saying: "If I had a good, spirited steed, I would go to fight against this enemy of the tsar." And when his friends heard of this, they told his intentions to the boyar. The boyar ordered that Savva be brought before him and that he be given a good steed and a weapon, but the boyar thought that the youth would perish at the hands of such a terrifying giant. Then Savva, as he was ordered by his brother, the Devil, galloped against this Polish knight, quickly defeated him, and brought him and his horse to the Muscovite regiments. And Savva was praised by all.

The next day there rode forth from Smolensk another glorious warrior who was in search of an adversary among the Muscovite armies. And once more Savva rode out, and defeated the knight. And everyone was stunned by his daring. However, Boyar Shein became wroth with Savva, but he concealed his rage in his heart.

On the third day, there once more came a warrior from the city of Smolensk, and this knight was more glorious than the previous two, and was looking for an adversary. Although Savva was afraid to ride against such a terrifying warrior, he followed the Devil's order and immediately rode against him. And then this Pole furiously charged Savva and wounded him in his left thigh with his lance. Savva recovered, however, charged the Pole, killed him, and brought his body and horse into the Russian camp. He terrified the Poles in Smolensk, while the entire army was stunned. Then the Polish sortie commenced, arm-clashed against army, and the battle began. And the flank of the Russian army, in which Savva fought with his brother, was winning, and the Poles turned their backs, and fled. The Devil and Savva killed an endless number of Poles, but they themselves were not injured by anyone.

When Boyar Shein learned of the courage of this youth, he could no longer conceal the wrath in his heart, but summoned Savva to his tent, and asked him, "Tell me, my youth, from which family are you and whose son are you?" And when Savva told him that he was the son of Foma Grudtsyn of Kazan, the boyar began to abuse him with all kind of crude words, and told him: "Why did you need to take part in such mortal combat? I know your father and your relatives. They are immensely wealthy. What is the reason for your forsaking your parent's home to come here? Was it persecution or poverty? I tell you, don't delay any longer, but return to the house of your parents and remain there, living in abundance with your parents. If you don't obey, and I hear about you once more and learn that you have remained here, then you will perish without mercy. I will order that you be beheaded!" Saying this to the youth, the raging boyar left him. And the youth left the tent in great sadness.

When he had left the tent, the Devil asked him: "Why are you troubled about this? If people do not want our services here, we shall return to Moscow and live there." And soon after, they left Smolensk for Moscow, and there they continued to live in the house of Captain Jacob Shilov. The Devil spent the day with Savva, while in the evening he would go to his abode in hell where he dwelt according to the ancient evil customs.

After a considerable length of time, Savva fell ill, and his illness was so severe, he was at death's door. The wife of the captain was a wise, God-fearing woman. She cared for Savva and told him on many occasions that he should summon a priest so that he might take Holy Communion and confess his sins. "You should do this," she said, "for you may die suddenly without having had the last rites."

Savva rejected her advice because, as he said, "My illness is certainly grave, but not fatal." His condition worsened from day to day, and the captain's wife incessantly urged him to take the last rites, because, as she said, "You may die without having taken them."

Finally Savva was forced by this God-loving woman to summon a priest. The captain's wife sent for a priest from the Church of St. Nicholas which is located in the Rooks' neighbor-

hood. The priest came to the ill man without delay. He was of
a mature age, with great experience, and was very devout.
When he came to the bedside of the ill man, he began to pronounce prayers before confession, as is the custom. When the
other people had left the room, the priest began to confess the
sick man.

Suddenly Savva noticed that the room had become filled with
a multitude of demons. His false brother, who was actually the
Devil, came with these demons, but this time he was not in the
image of man, but in his true bestial form. The Devil, who remained behind the crowd of demons, was in a frenzy of rage,
gnashing his teeth, and showing Savva the God-rejecting letter
Savva had given him in the vicinity of Solikamsk. And the Devil
told the ill man: "Look at this, you perjurer, do you realize what
it is? Did you write this or do you believe that by repenting
you can escape us? Oh, no, don't think that, for I will move
against you with all my forces." And the Devil told him this and
other evil threats. The sick man evidently heard them and was
as first frightened, but later he relied upon the power of God
and confessed everything in great detail to the priest. The priest,
although he was a man of the holy life, also became frightened,
since no one but he and Savva were in the room. And he was
deafened by the great uproar that came from the multitude of
demons, and only with great difficulty did the priest finish con-
fessing the sick man. Then he left for home without saying anything to anyone.

After the confession, the evil spirit assaulted Savva and began
to torture him mercilessly. One minute the Devil was beating
him against the wall; another minute he was throwing him
from the couch to the floor; then he throttled him until Savva
began to gasp and foam came from his mouth; then he tortured
him with many different kinds of torture. The aforementioned
captain, who was also a pious man, saw with his wife that the
youth was assaulted and tormented by the Devil. And they
grieved and bemoaned the fate of the youth, but were unable
to help him in any way. From day to day the assaults and
torments of the Devil became fiercer, and those who witnessed
them were terrified.

The master of the house, who saw the unusual fate of this
youth and who realized that, because of his courage, the youth
was known to the tsar himself, decided with his wife to inform
the tsar. They hoped that there might be some relative of the
youth in the tsar's palace. As soon as the man had decided this,

Portrait of a Russian boyar.
A seventeenth-century painting.

he sent his wife to her relative, telling her to inform the relative about everything and asking that she inform the tsar immediately. And he added, "In case the young man dies in such miserable plight, there may be litigation for not having informed the tsar."

His wife, without delay, hastened to her relative and told her exactly what she was ordered to say by her husband. Hearing these words, her relative was profoundly moved, grieved over the fate of the youth, and became sad at the situation of her relatives, fearing that this matter might bring them trouble. Therefore, without any delay, she went from her house to the tsar's palace and told the members of the tsar's court of these happenings. When the tsar heard about this youth, he showed mercy on him. He told the courtiers who were before him to send two sentries to the house of the captain where the sick man lay, whenever the daily changing of the sentries took place.

The tsar said, "They should watch over this youth with care so as to prevent him from killing himself by throwing himself into the fire or into the water, when he loses his senses because of the demons' torments."

And the pious tsar ordered that meals be sent daily to the sick man, and asked that the sick man appear before him in his palace as soon as he was cured. And so it was done. However, the sick man remained for a long time under the Devil's sway.

The first of July arrived, and on those days the youth was particularly tormented by the Devil. Finally he fell asleep, and while he was sleeping he began to talk as if he were awake and he shed tears from his exhausted eyes. And he said: "O Most Merciful Lady, Queen and Holy Virgin, have mercy upon me, our Lady, the Queen of Queens. I do not lie, I do not lie, but I shall do as I pledge."

The members of the captain's household and the sentries who watched him were astounded when they heard these words spoken by sick Savva, and they said, "He has a vision."

When the sick man woke from the sleep, the captain came to him, and said, "Tell me, Lord Savva, what kind of words did you speak while shedding tears in your sleep?"

And tears flowed steadily from Savva's eyes, and he said: "I saw that my couch was approached by a Lady from whom emanated light, and who shone with indescribable grace, and who was wearing a purple vestment. With her were two men distinguished by their venerable white hair. One of them was in an archbishop's vestment, while the other was wearing the robes

an Apostle. And I believe that they were none other than the
oly Virgin, the Friend of the Lord, John the Theologian, and
Metropolitan Peter, the ever vigilant guardian of our city,
Moscow, and the most glorious archbishop of bishops. I know
ell their images from the icons. And the Lady from whom
emanated light said: 'What has happened to you, Savva? Why
e you so full of sorrow?'

"And I said to her: 'I am full of sorrow, my Lady, because
he Son of our God is wroth with me, and because you, the
intercessor for the Christians, are wroth with me.' And, smiling
at me, she said: 'What do you think? How can you escape such
plight? How can you get your God-rejecting letter from hell?'
And I told her: 'It cannot be done, my Lady, except with the
succor of your Son and through your infinite mercy.' And she
old me: 'I shall implore my Son and God in your behalf; only,
you must follow to the word what I shall tell you. I shall deliver
you from this misfortune, if you will decide to take monastic
ows.'

"And so I vowed to her tearfully in my dream, and these
ere the words that you heard. And then she told me: 'Listen,
avva! On the holy day of my icon in my cathedral of the
on of Kazan, come to my church that is on the main square
the vicinity of the Rag Market. And then I shall perform a
iracle for you in the presence of all.' And after this, she be-
ame invisible."

The captain and the sentries who kept watch over Savva
arveled greatly upon hearing his words about his vision. And
e captain and his wife began to ponder how they should
form the tsar of this vision, and decided to send their relative
inform the courtiers in the tsar's palace and let them tell of
e vision to the tsar. When the aforementioned relative came
the captain's house, they told her of Savva's vision. When she
arned of this, she went immediately to the tsar's palace in
der to inform the courtiers in the tsar's palace and to let them
form the tsar of Savva's vision. When the tsar learned of it,
e marveled greatly.

When, on July 8th, the holy day of the Icon of the Blessed
irgin of Kazan arrived, there was a church procession with
oly icons and sacred crosses from the Cathedral of the Assump-
on of the Holy Virgin to the Holy Virgin of Kazan. In this
ocession participated the great sovereign, tsar, and grand
uke, Michael, the holy patriarch, with the bishops, and a great
any courtiers. And the tsar ordered that sick Savva be brought

to this church. Then, by the tsar's order, the ill man was rapidl
brought on a carpet to the Church of the Holy Virgin of Kaza
and was laid before the entrance to the church.

When the holy Mass begun, ill Savva was assaulted by th
evil spirit, and the Devil began to torment him ferociously, an
Savva called in a loud voice, "Help me, my Lady and Hol
Virgin! Help me, my Queen of Queens, the Mother of God
And when the choir began to sing the Song of the Cherubin
people heard a sound like thunder, and there came a voice an
nouncing: "Savva! Get up and come into my church!"

Then he got up from the carpet on which he had bee
brought, as if he had never been ill. He quickly came into th
church, fell on his knees before the Icon of the Most Hol
Virgin of Kazan, and prayed, shedding tears. At the san
moment there fell from the cupola of the church the God-rejec
ing letter of Savva that he had given to the Devil at Solikamsl
And all writing was erased from the letter, as if nothing ha
ever been written there. And then the same voice repeatec
"Savva! Here is the letter you wrote, and now fulfill my con
mandment, and don't commit the sin of disobedience." And h
arose, picked up the letter, and, shedding tears, spoke in a lou
voice before the icon: "Oh, Most Blessed Mother of Goe
Intercessor for all Christians, who prays for us to her Son an
to our God, absolve me of my sins and save me from the ver
pit of hell. And I will fulfill what I have pledged."

When the tsar, the patriarch, and all who were there hear
this and witnessed this most marvelous miracle, they thanke
God and His Most Holy Mother, and greatly marveled abou
such divine mercy that had delivered him from the very pit
hell. And, after the divine liturgy, they began to glorify Goe
and the entire clergy gave a service of thanksgiving for th
miracles that were performed before all.

Thereafter, the church procession with the holy icons an
sacred crosses left the church and went to the cathedral. An
the tsar returned to his palace rejoicing over this miracle, an
thanking God. And Savva returned in good health to the hous
of the aforementioned Captain Shilov, and never again did b
suffer from his disease. The captain and his wife saw thi
marveled greatly, and thanked God for his great mercy for a
men.

Savva remained living for a short time in the house of th
captain. Then he distributed all his wealth to the poor and
the churches, and left for the Monastery of the Miracle
Archangel Michael, which is called the Miracle Monastery an

which is located in the vicinity of the Cathedral of the Venerable and Glorious Assumption of the Most Holy Virgin. There he took his monastic vows, and remained laboring, fasting, and praying incessantly and thus pleasing God. There he lived for many years, and passed to the Lord in peace. And he was buried in this monastery.

42. *Frol Skobeev, the Rogue*

HARDLY any work of Russian seventeenth-century literature reflects so strikingly the drastic changes in both the way of life and the mentality of the Muscovite Russian as does the tale of *Frol Skobeev, the Rogue*. This story reveals the thorough secularization of Muscovite writings and the break with the traditions of the Age of Faith. The religious and moralistic tone in literature have vanished altogether. The solemn, ornate style, with an abundance of archaic Old Church Slavonic words, has given place to colloquial Russian and simple, short sentences. The subject itself of a rogue portrayed against the background of everyday Russian life was completely novel in Russian literature at that time, and the description of Frol Skobeev's life lacks the traditional clichés that dominated earlier biographical and hagiographic works. Amorous and erotic motifs now make their appearance. This work is a bitter satire on the new man who is shown as a rogue and cunning operator, and whose final success announced a new age for both Russian society and literature.

In some versions of this tale, the action takes places around 1680, the time when the customary barriers between the old, aristocratic boyars and the new gentry were crumbling, and the anonymous author gave the names of actual historical personages to his characters. The Skobeevs were small provincial squires of that time. Lovchikov actually did belong to the court and was a *stolnik* in the 1670's and 1680's. Only the name of Ordyn-Nashchekin, a famous statesman and diplomat during the reign of Tsar Alexis Mikhailovich, was slightly modified to Nadrin-Nashchekin. Still, it appears that the plot does not depict actual happenings, but reflects rather the new atmosphere and social trends in Muscovite Russia.

The present translation follows the oldest extant version of this tale, a manuscript written in the late seventeenth century and published by N. Skripil in *Russkaia Povest XVII veka*, Moscow, 1953, pages 155–166.

Some interesting passages indicating the further development of satirical and erotic themes in later versions of this tale have been interpolated from a manuscript published by N. K. Gudzy in *Khrestomatiia po drevnei russkoi literature*, Moscow, 1956, pages 415–425. These interpolated passages have been placed in brackets.

◆ ◆ ◆

In the district of Novgorod there lived the nobleman Frol Skobeev. In the same district were the estates of Stolnik[1] Nadrin-Nashchekin; and the stolnik's daughter, Annushka, was living at these Novgorodian estates.

Frol Skobeev, learning about the stolnik's daughter, came to the decision that he should have a love affair with her. But since he could not get to meet her, he decided to become acquainted with the steward of estates of Nadrin-Nashchekin. And so he began to visit him at his home. Some time later, Frol Skobeev happened to be at the steward's home when Annushka's nurse came to this steward. Frol Skobeev learned that the nurse lived with Annushka. When the nurse left to return to her mistress' home, Frol followed her and gave her a present of two rubles. And the nurse said to him, "My lord Skobeev, the favor you show me is beyond my service, for I haven't yet rendered you any service." And returning home to her mistress, the nurse said nothing to her of this matter. Frol spent a time at the steward's house, and then went home.

When the time of the Christmas holidays arrived, during which there is much merrymaking and the girls often have pretexts to pass the time gaily, the daughter of Stolnik Nadrin-Nashchekin, Annushka, told her nurse to go to all noblemen who had young daughters and whose estates were in the vicinity and ask them to come to Annushka's party and have some fun. The nurse went and asked all the daughters of noblemen, and they all promised to come to Annushka's party. Since the nurse knew that Frol Skobeev had a young sister who was unmarried, she went to Frol's house and asked his sister to come to Stolnik Nadrin-Nashchekin's house, to Annushka's party. The sister told

---

[1] Stolnik: an important rank at the Russian court in Moscow. At official banquets and receptions the stolniks served the tsar at the table. They usually were members of the aristocracy, and were often high officials in various governmental agencies or commanders in the army.

e nurse: "Wait a moment and I will go and ask my brother.
en I will tell you what he has decided."

The sister went to Frol and told him: "The nurse of Stolnik
drin-Nashchekin's daughter has arrived, and asks that I come
Annushka's party."

Frol Skobeev told his sister: "Go and tell this nurse that you
ll go, but with another girl, a nobleman's daughter."

The sister pondered on what her brother had told her to tell
e nurse. However, she did not dare to disobey her brother,
d told the nurse that she would go that very evening with the
ughter of another nobleman. Then the nurse returned to her
stress, Annushka.

In the meantime Frol Skobeev began to speak with his sister,
ing, "Well, sister, it is time for you to get dressed to go to
e party." When his sister began to don feminine attire, Frol
lered her: "Sister, bring me also a girl's attire. I shall don it,
I we shall go together to Annushka, the stolnik's daughter."
The sister was very much afraid that people might recognize
n, and then certainly there would be much trouble for her
other, for the stolnik was much liked by the tsar. Still, she did
: dare to disobey her brother, and she brought him the attire
a girl. Frol, having dressed himself as a girl, went with his
er to Annushka, the stolnik's daughter.

There had already gathered many daughters of noblemen,
: no one was able to recognize Frol in his feminine attire.
en the girls began to play parlor games, and enjoyed them-
ves. Frol also played the games, and was not recognized by
one. Finally Frol left the room for his needs, and was ac-
npanied through the corridor by the nurse, who carried a
er. On leaving, he told her, "Oh, my dear nurse, there are
ny girls here, and many of them ask services of you, but none
them would give you any gift for such services." Still the
se did not recognize him. Then Frol gave her five rubles,
ich she accepted gratefully.

Seeing that the nurse still did not recognize him, Frol fell
his knees and explained to her that he was a nobleman, Frol
beev, and that he had come in feminine attire so that he
ght marry Annushka. When the nurse realized that he really
; Frol Skobeev, she became frightened and did not know
at to do. Still, remembering both of his generous gifts, she
I to him, "Well, my lord Skobeev, I am ready to do every-
g you may ask, in view of your gracious generosity."

Returning to the place where the girls were enjoing them-
ves, she spoke not a word about Frol Skobeev, but soon after

she told her mistress: "Well, girls, you have had enough
these games. I suggest you play another game, one that v
played when I was young."

Annushka did not wish to disobey her nurse, and said on
"Well, my dear nurse, we shall play the games according to y
desires."

And the nurse told them of her game, saying: "Please, d
Annushka, play the role of the bride." Pointing to Frol Skobe
she said: "And this girl will be the bridegroom." And then s
led the two into a nice chamber, to the bed, as a bride a
bridegroom are usually led after the wedding. The girls
companied them to the bedroom and then, leaving the t
alone, went to the rooms in which they had been playing th
parlor games. And the nurse ordered the girls to sing loudly
that they might not hear any cries coming from the bedchamb
And Frol Skobeev's sister was very much afraid, fearing that
brother might get into trouble.

Lying with Annushka on the bed, Frol told her that he v
a nobleman, Frol Skobeev, from the district of Novgorod, a
not a girl. Annushka was seized by great fright. But F
despite the fact that he was himself afraid, became daring a
forced her to submit to his will. Thereafter, Annushka begg
Frol not to bring shame upon her by telling of this to othe
Later on, when the nurse and the girls returned to the cham
where Frol and Annushka were, they realized from Annushk
expression that something had happened. [Annushka had und
gone a tribulation she had never before experienced.] Howev
the girls still did not recognize Frol Skobeev, for he was ag
in feminine attire. But Annushka took her nurse by the ha
led her away from the girls, and said to her: "What have
done to me! The one who was with me was not a girl. He
man, Frol Skobeev."

However, the nurse answered: "I tell you the truth,
gracious lady, when I say that I was not able to recognize h
I thought that he was a girl like the others. If he has commit
such a shameful deed, we can kill him and hide his body
some secret place, for we have plenty of servants."

But Annushka took pity on Frol Skobeev [because she
begun to care for him, having lain with him in the b
chamber]. And she told the nurse, "Well, nurse, let it be
way, for never again shall I regain my chastity."

Thereafter, all the girls, as well as Frol Skobeev, went to
reception room, and all enjoyed themselves until late into

ht. Afterward, all the girls went to bed. And Annushka went
ped with Frol Skobeev [telling herself, "I wouldn't be able
find a better girl with whom to sleep." And they enjoyed
mselves throughout the night with carnal pleasures. And
ce that time a profound pity for Frol Skobeev dwelt in
nushka's heart. And only with great sorrow did she part from
l Skobeev.]

n the morning, when everyone had got up, the girls returned
their homes. Frol Skobeev also wanted to leave with his
er, but Annushka, who permitted all the others to go, kept
l Skobeev in her house. Frol Skobeev remained at Annushka's
se for three days, always in feminine attire, so that he might
be recognized by the house servants. And he and Annushka
pyed themselves, and only after three days did Frol go home
a his sister. Before leaving, Annushka gave Frol three hun-
d rubles. Frol [returned home, overjoyed, and from that
e the destitute Skobeev became richer, and began to live like
ealthy man and] began to have banquets with his fellow
lemen.

ometime thereafter, Stolnik Nadrin-Nashchekin wrote from
scow that Annushka should come to Moscow because there
e many noble young men, sons of stolniks, who were seek-
her hand in marriage. [Although Annushka was most un-
ing to do so,] she did did not want to disobey her father.
l so she soon left for Moscow. And when Frol Skobeev
ned that she had gone to Moscow, he became confused,
wing not what he should do. Although he was a nobleman,
was quite poor, and made his living working in Moscow
citing litigations at the court.[2] He decided [to mortgage his
te, which was just a wasteland, and] to go to Moscow in
er to take Annushka as wife. He began to make preparations
his trip to Moscow, although his sister was greatly grieved,
wanting him to go.

'rol Skobeev [took leave of his sister and] said: "Dear sister,
't grieve over anything. Maybe I will lose my life, but I will
give up Annushka. I will be either a colonel or a corpse. If
gs happen according to my plans, I will not leave you in

These solicitors were not formally trained, for there were no
ually educated lawyers in Muscovite Russia. The functions of
ers were performed by professional legal solicitors who repre-
ed their clients at the court and in governmental agencies. Many
hese solicitors, however, gained positions of great influence in
ernment administration.

need. However, in case misfortune occurs, please don't for
me in your prayers." And having made all the preparatio
Frol went to Moscow.

Arriving in Moscow, he took quarters in the vicinity of S
nik Nardin-Nashchekin's mansion. The next day Frol Skob
went to Mass, and in the church he met Annushka's nurse. A
the liturgy was over, Frol Skobeev left the church and awai
the nurse. When the nurse came out from the church, F
Skobeev approached her, bowed deeply, and asked her to
nounce his arrival in Moscow to Annushka. [The nurse promi
to support him.] Coming home, she told Annushka about Fr
arrival. Annushka became very happy, and told her nurse to t
him twenty rubles when he went to Mass the next day. A
the nurse did as she was told.

Stolnik Nadrin-Nashchekin had a sister who had taken v
in the Maiden's Convent.[3] Once the stolnik went to visit
sister in the convent. When he came there, the sister met I
with all due honors. And the stolnik passed a long time with
sister. They had many conversations, and once the sister as
the brother to permit her niece to visit her, since she had
seen her niece in many years. Stolnik Nadrin-Nashche
promised to permit his daughter to visit her at the convent. 7
sister added: "I would only ask you to give the necessary or
in your home so that your daughter may come whenever I se
my carriage, even if you yourself are not at home."

Some time later, Stolnik Nadrin-Nashchekin and his wife I
to go to visit some friends, and he ordered his daughter:
case my sister, your aunt, should send her carriage from
convent, please go to her." And he then went with his wife
visit the friends.

Annushka asked her nurse to go immediately to Frol Skob
and to tell him that he should procure a horse and carriage
soon as possible and come to her house, saying that he was s
from the Maiden's Convent by the stolnik's sister for Annush
The nurse went to Frol Skobeev and repeated the commands
her mistress.

When Frol Skobeev heard this, he didn't know what to
and whom to deceive in order to obtain a carriage, for all no
aristocrats knew that he was a poor nobleman and a great che
able only to solicit litigations. But he thought of a cert
stolnik named Lovchikov who had always been very kind

[3] The Maiden's Convent: the proper name of a convent in
vicinity of Moscow.

him. Therefore he went to this Lovchikov and had a long talk with him. Finally Frol began to beg Lovchikov to lend him his carriage and horses [so that he might go and look for a fiancée. Giving in to his requests, Lovchikov lent him his carriage and a coachman.] Frol went to his quarters and gave the coachman drinks until he was completely stupefied. Then he dressed himself in the lackey's clothes, sat on the coachbox, and went in the carriage to the home of Stolnik Nadrin-Nashchekin to get Annushka. There he was recognized by Annushka's nurse, who told Annushka that her aunt had sent her carriage for her from the convent. Annushka readied herself, sat in carriage, and went to Frol's quarters.

In the meantime Lovchikov's coachman had awakened, and Frol, realizing that the coachman was not sufficiently drunk, gave him more to drink. He then put him in the carriage, sat on the coachbox, and returned to Lovchikov's mansion. Arriving there, Frol opened the gate, drove the carriage into the yard, and left it there. When Lovchikov's servants found the carriage in the yard and the coachman inside, stupefied from drink, they went to Lovchikov and told him that the carriage was in the yard and that the coachman was dead drunk. Yet no one could learn who had brought the carriage and horses into the yard. Stolnik Lovchikov ordered the putting up of the horses and carriage in the stables, and added: "It's all right. At least the horses were not sold. What can one expect from Frol Skobeev?" In the morning Lovchikov asked the coachman where he went with Frol Skobeev, and the man answered, "I remember that we went to his quarters, but I do not actually know where I drove and what I did."

Soon afterward Stolnik Nadrin-Nashchekin returned from his friends and asked to see his daughter. He was told by the nurse that Annushka, by his order, had gone to the convent to his sister, since the sister had sent her carriage for her. Nadrin-Nashchekin answered, "Well, that's all right."

Thinking that his daughter lived with his sister in the convent, Nadrin-Nashchekin did not go for a while to his sister. In the meantime Frol and Annushka married. When Nadrin-Nashchekin finally did go to see his sister at the convent, and passed some time there without seeing his daughter, he remarked to his sister, "Well, sister, I haven't seen Annushka here." The sister answered: "Brother, don't joke. What can I do if you don't honor my requests? I asked you to send her to me, but apparently you don't trust me. As for myself, I haven't had time to send my carriage for her."

Stolnik Nadrin-Nashchekin replied: "My dear lady and sister
of what are you speaking? I don't understand a thing you have
said, because Annushka left for your convent a month ago when
you sent the carriage and horses after her. At that time I was
visiting friends with my wife. She was permitted to go, as I
ordered it so."

But the sister explained: "Brother, I have not sent a carriage
and horses for her, and neither has Annushka ever been in this
place."

Nadrin-Nashchekin grieved profoundly for his daughter, and
cried bitterly, for she had vanished without leaving the slightest
trace. Returning home, he told his wife that Annushka had disappeared and was not at the convent with his sister. And then
he began to question the nurse, asking who had come and with
whom Annushka had left. The nurse answered: "A coachman
came with a carriage and said that he had come from the
Maiden's Convent for Annushka. And Annushka left with him
according to your order."

The stolnik and his wife were greatly grieved, and wept
bitterly. The next morning the stolnik went to the tsar to tell
him that his daughter had vanished into thin air. The tsar
ordered that the disappearance of the stolnik's daughter be
made public, and he made the following pronouncement: "In
case someone is keeping her secretly and does not come forward
and admit it, this man will be sentenced to death when she is
found."

Hearing this, Frol Skobeev didn't know what to do. Finally
he decided to go to Stolnik Lovchikov, for this stolnik had always been good and kind toward him. When Frol came to
Lovchikov, they had a long conversation during which Lovchikov asked, "Have you taken a bride?" And when Frol answered
that he had, the stolnik asked, "And did you marry a wealthy
wife?"

Frol answered, "Up to now I haven't seen much wealth, but
we shall see what the future holds."

And Stolnik Lovchikov told Frol: "Well, Mr. Skobeev, now
you must start living in upright ways. Stop soliciting. It would
be much healthier if you were to live in your own domain."
Thereafter, Frol began begging Stolnik Lovchikov to intervene
for him.

Lovchikov answered: "Well, if it is a decent cause I shall
intervene for you, but if it is something dishonest, don't be
angry with me."

Frol then revealed to Lovchikov that he had married Stolnik

Nadrin-Nashchekin's daughter and that she was staying at this place.

Lovchikov answered, "You did this on your own, so accept the responsibility for it on your own."

But Frol threatened: "If you don't intervene for me, you also may be made responsible! I can testify against you, since you lent me the carriage and the horses to take her away. If you hadn't lent them to me, I wouldn't have been able to do it."

Lovchikov became very confused, and answered: "You are a real rogue! What are you trying to do to me? How can I intervene for you?" And then he suggested that Frol should go on the next day to the Cathedral of the Assumption of the Holy Virgin, for Nadrin-Nashchekin would be there for the Mass.[4] "After the Mass," he continued, "all of us will be standing together at St. John's Square. In this moment come and fall before the feet of Nadrin and tell him about his daughter. And I shall try to intervene on your behalf."

Frol Skobeev went the next morning to the Cathedral of the Assumption of the Holy Virgin and saw that Stolnik Nadrin-Nashchekin and several other stolniks were praying there. All of them, as was their wont, gather after Mass before the Bell Tower of John the Great[5] in John's Square. Nadrin-Nashchekin talked of his bereavement caused by the disappearance of his daughter. Lovchikov discussed the matter with him and was trying to convince him that he should be merciful no matter what happened. While they were talking, Frol Skobeev approached them and bowed to the stolniks, as was his custom, since they all knew him. Paying no heed to the others, Frol Skobeev fell to the feet of Nadrin-Nashchekin and began begging for forgiveness, saying: "My merciful lord and the first of the stolniks! Forgive me my guilt as if I were your humble slave who had daringly made an altercation with you!"

Nadrin-Nashchekin was already of advanced age and therefore had poor eyesight, and so could not recognize the man before him. He then drew Frol up with the handle of his cane, and asked: "Who are you? Tell me about yourself. What do you want from us?"

[4] In the seventeenth century the Cathedral of the Assumption of the Holy Virgin, which is located in the Kremlin, was in the center of the area of Muscovite governmental agencies.

[5] The Bell Tower of John the Great is the highest of the campaniles in the Kremlin. It was built by John IV, and, like the Cathedral of the Assumption of the Holy Virgin, was in the center of the area of governmental agencies.

But Frol repeated only, "Absolve me of my guilt."

Lovchikov came nearer, and said, "Before you stands Frol Skobeev, a nobleman who asks you to absolve him of his guilt."

Then Nadrin-Nashchekin exclaimed: "Get up, you rogue! For a long time have I known you, you rogue and knave! Tell me what has happened, you scoundrel! So you have once more got yourself into a predicament. If it is not too bad, I will help you. But if it is really base, then do as you want. For a long time I have told you, rogue, to live decently. Now get up and tell what is your evil-doing."

Frol got up from before the stolnik's feet and informed him that his daughter was at his place and that he had married her. Having heard that his daughter was Frol's wife, the stolnik began to sob, and lost consciousness. When he had slightly recovered himself, he began to rage: "What have you done, rogue? Do you know who you are? Who are you? Your evil-doing cannot be forgiven. How could you, such a rogue, dare to wed my daughter? I will go to the sovereign and ask that he punish you for this offense which is such a great affliction for me, you rogue!"

Lovchikov, for the second time, came near Nadrin-Nashchekin and tried to convince him not to go to the tsar, saying: "You had better go home and explain this to your spouse and then do your best as you both shall decide. You cannot undo what is already done. And he, Frol Skobeev, can find no shelter from your wrath."

Stolnik Nadrin-Nashchekin followed the advice of Lovchikov, and took his carriage and went home. In the meantime Frol Skobeev went to his house and told Annushka: "Well, Annushka, I don't know what will become of us. I have told your father of our marriage."

Stolnik Nadrin-Nashchekin came home, went to his wife's chambers, and, bitterly weeping and sobbing, told her: "My wife, my wife! Do you know what? I have found Annushka!"

And the wife asked him: "And where is she, Father?"

And Nadrin-Nashchekin told his wife: "That thief, rogue, and knave, Frol Skobeev, has married her."

When his wife heard these words, she knew not what to do, but only grieved deeply for her daughter. And both of them began to weep bitterly and to reprove their daughter. And knowing not what they should do, they cursed their daughter. When they had become calm, they began to ponder, and they deeply regretted the fate of their daughter. Finally they decided: "We must send a servant to learn where this rogue lives and if Annushka is still alive or not." And so they summoned a servant and ordered him to find the house of Frol Skobeev and to learn about Annushka and whether she was still alive and eating well.

When the servant came to the house of Frol Skobeev and Frol noticed that a man from his father-in-law's house had come into the yard, Frol told his wife to go to bed and to behave as if she were very ill. Annushka did as her husband willed. When the man, who was sent by her parents, entered the house and bowed deeply, as was the custom, Frol asked him, "What man are you and what is your business?" The man told Frol that he was sent by Stolnik Nadrin-Nashchekin to find out whether Annushka was in good health or not.

And Frol Skobeev told him: "Do you see, my friend, what kind of health she enjoys? This is the result of her parents' wrath, for, as you know, they reprimand her and curse her. They should at least give her their blessing."

The man bowed, left Skobeev, and returned to his master, Stolnik Nadrin-Nashchekin. And the stolnik asked him: "Did you find their quarters? Did you find Annushka? Is she alive or not?" The man answered that Annushka was very ill and would hardly remain alive much longer. And he asked them to send their blessings to their daughter. The stolnik and his wife grieved deeply and pondered what they should do with this rogue and knave.

Finally, the mother spoke: "Well, my friend, there is little we can do. Apparently God himself has willed that such a rogue be our daughter's husband. We, my friend, must send them the icon with our blessings. When our hearts become more merciful, then we shall see them." And they took down from the wall an icon decorated with gold and precious stones that were worth five hundred rubles. And they sent it with a servant, directing him to tell Annushka to pray to it and to tell Frol Skobeev not to sell the icon and then squander the money.

The servant took the icon and went to Frol Skobeev's house. Frol Skobeev saw the man coming, and told his wife: "Get up Annushka!" She got up and sat down with Frol. The servant entered the room and gave the icon to Frol. The latter accepted it, put it in a new place, and told the servant: "Such is the power of parental blessings. As soon as they had sent their blessings, God helped Annushka, and she recovered. And now, thanks be to God, she is in good health."

The servant returned to his master, told him that he had given the icon to Annushka, that her health had much improved, and that Annushka thanked her parents. The man then went to his lodgings.

Stolnik Nadrin-Nashchekin began to deliberate with his wife concerning their daughter. And they became sorry for her. The mother asked: "What should we do, my friend? Certainly this rogue will starve Annushka. How can this dog provide for her, when he himself is hungry? We must send her some provisions in a six-horse carriage." And so they sent provisions and a list of such to Frol Skobeev. Frol ordered that the provisions be put in an appropriate place without looking at the list. And he ordered the stolnik's servant to thank the parents for such gifts.

And from that time, Frol Skobeev lived like a wealthy man, and often visited important personages. And everyone wondered about Frol Skobeev and how he could have dared to carry through this affair.

Only a month later did the hearts of the parents become merciful to Frol and his wife. And they sent a man to them asking that they come to their house for dinner. And the man came and asked that they come that very day for dinner. And Frol answered the man, saying, "Report to the father that we are ready to come today to his grace." Frol and his wife dressed and went to the house of Frol's father-in-law, Stolnik Nadrin-Nashchekin. And when they came to the father-in-law's house, Annushka went to her father and fell before the feet of her parents. When Nadrin-Nashchekin and his wife saw their daughter, they began reprimanding her and visited their parental wrath upon her. But looking upon her, they began to weep bitterly because she had married against the will of her parents. Finally, their wrath subsided and they forgave her and ordered that she sit with them. But to Frol Skobeev they said: "And you, rogue, why are you standing? Sit down here. How can you, such a rogue, be married to our daughter?"

But Frol answered only: "Well, my lord and father, it was the will of God." And all sat down at the table, but Stolnik Nadrin-Nashchekin ordered the servants not to admit any visitors to the house, saying: "In the event that someone does come and asks if the stolnik is home, tell them that he is not, since I do not want to have other people see that we are eating with our son-in-law, that knave and rogue, Frol Skobeev."

After the meal, the stolnik asked, "Well, rogue, how will you make your living?"

And Frol answered: "Well, you know that better than I. I know only how to make my living by soliciting litigations."

And the stolnik told Frol: "Well, rogue, stop your soliciting.

In the district of Simbirsk I have an estate on which there are three hundred peasant families. You, rogue, can have it for your own, and live there permanently." Then Frol Skobeev and his wife bowed deeply and thanked the parents for this gift. But the stolnik said: "Don't bow, rogue. Better that you prepare the deeds to this domain."

Frol and Annushka remained only a short while longer at the parents' home, and then left. But on their way, Stolnik Nadrin-Nashchekin ordered that they return, and asked: "Well, rogue, how will you get supplies? Do you have any money?"

Frol answered: "Well, my father, you yourself know what kind of money I have, but perhaps I should sell the peasants on this estate."

Stolnik Nadrin-Nashchekin replied, saying: "No rogue, don't sell them. I shall give you some money. Take it." And he ordered that three hundred rubles be given to him. Frol Skobeev took the money and returned to his quarters.

Sometime later he received the deeds to this estate. Stolnik Nadrin-Nashchekin eventually was to make Frol Skobeev the heir of all his capital and domains. After the death of his father, Frol Skobeev married off his sister to the son of another stolnik, while Annushka's nurse remained living with Annushka and her husband in great honor to the end of her days.

43. *Misery-Luckless-Plight*

THE origin of *Misery-Luckless-Plight* has not been exactly determined, and it is of mixed genre. Found in a single copy that apparently was prepared in the eighteenth century, this tale-poem, in its content, philosophy, and language, belongs to the middle of the seventeenth century, when the problem of religious regeneration became so acute during the period of the movement of the Seekers After God (see Selection 39) and the Great Schism. Its theme is the salvation of a sinner. The story is in blank verse, and seems to have been written by a man well acquainted with both the ancient Russian tradition and oral folk poetry. The use of recurrent descriptions, its imagery, and repetition of traditional nature symbols and metaphors (for example, "The youth flew as a falcon," or "Misery after him as a gray hawk") relate the work to both the written and folklore traditions. The meter of four stresses is close to that of the historical *bylina*, while the psychological depiction of the prodigal young man seems to indicate that the author was familiar with religious literature. The writer's originality lies in the fact that his portrayal of the youth is distinctly different from the stereotyped characterizations of hagiographic writers.

For the present edition Leo Wiener's translation of the poem has been used. For readability, however, it has been divided into songs and stanzas, and the original Russian verse form has been retained. The translation has been partially revised.

✦ ✦ ✦

I. The Nature of Man

By the will of the Lord, our God, and our Savior,
Jesus Christ, Almighty
from the beginning of the age of man.
In the beginning of this passing age
God created heaven and earth,
God created Adam and Eve.
He ordered them to live in holy paradise,
and gave them this divine command:
He told them not to eat the fruit of the grapevine,
from the great tree of Eden.

But the human heart is unthinking and unruly,
and Adam and Eve were tempted.
They forgot God's command,
ate of the fruit of the grapevine,
from the great and wonderful tree,
and for that great transgression of theirs,
God's wrath rose against Adam and Eve.
And God drove Adam and Eve from the holy paradise of
    Eden.
He settled them upon the lowly earth,
blessed them that they might grow and multiply,
and told them to appease their hunger through their own
    labor
from the fruits upon earth.

God gave them this commandment:
there should be weddings and marriages
for the propagation of the race of men,
and for having beloved children.

But the human heart was senseless and disobedient;
from the very start it was not submissive,
looked with disdain at the father's instruction,
did not obey the mother,
was untrue to the advice of friends.

Then there came a weak and wretched race
that turned to reckless deeds
and began to live in turmoil and wrong,
and discarded humility of spirit.
And God grew wroth with them,
and imposed great calamities upon them,
and permitted that great misery be accorded to them,
and immeasurable shame,
evil plight,
fiendish visitations.
and evil, immeasurable nakedness,
and endless poverty and extreme want.
And he did it to humble us, to punish us,
to lead us on the path of salvation.
Such is the nature of man from his very birth from father
and mother.

II. PARENTS' ADMONITION

The youth had reached the age of discretion and absence of
wantonness.
His father and mother loved him much,
and they began to teach and instruct him,
to prepare him for good deeds:

"Dear child of ours,
listen to your parents' instruction,
listen to their saws,
good and cunning and wise,
and you will not be in want,
you will not be in great poverty.
Go not, child, to feasts and carousings;
do not seat yourself on a high place;
drink not two beakers at once;
be not tempted by good, beautiful women, fathers'
daughters.

Lie not down in the back yards.
Fear not the wise man;

fear the fool
lest the fools lay hands on you
and take off your costly garments,
and cause you great shame and dishonor,
and expose you to the scorn and empty prattle of men.
Go not, my child, to the dice-players and innkeepers,
and keep no company with tavern-goers.
Make no friends with the foolish and simple.
Steal not, rob not,
nor deceive, nor tell a lie, nor do wrong.
Be not tempted by gold and silver;
collect not unrighteous wealth.

Be not a witness to false swearing,
and think no evil of father and mother
or any other man—
that God may protect you from all evil.
Dishonor not, child, the rich and the poor,
but regard them all alike.
Keep company with the wise and sensible,
and make friends with friends you may rely upon,
who will not deliver you to evil."

III.   The Emancipation

The youth was then young and foolish,
not in his full senses, and imperfect in mind;
he was ashamed to submit to his father
and bow before his mother,
but wanted to live as he listed.
If the youth earned fifty rubles,
he found easily fifty friends,
and his honor flowed like a river;
the youth gained many friends for himself,
and they accounted themselves of his race.

And the youth had a trusted friend:
he named himself his plighted brother,
and he tempted him with tempting words;
he called him to the tavern yard,
led him into the hall of the inn,
brought him a cup of good wine,
handed him a beaker of heady beer,
and spoke to him the following words:

"Drink, my bosom friend, brother of mine,
to your joy and happiness and health.
Empty the cup of good wine
and follow it by a glass of sweet mead.
And if you drink, brother, until you be drunk,
lie down to sleep where you have drunk—
depend upon me, your plighted brother.
I shall sit down and keep watch over you:
at your head, dear friend,
I shall place a beaker of sweet mead,
by your side I shall place good wine,
and near you I shall place heady beer,
I shall watch well over you, dear friend,
and shall take you back to your father and mother."

At that time the youth depended
on his plighted brother; he did not wish to disobey him.
He settled himself near the heady drinks,
and emptied a cup of green wine,
followed it by a glass of sweet mead,
and he drank also the heady beer.
He drank until he lost his senses,
and where he had drunk, there he fell asleep;
he depended upon his plighted brother.

The day was inclining toward night
and the sun was in the west,
when the youth awoke from his sleep.
The youth looked all around him;
all the costly garments had been taken from him,
his shoes and stockings were all gone,
his shirt even was taken from him,
and all his property was stolen.
A brick was lying under his unruly head;
he was covered with a tavern sackcloth,
and at his feet lay ragged shoes;
at his head his dear friend was no more.

And the youth stood up on his bare feet
and began to clothe himself:
he put on the ragged shoes,
covered himself with the tavern sackcloth,
covered his white body
and washed his white face.

Sorrow entered the youth's heart,
and he spoke the following words:

> "Though God has granted me a good life,
>   I have now nothing to eat or drink!
> Since my money is gone,
>   even the last half-farthing,
> I have not a friend,
>   not even half a friend.
> They no longer account themselves of my race,
>   all my friends have disappeared!"

IV. THE EXPATRIATION

The youth felt ashamed to show himself
before father and mother,
and his race and family,
and to his former friends.
He went into a strange, distant, unknown land.
He found a court, a town in size,
and a house in that court, a palace in height.
In that house was given a splendid feast;
the guests drank, ate and made merry.

The youth came to the splendid feast,
made the sign of the cross over his white face,
bowed before the miraculous icons,
made his obeisance to the good people
on all four sides.

And when the good people saw the youth,
how well he made the sign of the cross,
how he acted according to the written rule,
they took him by the hands,
seated him at the oaken table,
not in the best place, nor in the worst,
they seated him in a middle place,
where the younger guests were seated.

And the feast was a merry one,
and all the guests at the feast were drunk and merry and
                        boastful;
but the youth sat, not merry at all,
gloomy, sorrowful, joyless,

nd neither ate, nor drank, nor made merry,
or boasted of anything at the feast.
aid the good people to the youth:

"Wherefore, O good youth,
do you sit, not merry at the feast,
gloomy, sorrowful, joyless;
you neither drink, nor make merry,
nor boast of anything at the feast.
Or has the cup of good wine not reached you,
or is not your seat according to your father's worth?
Or have small children insulted you?
Or are our children not kind to you?
Or foolish and unwise people made light of you, youth?

But the good youth remained sitting, and said:

"My lords and good people!
I will tell you of my great misfortune,
of my disobedience to my parents,
of my drinking at the inn, about the cup of mead,
the tempting drinking of heady wine.

When I took to drinking the heady wine,
I disobeyed both father and mother;
their blessing departed from me;
the Lord grew wroth with me
and to my poverty were added
many great and incurable sorrows
and sadness without comfort,
want, and misery, and extreme wretchedness.

Want has tamed my flowery speech;
sadness has dried up my white body.
For this my heart is not merry,
and my white face is sad, and my eyes dim.
I have lost my paternal honor,
any my youthful valor has left me.
My lords and good people!
Tell me and teach me how to live in a strange land,
among strange people,
and how to find dear friends!"

Said the good people to the youth:

"You are a sensible youth!
 Be not haughty in a strange land;
 submit to friend and foe,
 bow to old and young,
 tell not of the affairs of others,
 neither what you hear nor see.
 Flatter not friends nor enemies;
 have no tortuous fits,
 nor bend as a cunning snake;
 be humble before all
 but withal keep to truth and right—
 and you will have a great honor and glory.
 When people will find you out
 they will respect and honor you
 for your great truth,
 your humility and wisdom—
 and you will have dear friends
 who will call themselves your plighted brothers."

V. TEMPTATIONS OF MISERY-LUCKLESS-PLIGHT

And the youth went hence into a strange land
and began to live wisely,
and through his great wisdom acquired greater wealth tl
            before.
He looked out for a bride according to custom,
for he wished to marry.
The youth prepared a splendid feast,
according to his father's worth
and as best he knew,
and invited the honored guests and friends.
But through his own sin,
by God's will and the devil's temptation,
he boasted before his honored guests
and friends and plighted brothers.
A boastful word is always rotten,
and self-praise brings the destruction of man.
"I, a youth, have gained more possessions than ever!"

Misery-Luckless-Plight heard the young man's boasting
and spoke the following words:

"Young man, boast not of your fortune,
 praise not your wealth!
 I, Misery, have known people

who were wiser and richer than you,
but I, Misery, have outwitted them.
When a great misfortune befell them,
They struggled with me unto their death;
they were worsted by their luckless plight—
could not get away from me, Misery,
until they took their abode in the grave,
and I covered them forever with the earth.
Only then they were rid of nakedness,
and I, Misery, left them,
though luckless plight remained upon their grave."

And again it cawed ominously:

"I, Misery, attached myself to others,
for I, Misery-Luckless-Plight,
cannot live empty-handed; I, Misery,
wish to live among people
from whom I cannot be driven away with a stick;
but my chief seat and paternal home
is among the carousers!"

Spoke gray Misery the miserable:

"How am I to get at the youth?"

And evil Misery devised cunningly
to appear to the youth in his dream:

"Young man, renounce your beloved bride,
for you will be poisoned by your bride;
you will be strangled by that woman;
you will be killed for your gold and silver!
Go, young man, to the tsar's tavern,
save nothing, but spend all your wealth in drink;
doff your costly dress, put on the tavern sackcloth.
In the tavern Misery will remain,
and evil Luckless-Plight will stay—
for Misery will not gallop after a naked one,
nor will anyone annoy a naked man,
nor has assault any terrors for a barefooted man."

The young man did not believe his dream,
but evil Misery again devised a plan,

appeared as the archangel Gabriel,
and stuck once more to the youth for a new plight:

> "Are you not, youth,
>   acquainted with poverty and nakedness,
>   with hopes and security?
>   What you buy for yourself is money spent,
>   but you are a brave fellow
>   and can live without expense!
>   They do not beat, nor torture naked people,
>   nor drive them out of paradise,
>   nor drag them down from the other world;
>   nor will anyone annoy a naked man,
>   nor has assault any terrors for a naked man!"

VI. The Last Trial

The young man believed that dream:
he went and spent all his wealth in drink;
he doffed his costly dress,
put on the tavern sackcloth,
covered his white body.
The youth felt ashamed to show himself to his dear frien
He went into a strange, distant, unknown land.
On his way he came to a swift river.
On the other side were the ferrymen
and they asked for money to ferry him across;
but the youth had none to give,
and without money they would not take him across.
The youth sat a whole day,
until evening, and all that day until compline
the youth had nothing to eat,
not even half a piece of bread.
The young man arose on his swift feet,
and standing, he fell to grieving,
and he spoke the following words:

> "Woe to me, miserable Luckless-Plight!
>   It has overtaken me, young man,
>   has starved me, young man, with a hungry death.
>   Three unlucky days have I passed,
>   for I, young man, have not eaten half a piece of bread
>   I, young man, will jump into the swift river:
>   swallow my body, swift river!
>   And eat, O fish, my white body!

And that will be better than my shameful life;
will I ever be able to escape the hands
of Misery-Luckless-Plight?"

At that hour Misery leaped from behind a rock
near the swift river;
Misery was barefooted and naked
and there was not a thread upon it,
and it was girded with a bast thong,
and it called out with a mighty voice:

"Wait, young man, you will not escape from me, Misery!
Jump not into the swift river,
nor be in your misery doleful!
Though you live in misery, you need not be doleful,
and you should even let your dolefulness die in misery!
Remember, young man, your former life;
how your father spoke to you, and your mother
            instructed you!
Why did you not then obey them?
You would not submit to them,
and were ashamed to bow to them,
but wanted to live as you listed!
But he who will not listen to the good teaching of
            his parents
will be taught by me, Misery-Luckless-Plight!

Luckless-Plight spoke the following speech:

"Submit to me, impure Misery;
bow before me, Misery, to the damp earth,
for there is no one wiser in the whole world than I,
            Misery;
and you will be ferried across the swift river,
and the good people will give you to eat and drink."

The young man saw his inevitable calamity,
and he submitted to impure Misery,
bowed before Misery to the damp earth!

The good fellow went ahead with a light step over the steep,
        fair bank,
over the yellow sand.
He went happy, not at all doleful,

for he had appeased Misery-Luckless-Plight.
And as he went, he thought a thought.
    "Since I have nothing,
       I need not worry about anything!"
And as the youth was not sorrowful,
he started a fair song,
a mighty, sensible song it was:

    "Sorrowless mother has borne me:
      with a comb she combed my little locks,
      dressed me in costly garments,
      and stepping aside shaded her eyes
      and looked at me:
      'Does my child look well in costly garments?
      In costly garments my child is a priceless child!'
      Thus my mother always spoke of me!
      And then I learned and know it well,
      that a costly gown cannot be made without a master,
      nor a child be comforted without a mother,
      nor a drunkard ever become rich,
      nor a dice-player be in good renown,
      and I was predestined by my parents to be a well-dressed
          boy
      who was born devoid of everything."

The ferrymen heard the good fellow's song,
took the young man across the swift river,
and took nothing from him for the ferrying.
The good people gave him to drink and to eat,
took off his tavern sackcloth,
gave him peasant's clothes.
And these good people spoke to him:

    "You are a good fellow,
      so go to your home,
      to your beloved, respected parents,
      to your father and mother dear,
      greet your parents, father and mother,
      and receive from them the parental blessing!"

From there the youth went to his home.
When he was in the open field,
evil Misery had gone before him;
it met the youth in the open field,
and began to caw above the youth,

like an ill-omened crow above a falcon.
Misery spoke the following words:

> "Wait! you have not gone away from me, good fellow!
> Not merely for a time have I, Misery-Luckless-Plight,
>   attached myself to you;
> I shall labor with you to your very death!
> And not I, Misery, alone, but all my relatives,
> and there is a godly race of them:
> we are all gentle and insinuating,
> And he who joins our family will end his days among us!
> Such is the fate that awaits you with us.
> Even if you were to be a bird of the air,
> or if you went into the blue sea as a fish,
> I would follow you at your right hand."

The youth flew as a clear falcon,
and Misery after him as a white gyrfalcon;
the youth flew as a steel-blue dove,
and Misery after him as a gray hawk;
the youth went into the field as a gray wolf,
and Misery after him with greyhounds;
the youth became the feathergrass in the field,
and Misery came with a sharp scythe,
and Luckless-Plight railed at him:

> "You, little grass, will be cut down;
> you, little grass, will lie on the ground,
>   and the boisterous winds will scatter you!"

The youth went as a fish into the sea,
and Misery after him with close-meshed nets,
and Misery-Luckless-Plight railed at him:

> "You, little fish, will be caught at the shore,
>   and you will be eaten up and die a useless death!"

The youth went on foot along the road
and Misery at his right hand.
It taught the youth to live as a rich man by killing and
        robbing,
so that they might hang the young man for it,
or might put him with a stone in the water.

The youth bethought himself of the road to salvation
and at once the youth went to a monastery to be shorn a monk,
and Misery stopped at the holy gates—
no longer clung to the youth.

And this is the end of the story:
Lord, preserve us from eternal torment,
and give us, O Lord, the light of paradise!
Forever and ever, amen!

POETRY

44. Poems From the Collection of Baccalaureus Richard James

In 1619 a young British scholar, baccalaureus Richard James, visited Russia and brought back to England six short poems, or songs, which he had transcribed phonetically in Russian, using Latin letters. F. Buslaev, the first scholar to study and publish them, believed that they were specimens of Russian folklore, but contemporary scholars believe that all of the poems were written by an unknown Russian poet of the early seventeenth century. The use of rhymed verses, completely uncharacteristic of Russian folklore of the time, their vocabulary—which betrays an author well-versed in the Russian literary language—as well as their subjects strongly confirm the latter opinion. The poems reflect political events of the time, and one of them, "Ode on the Return to Moscow of Patriarch Filaret," even deals with an event that occurred in the same year as the transcription of these poems.

The first is about the second raid against Moscow by the Khan of Crimea, Devlet Girey. In 1571 the Tatars of Crimea, under Khan Devlet, cleverly circled Russian armies guarding the access to Moscow and attacked and burned the Russian capital. Over a million Russians perished during this raid, while hundreds of thousands of prisoners were captured by the Tatars, later to be sold on the Middle Eastern and Mediterranean slave markets. In 1572 Devlet repeated his raid, but was defeated by Russian troops under Prince M. Vorotynsky. Out of a hundred and twenty thousand Tatar warriors, only twenty thousand returned home. The poem depicts the Tatars' hope of inflicting a final blow on Moscow and of conquering the other Russian cities. The "seventy Apostles" mentioned in the poem are the Muscovite churches, dedicated to seventy pupils of Christ, while the expression "Holy Fathers" refers to the churches dedicated to the three theologians of the early Christian Church: St. Basil the Great, St. Gregory the Theologian, and St. John Chrysostom (Golden Mouth).

The second poem voices the feelings and lament over her fate of Princess (Tsarevna) Xenia, the daughter of Tsar Boris

Godunov. After the death of Tsar Boris, when the impostor, Pseudo-Dmitry, seized Moscow and became tsar, he abused the daughter of his enemy and then sent her to a convent in Ustiuzhna-Zhelezhnaia, in northern Russia, where she was forced to take monastic vows.

The last of the poems offered here from the James Collection is an ode glorifying the return from a Polish prison of Metropolitan Filaret (who soon became Patriarch), father of Michael Romanov, the first tsar of the dynasty which was to rule Russia until the revolution of 1917. Fedor (Filaret was his monastic name) Nikitich Romanov had been captured along with other Russian aristocrats by the Poles during the Time of Troubles, and only after the Russian-Polish armistice of 1618 was he permitted to leave the Polish-Lithuanian Condominium and return to Moscow.

The text of the *Raid of the Crimean Tatars* and *Ode to the Return of Filaret Romanov* follow the translations of Leo Wiener, while the text of *Song of Princess Xenia* is taken from W. R. Morfill's *Story of Russia*, New York and London, 1890. All three texts have been revised by the present editor.

◆ ◆ ◆

RAID OF THE CRIMEAN TATARS

Not a mighty cloud has covered the sky,
Nor mighty thunders have thundered:
Whither travels the dog, Crimea's khan?—
To the mighty Tsardom of Muscovy.
 "Today we will go against stone-built Moscow,
 But coming back, we will take Riazan."
And when they were at the river Oka,
They began their white tents to pitch.
 "Now think a thought with all your minds:
 Who is to sit in stone-built Moscow,
 And who is to sit in the city of Vladimir,
 And who is to sit in the city of Suzdal,
 And who will hold the old city of Riazan,
 And who will sit in the city of Zvenigorod,
 And who will sit in the city of Novgorod?"
There stepped forward Divi Murza, son of Ulan:
 "Listen, our lord, Crimea's khan!
 You, our lord, shall sit in stone-built Moscow,
 And your son in Vladimir,

And your nephew in Suzdal,
And your relative in Zvenigorod,
And let the equerry hold old Riazan,
But to me, O lord, grant Novgorod:
There, in Novgorod, lies my luck."
The voice of the Lord called out from heaven:
 "Listen, you dog, Crimea's khan!
 Know you not the Tsardom of Muscovy?
 There are in Moscow seventy Apostles,
 Besides the three Holy Fathers.
 And there is in Moscow still an Orthodox tsar."
And you fled, you dog, Crimea's khan,
Not over the highways, nor the main road,
Nor following the black banner.

SONG OF PRINCESS XENIA, DAUGHTER OF TSAR BORIS GODUNOV

There weepeth a little bird,
A little white quail:
 "Alas, that I so young must grieve!
 They wish to burn the green oak,
 To destroy my little nest,
 To kill my little ones,
 To catch me, quail."
In Moscow the Princess weepeth:
 "Alas that I so young must grieve!
 For there comes to Moscow the impostor
 Grishka Otrepiev, the defrocked monk,
 Who wants to take me captive,
 And having captured make me a nun,
 To send me into the convent.
 But I do not wish to become a nun,
 To go into a monastery:
 I shall keep my dark cell open,
 To look at the fine fellows.
 O our beautiful corridors!
 Who will walk over you
 After our life as the tsar's family
 And after Boris Godunov?
 O our beautiful palace halls!
 Who will be sitting in you
 After our life as the tsar's family
 And after Boris Godunov?"

And in Moscow the Princess weepeth,
The daughter of Boris Godunov:
   "O God, our merciful Savior!
    Wherefore is our Tsardom perished—
    Is it for father's sinning,
    Or for mother's not praying?
    And you beloved palace halls!
    Who will rule in you,
    After our life as the tsar's family?
    Fine stuffs of drawn lace!—
    Shall we wind you around the birches?
    Fine gold-worked towels!
    Shall we throw you into the woods?
    Fine earrings of hyacinth
    Shall we hang you on branches,
    After our life as the tsar's family,
    After the reign of our father,
    Glorious Boris Godunov?
    Wherefore comes to Moscow the defrocked monk,
    And wants to break down the palaces,
    And to take me, princess, captive,
    And to send me to Ustyuzhna Zheleznaia,
    To make me, princess, a nun,
    To place me behind a walled garden?
    Why must I grieve,
    As they take me to the dark cell,
    And the abbess gives me her blessing?"

ODE TO THE RETURN OF FILARET ROMANOV, FATHER OF TSAR MIKHAIL, TO MOSCOW

The Tsardom of Muscovy was happy
And all the holy Russian land.
Happy was the sovereign, the Orthodox tsar,
The Grand Duke Mikhail Fedorovich,
For he was told that his father had arrived,
His father Filaret Nikitich,
From the land of the infidel, from Lithuania.
He had brought back with him many princes and boyars,
He had also brought the boyar of the tsar,
Prince Mikhail Borisovich Sheyn.
There had come together many princes, boyars, and
      dignitaries,

In the mighty Tsardom of Muscovy:
They wished to meet Filaret Nikitich
Outside the famous white stone-built Moscow.
'Tis not the beautiful sun in its orbit—
'Tis the Orthodox tsar that has gone out,
To meet his father dear,
Lord Filaret Nikitich.
With the tsar went his uncle,
Ivan Nikitich the boyar—
  "The Lord grant my father be well,
  My father, lord Filaret Nikitich."
They went not into the palace of the tsar,
They went into the cathedral of the most Holy Virgin,
To sing a holy Mass.
And he blessed his beloved child:
  "God grant the orthodox tsar be well,
  Grand Duke Mikhail Fedorovich!
  And for him to rule the Tsardom of Muscovy
  And the holy Russian land."

45. *Prince Ivan Khvorostinin: Autobiographical Verses*

PRINCE Ivan Khvorostinin (1585? to 1625) was one of the most controversial Russian writers of the first quarter of the seventeenth century. Scion of an ancient noble family and the son of the valiant defender of Pskov against King Stephen Bathory, Ivan Khvorostinin appeared at the Muscovite court quite early. He later became one of the intimate friends of Pseudo-Dmitry, who became tsar in 1605. After the fall of this impostor, Khvorostinin was banned from Moscow, but some years later he reappeared as commander of one of the armies that fought against the Poles in southwestern Russia. It seemed at the time that this talented aristocrat had a brilliant career before him, but his debauchery, dissoluteness, and unorthodox behavior caused him difficulty once more. He was apparently very unhappy in Moscow society, for he often criticized his surroundings, and complained that there weren't any clever people there, nor anyone worth being acquainted with. In one of his satirical verses, he claimed:

"These Muscovite people
cultivate much rye,
but live only by the lie."

Such verses aroused the indignation of the court, and a new
investigation of his case showed that he wanted to flee to the
West, to Italy, and that he denied such basic dogmas of the
Orthodox Church as resurrection after death, and the Trinity
He apparently followed the teachings of the Unitarians. This
early Russian Westernizer was then sent to the Monastery of St
Cyril where, in 1623, he decided to recant, and was then per
mitted to return to Moscow. Soon after his return he wrote his
monumental *Exposition Against the Blaspheming Heretics,* in
which he ambitiously attacked both the Roman Catholic and
Protestant churches. This exposition, which is about 1,333 verses
long, is written in rhymed couplets. His verses have no meter
and the line varies from six to fourteen syllables. This first Rus
sian poem of considerable length deserves attention not only
because of its size, but also because of the great variations in
rhyme and the autobiographical elements of its final part. In
this last section Prince Khvorostinin bitterly complained of the
unfaithfulness of his servants and friends, who apparently in
formed the government of his unorthodox behavior and think
ing. Besides this religious poem, he was the author of a number
of other historical and polemical works in which he displayed a
skillful command of contemporary literary devices and in which
he often introduced rhymed passages.

The following translation of the final part of the *Exposition
Against the Blaspheming Heretics* is based on the text published
in *Letopis zaniatii arkheograficheskoi komissii,* Volume XVIII
St. Petersburg, 1907, pages 77–80.

❖ ❖ ❖

Look, reader, upon the Roman mores
and be faithful to God's glories.
Do not look for truth in any foreign creeds.
Do not betray the holy fathers' deeds.
Take care, for the Western Church's revelations
can certainly destroy our foundations.[1]
The Western Church is dark both day and night,
and bitter fruits grow like a blight.

[1] Under the expression "Western Church" Prince Khvorostinin
means both the Catholic and the Protestant churches.

Their Eighth Council[2] did many wrong deeds,
betraying many of the holy fathers' creeds.
They want to condemn us to evil torments,
and they give their warriors heretical armaments.
The wave of their wrath is great,
but ever shall I their teachings berate.
I have wanted to bequeath something to my nation,
which is built upon a holy and Christian foundation.
But there were many evil doers,
who have confused our blessed rulers.
I have wanted to lend my hand to the work of salvation,
and for the destruction of their heretical creation.
But in place of ink, I had to use tears
and in irons I found the end of my career.
In prison I passed many days,
for a long time I did not see the sun's rays.
I have wanted to escape their evil gold,
and for such, never have I my soul sold.
I was forced to hide from treacherous detestation,
and thus could not continue my affirmation.
As an army commander I was always brave,
not wanting to bring my friends to the grave.
On Him who knows my heart have I always relied,
and He has always been my friend, true and tried.
His commandments I have never rejected,
but to His protection have I myself directed.
And before the time of my misfortune,
I had always rejected a heretical fortune.
I did so by the Holy Scriptures,
and following the holy fathers' strictures.
I have remained the faithful son of my faith
and firmly stood for the Eastern Church's Grace.
It was not my wont to debate with the ignorant,
nor did I care for their argument.
By much misfortune have I been accosted,
but by the absence of friends I was sore exhausted.
And no one would fain take a stand for me,
but only the Lord His help granted me.
I have written many words against the enemy
        of the faith,

[2] Eighth Council was the first council of the Western Christian
Church, which is considered by the Catholics an Ecumenical Council;
but it is not recognized by the Eastern Orthodox, who did not take
part in its works.

and still I was thrown into such a bitter place.
Many a friend denounced my writing
and launched against me bitter fighting.
They took me from my holy task,
and not a word of thanks could I ask.
As a heretic was I condemned,
and thus my task came to a bitter end.
Look upon their evil doings,
and contrite hearts be not eschewing.
Even my servants became my enemies,
thus depriving me of any serenity.
They took away from me their comfort and support,
and prepared against me the trial in court.
Their lawless hatred was evil,
and they prepared me for burial.
They did so, for they belong to a kind most base,
worse than if they were of a devilish race.
They spewed their poisons at me,
and in their betrayal they agreed.
Their weapons were denunciations,
spreading against me all kind of calumniation.
O Lord, our God, show your might
and judge whether they or I be right.
You alone know of all my devotions
and you will divine the truth in their motions.
They were fed on my bread,
yet they turned my good deed to one of dread.
Yet sweeter than the sweetest flower,
is being in the Lord's power.
Let the work of my slaves be cursed,
let us hope their design will be dispersed.
Don't throw pearls before swine,
for they will be defiled, whether they be yours
        or mine.
And I underwent many hardships because of my
        slaves,
and they nearly brought me to the brink of the
        grave.
They forgot the words of Christ's admonitions
and I could not escape their evil intentions.
Their words were as ensnaring as a spider's web,
and their hatred was like an evil web.
Over them I was placed by my Creator,

by God was I placed over these evil traitors.
I stood alone against this evil horde,
but I was raised above them by my dear Lord.
But they became my bitter enemies,
and they profaned their own souls with their
    calumnies.
To win their own freedom,
they wanted to escape their serfdom.
They hurled their words like arrows against their
    lord,
and I wonder about those who approve of such
    a horde.

46. The Orderly of Colonel Theodore Zay
A Love Letter from the Year 1698

accidental arrest of a certain Savva Kartsev, who was sus-
ted of participating in political conspiracy, preserved in the
ives of the Russian police a love letter written by the
erly of Colonel Theodore Zay. The letter was written for the
nel's son, who had recently married without parental con-
, and was to be delivered by Savva Kartsev to the wife of
young man. The intervention of the police prevented its
very, but preserved the letter for posterity. The rhymed
plets of this letter demonstrate a new poetic vogue, while the
re, epithets, and vocabulary resemble the love songs of Rus-
folklore.
his poem is translated from the text published by L. Maikov
)cherki po istorii russkoi literatury XVII i XVIII stoletii, St.
ersburg, 1889, page 230.

◆ ◆ ◆

To the most glorious light which has ever appeared
    before my eyes,
to the nicest person whom I advise.
May my beloved live for many years,
and not forget the pledge given to me here.
Do not forget our pledge taken before the Lord,
when we exchanged rings of our future concord.

At that time we had our wedding crowns on our
  heads,
crowns of gold for the commemoration of the
  happy, holy event.
Do not forget me in your prayers,
for I shall forget you never.
And I am so sad without you,
that I could fly from here as if I were a bird,
and I would come to you, my beloved.
We could lock ourselves in our chambers,
and confide in each other's secrets.
O my dear, blue flower, the beloved of my life!
What did I do when I came to my lord-father
and when I saw my lady-mother?
When I looked into their eyes,
I saw that our joy was beshadowed.
I awaited kind words from their graces,
but their words betrayed my faith.
"You can marry
someone with considerable wealth,
but you should marry her that we would care for,
and whom you should love.
You should marry a girl from the house of a
  Muscovite nobleman."
But I, my dear nightingale, only thanked them
  for their advice,
and now I send you this love letter with my best
  regards.

47. *Peter Kvashnin*

AROUND 1680 Peter Kvashnin, a member of an ancient
noble family, wrote about fifty lyric poems, some of which
more than a hundred lines in length. This poetry was first p
lished in 1932 by M. N. Speransky, who thought it was
product of Russian folklore. But the form, vocabulary, and
usual epithets, as well as partially rhymed lines, seem to pr
that the poems are instead the personal creations of Kvash
or of one of his friends. Only in a few aspects do they follow
folklore tradition. The fact, also, that many of them are un

d would indicate that they are the product of Kvashnin's own
tic creativeness. All the poems have a common topic, that of
ful and unrequited love, and are filled with pathos.

he translations of the two poems given here are based on
N. Speransky's texts published in *Izvestiia Akademii Nauk
R*, Volume 7, 1932, pages 721–724.

he subject of the first poem is the tender love of a sister for
brother.

◆ ◆ ◆

DEAR BROTHER

It was not a she-turtledove that cooed with a
     turtledove.
It was a sister that spoke with her brother.
And speaking with her brother, the sister
began to praise the darling little brother:
"Oh, my dearest little brother, my fond heart,
my dearest of friends, my beloved.
I cannot cease my enjoyment of looking upon you.
You are my precious darling, beautiful as an apple.
You are handsome, my fair brother, like a poppy
     blossom.
You appear, my young, dear brother, as a cherry.
When I don't see you, my brother,
I could die from sorrow.
And I remember my brother,
but I can only sigh after him.
And I dream steadily of him,
my friendship for him is firm."
The sister speaks with her brother,
and the sister begins to lament:
"Bitter is my life, my brother,
for I hear nonsense and senseless rumors.
Why do those people hate me?
O God, judge those who envy us,
who want to abuse me, a young girl,
and who want to separate me from my brother.
I should rather lose my reputation
than be separated from my brother.
Even if they spread calumnies about me,
I shall never forsake my brother. . . ."

                [This poem is unfinished.]

I THOUGHT

I thought, I pondered,
I followed the reasoning of another,
and I said no to my love, straight to his face.
              [A hiatus of several lines]
And he decided to take a young wife, a maiden
              fair.
Oh, come to me, my beloved, on the eve of your
              wedding!
I shall give you, my beloved, a beautiful linen
              shirt,
A shirt adorned with muslin.
I waited for my dear friend the whole day until
              evening.
And my beloved came to me
early in the morning, when a beautiful sun had
              risen.
And you, my nurses and servants, bring me my
              trunk with iron bars.
And open this trunk with the iron bars,
and take from it two steel knives
for me and for my friend.
Since I could not keep him with me,
you had better open his white breast.
And then he, my beloved, will belong
neither to me, nor to my sister,
nor to that strumpet who separated us.
But you, my beloved, will belong to our mother,
              the damp earth.
And only an oaken board will preserve my secret.

A Short Glossary of Some Russian Terms
Used in This Anthology

I. CURRENCY AND MEASURES

ivna An old Russian unit of money equivalent to the old English pound. It was in the form of a silver ingot.

una From the Russian word for marten. A monetary unit, there being twenty-five *kunas* in a *grivna*.

ogata A unit of money, there being twenty *nogatas* in a *grivna*. It was a vair.

ezana A vair. There were fifty *rezanas* in a *grivna*.

able A Russian monetary unit since the fifteenth century. Equal to about one English pound at that time.

rsta or *poprishche* Units of measure equal to about ⅔ of a mile.

II. RANKS AND TITLES

etropolitan The head of the national Orthodox Church, in particular head of the Russian Church until the end of the sixteenth century. Since the end of the sixteenth century the term has come to denote an archbishop in charge of a large diocese.

sadnik An elected high official in the cities of early Kievan Russia and in both the Novgorodian and Pskovian republics until the fifteenth century. Similar to rank of commissioner.

tnik An officer who commanded a *sotnia*, a company of one hundred men. A centurion.

olnik A high official at the tsar's court or of the civil administration.

relets (pl. *streltsy*) Professional infantrymen. The corps of *streltsy* was created in the sixteenth century.

siatsky An elected commander of the army in the earlier Kievan period and in the Novgorodian and Pskovian republics.

oevoda A high-ranking officer either in the civil administration or in the army. A rank equivalent to that of general or governor.

Chronology of Russian History and Culture

venth Century B.C. Occupation of the southern prairies of Russia by the Scythians, and the founding of Greek cities on the northern shore of the Black Sea.

ird Century A.D. Goths occupy the southern prairie of Russia.

urth Century The Huns penetrate into Europe from Asia, thus causing the Great Migration. The Antes (Slavs?) founded a state in what is present-day southern Russia.

inth Century Appearance of the Viking (Varangian) tradesmen in Russia.

2 The legendary founding of the Russian state by Rurik.

7 Oleg's first campaign against Constantinople.

5 Olga travels to Constantinople, and takes baptism there.

38 or 989 The Christianization of Russia by Prince Vladimir.

Early Eleventh Century   The Kumans drive out the Pechenegs fro
   the southern prairies of Russia.

Circa 1030   The oldest known Russian literary work, the *Serm*
   of Luke Zhidiata.

1019–1054   The reign of Yaroslav the Wise.

Circa 1050   The writing of the *Primary Chronicle* begins.

1113   Monk Nestor ends the writing of the *Primary Chronicle*.

1113–1125   The reign of Vladimir Monomakh, the last great prin
   of the Kievan Period to be recognized as ruler of all Russi

1185   Igor's unfortunate campaign against the Kumans.

1186 (?)   The writing of the *Lay of Igor's Campaign*.

1223   Russians are defeated by the Mongols at the river Kalka.

1237–1240   The Mongol conquest of Russia.

1283–1304   Daniel, Prince of Moscow, founds the Muscovite stat

1261   The beginning of the Muscovite branch of the Rurik dynast

1326   Metropolitan Peter, the head of the Russian Church, mov
   his office to Moscow.

1328   Ivan Kalita receives the title "Great Prince of All Russia."

1314–1392   St. Sergius of Radoniezh, the founder of monasticism
   northern Russia.

1380   Russia defeats the Tatars at the Battle of Kulikovo.

1386 (?)   The writing of *Zadonshchina*.

1420   The death of Epiphanius the Wise, author of the lives
   St. Sergius and St. Stephen of Perm.

1427 or 1430   Death of the greatest Russian painter of the mediev
   era, Andrew Rublev.

1462–1505   The reign of Ivan III, the unifier of northern Russia.

1533–1584   The reign of Ivan IV.

1550–1570   The compilation of *Chetii Minei (The Book of the Liv*
   of Saints*), of the *Book of Grades*, and Nikon's *Illustrat*
   Codex.

1598   The death of Tsar Fedor, and the consequent end of th
   Rurik dynasty.

1598–1605   The reign of Tsar Boris Godunov.

1605–1613   The Time of Troubles.

1613–1645   The reign of the first Romanov, Tsar Michael.

1620–1630   Avraamy Palitsyn, M. Katyrev-Rostovsky, and I. Khv
   rostinin write their works on the Time of Troubles. Probab
   time of the writing of the *Life of Yuliania Lazarevskaia*.

1645–1676   The reign of Tsar Alexis.

1653   The first reforms of Patriarch Nikon.

1663   Simeon Polotsky comes to Moscow. Beginning of Russia
   syllabic verse.

1667   The Church Council of Moscow and the consequent schis
   within the Russian Church.

1672   *Esther*, the first Russian play, is staged in the tsar's theatre.

1673   Avvakum writes his *Life*.

1682–1725   The reign of Peter the First, and the consequent wes
   ernization of Russia.